THE MEDIÆVAL HOSPITALS
OF ENGLAND

THE SOUTH-EAST VIEW OF THE HOSPITAL OR MAISON-DIEU AT DOVER.

HUBERT de BURGH Earl of Kent and Lord Chief Justice of England Founded A.D. 1227, at the South East entrance of the Town of Dover an Hospital for Brothers and Sisters; to the Honour of the Blessed Virgin Mary, King Hen. III as the same time giving them the Tythe of all the Profitts arising from the Refuge of Dover-Port And in the 13 Year of his Reign, bestow'd on them at yearly Rent of £10, payable out of the profitts of y.e said port But this Hospital at the General Dissolution, sharing the Fate of other Religious places, is become the Ruine here represented.

ST. MARY'S HOSPITAL, DOVER

THE
MEDIÆVAL HOSPITALS
OF ENGLAND

ROTHA MARY CLAY

NEW YORK

BARNES & NOBLE, INC.

Publishers · Booksellers · Since 1873

Published by Frank Cass & Co. Ltd.,
10 Woburn Walk, London W.C.1
by arrangement with Methuen & Co.

Published in the United States
in 1966
by Barnes & Noble, Inc.
105 Fifth Avenue, New York, 10003.

First Edition   1909
Second Impression   1966

Printed in Great Britain

DEDICATED TO

FRANCES ARNOLD-FORSTER

WITH GRATEFUL AFFECTION

PREFACE

WHEN the able author of this book asked me to write a Preface to a work on Hospitals, I replied that I must first see the sheets in proof. This was not due to any doubt of the ability of the writer, it was due to some doubt as to the adequacy of the material at her disposal. This doubt has been much more than removed. The mass of the material collected is remarkable. Still more remarkable is the evidence of the very large part played by Hospitals—in the widest senses of the word—in the social life of the people of this land in the earlier Middle Ages. For the fuller understanding of the social life of our ancestors, this book contributes information of the most luminous character. It will serve also as an example and pattern for young and earnest students of real history, the history of ordinary human beings rather than of generals and of kings. And it must be added that, although the division into numerous headings leads to frequent repetitions of the names and characters of institutions of the nature of Hospitals, it has the great advantage of reducing to order a mass of material which might under less careful treatment have had a chaotic appearance. As a book of reference for readers and writers, this treatise on the Mediæval Hospitals of England ought to hold a distinguished place.

G. F. BRISTOL

July, 1909.

CONTENTS

LIST OF ILLUSTRATIONS IN THE TEXT

* Asterisk denotes that buildings remain in much the same condition
as shown.

The seals are copied mainly from impressions in the British Museum.

xii MEDIÆVAL HOSPITALS OF ENGLAND

LIST OF ILLUSTRATIONS IN THE TEXT xiii

LIST OF PLATES

LIST OF PLATES XV

INTRODUCTION

"And to relief of lazars and weak age,
Of indigent faint souls, past corporal toil,
A hundred almshouses, right well supplied."
(Shakespeare : Henry V., i. 1.)

WHILE we are justly proud of our institutions for the amelioration of the lot of the infirm and destitute, we are apt to forget that they are not the outcome of any modern philanthropic movement, but are rather England's inheritance for above a thousand years.

Much has been written of the regular monastic houses. These are situated, as it were, upon the high-roads of ecclesiastical history ; but comparatively little attention has been paid to the existence and development of the foundations known as "Hospitals." Although it is with some trepidation that we tread the less-frequented by-paths of history, an attempt will be made in this volume to illustrate the place of the hospital in pre-Reformation times, and by this means to secure a fuller recognition of the widespread activity of the Church of England in former days. Hospitals played an important part in the social life of the Middle Ages, and from the study of them much may be learnt of the habits of a distant past.

At the outset it will be well to make clear what the hospital was, and what it was not. It was an ecclesiastical, not a medical, institution. It was for care rather than cure : for the relief of the body, when possible, but pre-eminently for the refreshment of the soul. By manifold religious observances, the staff sought to elevate and dis-cipline character. They endeavoured, as the body decayed, to strengthen the soul and prepare it for the future life. Faith and love were more predominant features in hospital life than were skill and science.

It will surprise many to learn that—apart from actual monasteries and friaries—there existed upwards of 750 such charitable institutions in Mediæval England.[1] To appreciate the relative magnitude of this number, it must be remembered that the total population was smaller than that of London at the present day. The fact proves that clergy and laity were battling bravely with social problems. There existed a sense of responsi-bility, causing real charitable effort, although mediæval methods may appear mistaken in the light of modern scientific and economic principles.

The study of these ancient charities calls attention to the following points. The first is the extent of leprosy in England. There are, indeed, conflicting opinions con-cerning the prevalence of the disease, but it is certain that the figure mentioned above includes over 200 hospitals occupied at one time by lepers. Secondly, a number of the early foundations were in the main houses of hospitality for strangers; and this testifies to the widespread practice of pilgrimage. There were also general hos-pitals in which temporary and permanent relief was

[1] Nearly 800 are set down in the appended list, but some are uncertain.

given to needy persons of all sorts and conditions. Some
were very small institutions, mere cottage-hospitals. It
is often impossible to ascertain the character of an ancient
charity. As long ago as 1594, it was reported concerning St. Edmund's, Gateshead: "the poor . . . are
and have been indifferently of both kindes as men and
women; but whether sicke or wholl, lepers or way
fairinge, so they be poore, needie, and indigente, is note
respected." On the other hand, in the case of large
towns, hospitals were often differentiated. Situated in the
main street, perhaps, was an infirmary-almshouse for the
sick and helpless; near a frequented gate stood a hostel
for passing pilgrims and others; outside the walls there
would be at least one leper-hospital.

It is not possible to be precise in chronology, or even
to give approximate dates. In Chantry Surveys there is
often a memorandum that no foundation can be shown,
this being lost in obscurity, and the house founded "before time of memory." Probably the earliest authentic
fact relating to charitable houses other than monasteries
is that concerning the Saxon hospital at York, for although, in the words of Canon Raine, "its beginning is
enveloped in an atmosphere of historical romance," the
munificence of Athelstan enables us to date its origin
about the year 937.

The year 1547 serves as a useful limit to our period, and
may well for the purposes of this book denote the close
of the Middle Ages in England. Its selection in no way
implies a lack of continuity in the Church with which
every hospital was intimately associated,—yet it marks

a time of transition. Charity was crippled for a time by the confiscations of endowments designed for the relief of the destitute, until a new generation of philanthropists arose and endeavoured to replace them. Thomas Fuller truly says, "the reformed Religion in England hath been the Mother of many brave Foundations." To support this he instances certain famous hospitals, as that at Warwick, built by the Earl of Leicester (1571); Croydon, by Archbishop Whitgift (1596); Guildford, by Archbishop Abbot (before 1617), and Sutton's Charterhouse (1611). There is, indeed, no fundamental difference between the earlier and later almshouses of the sixteenth century. The author of *A History of English Philanthropy* gives two reasons for using the period of the dissolution of monasteries as a starting-point. "It was then," he says, "that modern problems began to formulate themselves with great precision; and charity was then ceasing to be under the immediate direction and tutelage of the Church." For the same reasons, the year 1547 is here used to conclude the earlier philanthropic era.

A tabulated list of hospitals will be found in Appendix B. Additions and corrections are earnestly invited by the author, as local and particular knowledge is required to make it accurate and exhaustive. From this list are excluded such infirmaries as formed an integral part of a monastic house; but in cases where some abbey maintained a separate institution outside its gates (with distinct constitution, separate dedication-name, and sometimes a separate seal), the foundation is set down as a hospital. The institutions known as Colleges have no place unless, indeed, they maintained bedemen. The "House of Converts" does, however, rightly belong to our subject, for it was an almshouse and industrial home. "Hospitals" of the Orders of the Temple and St. John of Jerusalem are excluded, because they differ in character, although the work they carried on was partly the same. Moreover, as they formed part of great societies, famous in and beyond Europe, they have their own historians. Houses of the Knights of St. Lazarus must, however, consistency notwithstanding, find a place, because any account of relief provided for lepers would be incomplete if that comparatively small Order were passed over. "Hospital" was a wide-embracing term, and the occasional application of the word to religious foundations of one kind or another has not always been accounted a reason for their inclusion.

The history of many houses is obscure, limited in some cases to a single reference. The great scholars Bishop Tanner and Sir William Dugdale reaped harvests, which are garnered in their Monasticons; yet even a humble student may now glean after them by means of the invaluable printed Calendars of the Public Record Office. The labours of the Historical Manuscripts Commission are likewise fruitful. Wills are useful as showing the period up to which these institutions had popular support. Although Appendix B was mainly compiled before the issue of the Victoria County History, certain shires have received several additions from that great work, the forthcoming volumes of which will doubtless supplement the present list. Episcopal archives throw light upon hospital-life, as upon every department of ecclesiastical history; fresh information and confirmatory evidence about which will be forthcoming when, by means of the Canterbury and York Society and other Record Societies, more Registers become accessible. It is much to be desired that local Archæological Societies should take up and develop the history of particular houses. It is difficult to ascertain which ancient charities still continue, but an attempt has been made to record approximately in the appended table such endowments as now exist.

Grateful thanks are due to those who have assisted the writer in her task. And first, to the Lord Bishop of Bristol, whose kind offer to contribute the Preface to this volume is only the latest proof of the ever-helpful interest he has taken in the whole work. Mention must also be made of Mr. R. C. Fowler, of the Public Record Office, who, after personally examining the List of Foundations, gave hints for its improvement. The Rev. C. S. Taylor, F.S.A. and the Rev. Canon Wordsworth have given invaluable assistance, particularly by the translation of the Office found in Appendix A. In various ways help has been rendered by Miss Arnold-Forster, Professor G. H. Leonard, Mr. W. F. Rawnsley, and by friends and correspondents too numerous to mention. Lastly, it remains for the writer to acknowledge her indebtedness to the Rev. Dr. Cox, General Editor of the Series, without whose kindly encouragement she would never have ventured to go beyond a private study of the subject in hand.

The Spyttell hous.[1]

ℭ. Copland.

ℭ. Syr, J pray you, who hath of you relefe?

ℭ. Porter.

ℭ. Forsoth they that be at suche myschefe
That for theyr lyuyng can do no labour
  And haue no frendes to do them socour
As old people seke and impotent
  Poore women in chyldbed haue here easement
Weyke men sore wounded by great byolence
  And sore men eaten with pockes and pestylence
And honest folke fallen in great pouerte
  By mischaunce or other infyrmyte
May faryng men and maymed souldyours
  Haue theyr relyef in this poore hous of ours
And all other which we seme good and playne
  Haue here lodgyng for a nyght or twayne
Bedred folke, and suche as can not craue
  In these places moost relyef they haue
And yf they hap within our place to dye
  Than are they buryed well and honestly
But not euery unseke stoborne knaue
  For than we shold ouer many haue.

---

[1] From *The hye way to the Spyttell hous* (*circa* 1536), in which Robert Copland speaks with the Porter of a London hospital, probably St. Bartholomew's.

MEDIÆVAL HOSPITALS OF ENGLAND

PART ONE

CHAPTER I

HOSPITALS FOR WAYFARERS AND THE SICK

" Founded for the maintenance of poor pilgrims and other infirm persons resorting thither to remain until they are healed of their infirmities."
" For the poor, for persons going to Rome, for others coming to Canterbury and needing shelter, and for lying-in women." (St. Thomas', Canterbury.)

i. ST. JOHN'S HOSPITAL, OXFORD

THE earliest charitable institutions of England were houses of hospitality. In sketching the development of these guest-houses we must bear in mind that the hospital (derived from *hospes*, a host or guest) was a wayside shelter for all comers.

FIRST PERIOD (*circa* 925–1170)

Travellers were exposed to peril by the rudeness of the times, but in those early days hospitality was regarded as a solemn obligation. To receive any stranger was a duty: to welcome the passing pilgrim was a sacred privilege. Although the private entertainment of guests was widely practised, some public institutions were required. Tradition tells of at least two "hospitals" or hospices founded in the tenth century (925–940). Both were in Yorkshire,[1] one being in the distant country parts, the other in the populous town. At Flixton in Holderness was a house of refuge "to preserve travellers from being devoured by the wolves and other voracious forest beasts."[2] The city of York, on the other hand, was so great a place of thoroughfare that it was impossible to entertain all who came. Athelstan, recognizing that the Canons of the Minster were men of holy life, active in helping the needy who flocked to them, assisted them in their hospitality by the foundation of St. Peter's hospital.

Two other early houses of charity are ascribed to the Saxon bishops Oswald and Wulstan of Worcester. In the eleventh century at least we emerge from tradition, for it seems clear that St. Wulstan founded that hospital near his cathedral city which afterwards bore his name. It will be remembered that bishops were especially bound by their vows at consecration to be given to hospitality. In pre-Norman days, the solemn question was in substance what is asked to-day: "Wilt thou shew mercy and kindness, for the name of the Lord, to the poor, the stranger, and all in want?" (*pauperibus et peregrinis omnibusque indigentibus*). To this the elected bishop re-

---

[1] There were probably other Saxon hospitals. Leland notes the tradition that St. Giles', Beverley, and St. Nicholas', Pontefract, were founded "afore the Conquest."

[2] Dugdale, charter temp. Henry VI.

plied, "I will." This formula occurs in the Exeter Pontifical, compiled about nine hundred years ago, and is repeated in Osmund's Sarum Use.

There were, of course, pilgrims among those who sojourned in early hostels. Englishmen have always loved travel. Not only did our Saxon forefathers journey to Rome (receiving shelter by the way in hospitals of English foundation), but they constantly visited their national shrines. Probably a fresh impetus was given to pilgrimage by the coming of the Normans. Monastic life was strengthened, and this was a guarantee of hospitality. "Guests are to be received as if they were Christ Himself," said the rule of St. Benedict. In the century after the Conquest, as in those which preceded it, the chief works of mercy were done in the monastery. There was the *hospitium* within the abbey-gate, as at St. Mary's, York; and the "Strangers' Hall" at Winchester. Then followed the shelter outside the walls, as at Battle, referred to (*circa* 1076) as "the house of the pilgrims which is called the hospital." During the twelfth century more independent foundations became common. All sorts and conditions of men were lodged—wayfarers, invalids, and even lepers.

About the year 1148, St. Bartholomew's, Smithfield, was the resort of sick pilgrims, of whom "many and innumerable were schewid tokynnys of myracles." The patients who flocked to the famous shrine and hospital were "langwissyng men greuyd with uariant sorys"; one sought "remedie of his akynge hede," another suffered from "bleriednes of yen" (eyes), and yet another from "ryngyng of his erys." Victims of the falling sickness (epilepsy), paralysis, dropsy, fevers, insanity, found relief; deaf and dumb were healed; a child born blind received sight from "the heuenly leche."

Theobald, Archbishop of Canterbury, about 1141, invited help for "the hospital house of Dover, which two brethren, Osbern and Godwin, are diligently building for the reception of the poor and strangers." This hospital of St. Bartholomew (Buckland) was also used for lepers. The need of further provision for travellers was felt, and a benefactor made extensive grants on condition that a house was provided for the reception of needy people disembarking from ships : before 1163 reference is made to the *hospitium* for strangers. It was doubtless frequented by voyagers returning from the Crusades ; but before long an event occurred which brought multitudes to Dover, and then the old hospital proving insufficient, became chiefly the resort of lepers, and a new Maison Dieu was built near the quay. (See Frontispiece.)

SECOND PERIOD (*circa* 1170–1270)

The year 1170 marks an epoch, ushering in the great pilgrimage within and towards England. When the shrine of St. Thomas of Canterbury became the goal of pious wayfarers it was necessary to find accommodation for them. The hospitals of Canterbury and Southwark bearing the martyr's name were among the earliest. Within a few years such houses (often called *Domus Dei*) were founded in most of the southern ports and along the Pilgrims' Way, as at Dover, Ospringe, and Maidstone. At Strood "the poor, weak, infirm and impotent, as well neighbouring inhabitants as travellers from distant

PLATE 1

places," were cared for "until they die or depart healed."
Norfolk, like Kent, was studded with houses of charity,
especially near the highway to Walsingham. Thirteen
pilgrims were lodged at Bec, near Billingford. At
Thetford there was a hospital near the passage
of the river. Among other early hostels we may
enumerate those of Newcastle, Hexham, Ripon, Stamford, Aynho, London (St. Mary's), Bridgwater, and
Ledbury.

The hospital was a guest-house and infirmary in one.
That on the outskirts of Oxford was called in a charter
(*circa* 1194) *Herebergeria Hospitalis S. Joh. Bapt.;* in
1233 this was refounded (Fig. 1) "that therein infirm
people and strangers might receive remedy of their health
and necessity." The inmates of St. Nicholas', Salisbury,
are described as passengers (*transeuntes*) and as sick
and infirm (*egroti et infirmi*). The same two-fold work
of charity was carried on at Chichester, as shown by
St. Mary's statutes :—

"If anyone in infirm health and destitute of friends should
seek admission for a term, until he shall recover, let him be
gladly received and assigned a bed. . . . In regard to the
poor people who are received late at night, and go forth
early in the morning, let the warden take care that their
feet are washed, and, as far as possible, their necessities
attended to."

There is a MS. in the British Museum entitled *The
Pilgrim.* It is an allegorical poem in the manner of the
"Pilgrim's Progress," and sets forth the adventures of
the traveller. The illustration (Pl. I) and description
were probably taken from experience of earthly pilgrimage. "Charity" is seen welcoming strangers,

at which work she was always busy in mediæval
England :—

> " And I suppose for my beste
> There to herborewe and to reste
> On ther cam and preyed me
> And her name was *Charite*
> To pylgrymes in goodly wyse
> Sche dyde moste trewely the seruyse
> With chere benygne and glad uysage
> She brought hem to ther herbergage."[1]

Among shrines which the pious Englishman visited may
be mentioned Bury St. Edmunds, Westminster, Durham,
Beverley, St. Albans, Waltham.[2]

THIRD PERIOD (1270–1470)

(a) *Pilgrimage and Vagrancy.*—The greatest century
of pilgrimage was past, but vagrancy was an ever-
increasing problem, and inasmuch as
it affected the social life of England, it
affected hospitals, directly or indirectly.
In the Statute of Labourers, drawn up
in 1350, an attempt had been made to
restrain desultory wandering, idleness,
mendicancy and indiscriminate almsgiving. This was followed by many
ordinances, local and general. By a
proclamation in 1359 the municipal
authorities of London de-
clared that such unworthy
beggars "do waste divers
alms, which would otherwise

2. A PILGRIM

be given to many poor folks, such as lepers, blind, halt,

[1] Cott. Tib. A., vii. f. 90.
[2] See also J. C. Wall, *Shrines of British Saints* in this Series.

and persons oppressed with old age and divers other maladies." In 1369 they issued a precept "for mendicants, vagrants and pilgrims to leave the city." The Statute of Westminster (1383) ordered inquiry concerning vagabonds "wandering from place to place, running in the country more abundantly than they were wont in times past." The Act of 1388 declared that those who "go in pilgrimage as beggars" when fit for employment, should be dealt with according to the previous Statute. It will be observed that these measures were framed from an economic standpoint, not to check pilgrimage as such.

Although pilgrimage was declining, there were still many pilgrims. Some of these were professional palmers, and hirelings fulfilling vows by proxy; for there are numerous bequests in the fourteenth century to persons undertaking journeys on the testator's behalf to Canterbury, Walsingham, and Bury St. Edmunds, as well as to St. James of Compostella, Rome, or the Holy Land. The special "Jubilee" at Canterbury in 1420 was attended by 100,000 persons, and in 1434 thousands set sail for Compostella.

(b) *Provision for temporary relief.*—Existing houses of hospitality were kept up, but a growing tendency to discriminate amongst applicants may be noticed. In many cases more beds were reserved for chronic invalids than for casual comers. St. Thomas' hospital, Canterbury, carried on its old work, but the renewed statutes of Archbishop Stratford (1342) direct "that poor pilgrims in good health shall be entertained only for one night . . . that greater regard shall be had for the sick than for the well pilgrims." With some diplomacy it describes itself, in a petition to the Pope, as designed "for persons going to Rome (*Romipete*), for others coming to Canterbury and needing shelter,"[1] etc.

The chief building period was over, as far as this particular kind of temporary provision is concerned, but one or two new foundations must be mentioned.   St. John's, Winchester, was built about 1275 "for the relief of sick and lame soldiers, poor pilgrims, and necessitous wayfaring men, to have diet and lodging thereto fit and convenient for one night or longer, as their abilities to travel gave leave."   In 1393, the Bishop of Ely offered an indulgence to persons contributing to the sustentation of a hospital at Brentford, which consisted of a chapel, newly constructed, "with two houses built there, furnished with beds and other necessaries for the entertainment of poor travellers."   The old hospital at Brackley was reconstituted for the same purpose (1425).   It was, however, suppressed sixty years later, because hospitality was being neglected.

One special form of temporary relief came to the front about this time.   The assistance of women in childbirth was named in the Petition and Statute of 1414 as part of the recognized aim and scope of hospital charity.   The heading to this chapter alludes to the work undertaken at St. Thomas', Canterbury, in 1363.   The foundation deed of Holy Trinity, Salisbury, sets forth that "lying-in women are cared for until they are delivered, recovered and churched."   The Spital near Blyth was newly constructed in 1446 for the lodging of strangers and distressed women.

It is recorded that the two London infirmaries of St. Mary without Bishopsgate and St. Bartholomew under-

---

[1] Cal. Pap. Letters, 4, p. 36.

PLATE II

HOSPITAL OF ST. THOMAS, CANTERBURY

FOR PILGRIMS

took this work ; in both institutions the touching provision was made that if the mother died, her child should be brought up there until the age of seven.[1] In the year 1437 privileges were granted to the latter hospital "in consideration of their great charges in receiving the poor, feeble and infirm, keeping women in childbirth until their purification, and sometimes feeding their infants until weaned." William Gregory, a citizen of London, describing in his commonplace book various foundations, says of "Bartholomewe ys Spetylle" :—

"Hyt ys a place of grete comforte to pore men as for hyr loggyng, and yn specyalle unto yong wymmen that have mysse done that ben whythe chylde. There they ben delyueryde, and unto the tyme of puryfycacyon they have mete and drynke of the placys coste, and fulle honestely gydyd and kepte."

General hospitals for the sick were thus in process of development. St. Bartholomew's was steadily fulfilling its founder's vow to provide a place for the "recreacion of poure men." After three and a half centuries of usefulness, a roll of 1464 records with approbation "works done within the hospital in relief of poor pilgrims, soldiers, sailors and others of all nations."

FOURTH PERIOD (*circa* 1470–1547)

(*a*) It is evident that pilgrimage was no longer an important factor in the social life of the country. The daily resort to shrines had practically ceased, but the special anniversaries were kept. Such pious travellers as there were, lodged chiefly in inns. At Glastonbury a Pilgrims' Inn was built by Abbot John, about the year 1475, to accommodate those visiting the holy places of

---

[1] Close Rolls 1344, 1353.

St. Joseph of Arimathæa and St. Dunstan. A later abbot, Richard Beere, writing to Archbishop Warham to defend the genuineness of St. Dunstan's relics, stated that people had come from far and near to visit the new shrine, especially upon St. Dunstan's Day (1508).[1] Although the regular stream of pilgrims to Canterbury was no longer seen day by day, the great " Jubilee " celebrations were popular, the last one being kept in 1520. At that time the needs of visitors were met by special provision, a post being set up in the main street with "letters expressing the ordering of uitell and lodyng for pylgrymes." Probably the bailiffs and citizens made all arrangements for bed and board as they had done in 1420.

Vagrancy still constituted an increasingly grave problem. By " An Acte agaynst vacabounds and beggers," in 1495 (re-enacted 1503), previous legislation was amended and "every vagabound heremyte or pilgryme," partially exempt hitherto, was henceforth compelled to fare like wandering soldier, shipman or university clerk. In a letter from Henry VIII to the Mayor of Grimsby it is observed that the relief of the impotent is much diminished by the importunate begging of the sturdy and idle, and it is required that measures be taken " that the weedes over growe not the corne."[2] The Statutes became increasingly stern, and able-bodied beggars were scourged with the lash from town to town by the Act of 1530–1. But " the greatest severities hitherto enacted were mild in comparison with the severe provisions of the enactment " of the first year of Edward VI (1547). If the young king's father had literally chastised beggars with whips, his own counsellors desired that they should be chastised with scor-

---

[1] Chron. and Mem. 63, p. 434.   [2] Hist. MSS. 14th R. (8) 249.

pions. They might be reduced to the condition of slaves : their owners might put a ring round their necks or limbs, and force them to work by beating and chains, whilst a runaway could be branded on the face with a hot iron.[1] This brutal law was repealed two years later.

(*b*) Where towns were few and far between, the need of shelter for strangers was especially felt. Extensive works of hospitality were done by religious houses, particularly in the northern counties. That fresh provision, although on a small scale, was still made for shelter, indicates its necessity. When an almshouse was built at Northallerton (1476), accommodation was made not only for thirteen pensioners, but for two destitute and distressed travellers, who should stay a night and no longer. A hostel solely for temporary shelter was founded at Durham (1493). One Cuthbert Billingham directed the provision of eight beds in a "massendeue or spittel," where "all poore trauellyng people ther herbery or logyng asking for the loue of Gode shall be herbered and logide." In Westmorland, a little hospital, with two beds for passers-by, was built by John Brunskill at Brough-under-Stainmoor (1506): it was situated on the pass into Yorkshire.

At seaports and in places of thoroughfare, shelter was still provided for travellers. God's House, Southampton, expended £28 annually upon "daily hospitality to wayfarers and strangers from beyond the sea," and similar charity was provided at Dover. Leland describes St. Thomas', Canterbury, as "An Hospital within the Town on the Kinges Bridge for poore Pylgrems and way faring men." At Sandwich there was a "Harbinge" attached to St. John's almshouse. Provision was made for lodgers,

[1] C. J. Ribton-Turner, *Vagrants and Vagrancy*, 1887.

and the buildings included "the chambre of harber for strange wemen, the gentilmen chambre and the long harbur chamber " (1489). The town authorities ordered "that no persons do harbour beggars, who are to resort to St. John's Hospital " (1524).

The existing provision for temporary relief was in fact wholly inadequate. In the metropolis, for example, there was a crying need. It was stated by Henry VII in 1509 that :—

"there be fewe or noon such commune Hospitalls within this our Reame, and that for lack of them, infinite nombre of pouer nedie people miserably dailly die, no man putting hande of helpe or remedie."

The king, recognizing the need, planned to convert the old Savoy Palace into a magnificent institution (Pl. XIV) in which "to lodge nightly one hundred poor folks." If this charity corresponded with the recent Statute, it would relieve those vagrants who alone were exempt, namely, women in travail and persons in extreme sickness. The king contemplated building institutions similar to the Savoy in York and Coventry, but the design was not carried out.

The problems arising from true poverty and false mendicancy were, of course, intimately connected with hospital life. A graphic picture of the difficulties which beset administrators of charity about the year 1536 is given by Robert Copland in *The hye way to the Spyttell hous*. The author states that one wintry day, he took refuge from the snow-storm in the porch of a hospital, probably St. Bartholomew's. Here he got deep into conversation with the porter of the house. While they talked, there gathered at the gate people of very poor estate,—lame, blind, barefoot—and Copland, who does not despise the honest poor, only those who live in need and idleness, inquires whether they admit all who ask for lodging. The porter at first answers, " Forsooth, yes," and Copland goes on to protest against indiscriminate hospitality :—

> " Me thynk that therin ye do no ryght
> Nor all suche places of hospytalyte
> To confort people of suche iniquyte.
> But syr I pray you, of your goodnes and fauour
> Tell me which ye leaue, and which ye do socour."

The porter replies that the house is no supporter of sham beggars. There are some who counterfeit leprosy, and others who put soap in their mouth to make it foam, and fall down as if they had "Saynt Cornelys euyll." He goes on to describe those who hang about by day and sleep at night at St. Bartholomew's church door —drunkards, spendthrifts, swearers and blasphemers, those who wear soldiers' clothing, but are vagabonds, and men who pretend to have been shipwrecked. Many of these live by open beggary, with bag, dish and staff :—

> " And euer haunteth among such ryf raf
> One tyme to this spyttell, another to that."

The porter intimates that an effort is made to discriminate among those daily harboured, but he confesses that they are obliged to receive many unsatisfactory men, and disreputable women so numerous that they are weary of them ; but they refuse stubborn knaves who are not ill, for they would have over many. Indeed, the aim of the hospital is to relieve those who cannot work and are friendless—the sick, aged, bedridden, diseased, wayfaring men, maimed soldiers, and honest folk fallen into poverty. (See p. xxiv.)

It is clear, however, that during the sixteenth century there was much genuine distress besides unthrifty beggary and sham sickness. From various economic causes there was a considerable increase of destitution. Legislation entirely failed to solve the problem of an ever-shifting population. The Statute of 1530-1 had recognized the value of charitable foundations by its clause :—" provided also, that it be lawful to all masters and governors of hospitals, to lodge and harbour any person or persons of charity and alms." Although hospitals had been abused, the neglect of the sick and homeless which their reduction involved was a far worse evil. One writer after another breaks out into descriptions of the increased poverty and pain. Brinklow, in *The Lamentacyon of a Christian agaynst the Cytye of London* (1545), bewails the condition of the poor :—

" London, beyng one of the flowers of the worlde, as touch-inge worldlye riches, hath so manye, yea innumerable of poore people forced to go from dore to dore, and to syt openly in the stretes a beggynge, and many . . . lye in their howses in most greuous paynes, and dye for lacke of ayde of the riche. I think in my judgement, under heaven is not so lytle prouision made for the pore as in London, of so riche a Cytie." [1]

Again, referring to the old order and the new, *A Suppli-cation of the Poore Commons* (1546) speaks of poor impotent creatures as " now in more penurye then euer they were." Once they had scraps, now they have nothing. " Then had they hospitals, and almeshouses to be lodged in, but nowe they lye and storue in the stretes. Then was their number great, but nowe much greater."

[1] Early Eng. Text Soc. Extra Series 22, p. 90.

PLATE III

ST. JOHN'S HOSPITAL, CANTERBURY

CHAPTER II

HOMES FOR THE FEEBLE AND DESTITUTE

' Hospitals in cities, boroughs and divers other places . . . to sustain blind men and women . . . and people who have lost their goods and are fallen into great misfortune." [1]

THE majority of hospitals were for the support of infirm and aged people. Such a home was called indiscriminately "hospital," "Maison Dieu," "almshouse" or "bedehouse." It was, as in the case of Kingston-upon-Hull, "God's House . . . to provide a habitation for thirteen poor men and women broken by age, misfortune or toil, who cannot gain their own livelihood." It occupied the place now filled by almshouses, union workhouses, and homes for chronic invalids or incurables.

(I) ALMSHOUSES IN CITIES

One of the most ancient hospitals for permanent relief was St. John's, Canterbury, founded about 1084, and still existing as an almshouse. (Pl. III.) Eadmer tells us that it was intended for men suffering from various infirmities and for women in ill health. The inmates are described as a hundred poor, who by reason of age and disease cannot earn their bread ; and again, as a hundred brothers and sisters blind, lame, deaf and sick. It is

[1] Rolls of Parl. 2 Hen. V, Vol. IV, p. 19 b Petitions, No. III.

15

characteristic that the earliest foundation of this type
should be found in the chief cathedral city of England :
every such town had a hospital in connection with the
See.   The prince-bishops of Durham, for example,
provided houses of charity around the city and at their
manors.   Ralph Flambard built St. Giles', Kepier ; Philip
of Poitiers founded St. James' near Northallerton ;
Robert de Stichill, St. Mary's, Greatham ; and Nicholas
of Farnham, St. Edmund's, Gateshead.   The most
famous episcopal hospital remaining is that of St. Cross,
near Winchester. (Pl. VIII.)

Other charities were associated with cathedral clergy.
There was a hospital for the poor in the precincts of
St. Paul's Cathedral.   Before the year 1190, one of the
canons gave his house for the purpose, and the Dean
endowed it with certain tithes.   St. Nicholas', Salisbury,
founded by the Bishop, was afterwards committed to
the Dean and Chapter.   The existing almshouses in
Chichester and Hereford were likewise associated with
those cathedrals.

(2) ALMSHOUSES IN BOROUGHS

The municipal control of charity is an ancient custom.
Before burgesses were called to Parliament, townsmen
of Exeter, Northampton, Nottingham and Wallingford
were trustees of the hospitals of St. John in those
places.   The leper-houses of Lynn and Southampton
were also early instances of municipal administration.   In
the reign of Edward I the hospitals in Scarborough were
declared to have been "founded by burgesses of the
town of old."   During the fourteenth century, if not
before, the "keepers" of Beverley, the "jurats" of Hythe,

and the commonalties of Bedford, Gloucester, Huntingdon, Pevensey, Sandwich, Wilton, etc., controlled almshouses in those towns.[1] Old deeds of the Winchester corporation refer to Devenish's hospital as "oure hous of Synt John." Freemen had an advantage, if not a monopoly, when seeking entrance into houses under municipal supervision. The "Customals" of Rye and Winchelsea show that men and women "who have been in good love and fame all their time, and have neither goods nor chattels whereof to live" were received without payment into the hospitals of the town. Bubwith's almshouse, Wells, was to receive men so poor that they could not live except by begging, and so decrepit that they were unable to beg from door to door. Reduced burgesses were assigned "the more honourable places and beds." At St. Ursula's, Chester, candidates were preferred who had been one of "the twenty-four," or the widows of aldermen and common council-men.

In some towns charities were not directly connected with the municipality but with local trustees. St. Katherine's, Rochester, was under the governance and correction of the parish priest, the city bailiff and the founder's heirs. Davy of Croydon put his almshouse under the vicar and other townsmen, answerable ultimately to the Mercers' Company, and provided that his pensioners should be "householders or trewe labourers" from within four miles, preference being given to residents of long standing, if of good character and destitute.

---

[1] St. John's, Bedford, was intended only for townsmen; all such applying to the master for relief were to be received, but "all poore folkes dwellyng without the same town to be expulsed and put out." *Chantry Cert.* (ed. J. E. Brown).

(3) GILD ALMSHOUSES

The gilds were an important factor in the economy of towns, and their works of piety sometimes included hospital maintenance. St. Cross, Colchester, having been practically disendowed—the advowson was granted to the commonalty in aid of the repair of the town walls—was revived in 1407 as an almshouse under the auspices of St. Helen's gild. Barstaple of Bristol founded his almshouse for twenty-four poor, (granting the advowson to the mayor and commonalty,) and also a fraternity for himself, his wife and others who wished to join. The institutions were incorporated separately. Each community was ruled by a warden, possessed a common seal, and had power to make ordinances.[1] In other cases a private individual attached his charity to an existing association to secure continuity of rule. Hosyer's almshouse in Ludlow, e.g., "appertained" to the Palmers' gild. These religious societies often began in connection with some trade. At Winchester, financial assistance was given to St. John's by "the fraternity of St. John, in the hospital there by providence of the Tailors of Winton first ordained."

The craft-gilds and city companies supported disabled members in places like the Maison Dieu of the Shoe-makers at York, called also the Bedehouse of the Cordyners. There are countless references in wills to the poor of the Drapers' or Fullers' Halls, etc. Although such institutions were really almshouses, they are not (with certain exceptions) included in the appended list, and their history must be sought in connection with the trades.

[1] Pat. 9 Hen. IV, Pt. i. m. 8.

In ports, special provision was made for seafaring men. Leland remarks that St. Bartholomew's, Sandwich, was "fyrst ordened for Maryners desesid and hurt." The Fraternity of the Blessed Trinity at Kingston-upon-Hull maintained "an house of alms of poor mariners," and a similar institution was incorporated with Trinity House, Newcastle-upon-Tyne. A society of merchants at Bristol provided for poor seamen within the old hospital of St. Bartholomew (1445). Upon arrival in port, masters and mariners alike contributed to the charity because "the wheche prest and pore peple may nott be founden ne susteyned withoute grete coste." This fraternity was in fact a benefit-club, for members became eligible for admission after paying their dues for seven years. The community was especially bound to pray for seamen in time of peril.

(4) PRIVATE ALMSHOUSES

In villages, the lord of the manor or squire provided a charity for his retainers, tenants or neighbours. This was done at Arundel, Donnington near Newbury, Heytesbury, Ewelme, Thame, etc. A man who had risen to prosperity occasionally remembered his birthplace in this way, as Chichele did at Higham Ferrers.

Although most hospitals were of a general character, some were designed for particular classes of persons, such as homeless Jews, poor clergy, decayed gentle-people, women and children.

(5) HOMES FOR JEWS

The chief "hospital" for Jewish converts was in London. The inmates were not ailing in health, but they needed succour because they were unable to earn a living, and were cut off from their own families as apostates. Converts were often sent to monasteries for maintenance. The names of almost five hundred, together with the particular houses that received them, are recorded in one roll of 39 Henry III.[1]

Special provision for the maintenance of converted Jews was made in 1232, when Henry III founded the House

3. HOUSE OF CONVERTS, LONDON

of Converts, Hospital of St. Mary or "Converts' Inn," near the Old Temple. Within twenty years Matthew Paris described its purpose, also making a drawing (Fig. 3) in the margin :—

"To this house converted Jews retired, leaving their Jewish blindness, and had a home and a safe refuge for their whole lives, living under an honourable rule, with sufficient sustenance without servile work or the profits of usury. So it hap-

---

[1] Tovey, *Anglia Judaica*, 227.

pened that in a short time a large number were collected there. And now, being baptized and instructed in the Christian law, they live a praiseworthy life under a rector specially deputed to govern them."[1]

The year of this chronicler's death (1256), upwards of 160 convert brothers received tunics from the king's almoner. Probably about half were inmates, and half unattached pensioners. The number may have been increased from interested motives on account of the persecution of Jews which followed the supposed "horrible crime lately perpetrated in the city of Lincoln, of a Christian boy crucified." In January 1256, pardon was granted to John the convert, who was a Jew of Lincoln when the so-called "little St. Hugh" was put to death.

The *Domus Conversorum* was rebuilt by Edward I, who bestowed much attention upon it. By his ordinance, the pensioners were taught handicrafts and trained to support themselves. He ordered that school should be kept and that suitable converts might be educated as clerks or chaplains. St. Mary's was an industrial home or training institution for persecuted Jewish Christians, who were safe only under royal protection. Another roll of the same year shows that a special effort was made at that time to evangelize the Jews. Orders had recently been given to repress notorious blasphemers, and those who after baptism had been "perverted to Jewish wickedness" Edward also directed that strenuous efforts should be made by the Friar Preachers for their conversion. Finally he set himself to improve the endowments of the institution :—

" He therefore, in order that those who have already turned

[1] Chron. and Mem. 44, iii. 262.

from their blindness to the light of the Church may be strengthened in the firmness of their faith, and those who still persist in their error may more willingly and readily turn to the grace of the faith, has taken measures, under divine guidance, to provide healthfully for their maintenance."[1]

The House of Converts was then supporting ninety-seven persons. Of these fifty-one remained in 1308. After the great expulsion in 1290, the numbers were quickly reduced. In 1327, there were twenty-eight. In 1344, the institution supported eight converts and seven admitted for other causes. After that date the pensioners dwindled to two. During the fifteenth century, a few foreign Jews were received from time to time, the household varying between eight and three. The hospital was empty in the days of Edward VI, and remained so until 1578 ; its subsequent history is related by Adler.

The *Domus Conversorum* in Oxford was likewise founded by Henry III. There, says Wood, "all Jews and infidells that were converted to the Christian faith were ordained to have sufficient maintenance. By which meanes it was soe brought about that noe small number of these converts had their abode in this place and were baptized and instructed." The building (figured in Skelton's *Oxonia Antiqua*) subsequently became a Hall for scholars.

According to Leland and Stow there were homes, or, at least, schools, for Jews in London and Bristol before Henry III turned his attention to this work. Stow, referring to the original foundation of St. Thomas' hospital, Southwark (1213), says that it was a house of alms for converts and poor children. Leland, quoting from a manuscript of the Kalendars' Gild in Bristol, states that

[1] Pat. 8 Edw. I, m. 17.

in the time of Henry II there were "Scholes ordeyned in Brightstow by them for the Conversion of the Jewes." The information (which he gleaned from the *Little Red Book*) originated in the bishop's inquisition made in 1318, which found that Robert Fitz-Harding and the Kalendars "established the schools of Bristol for teaching Jews and other little ones under the government of the same gild and the protection of the mayor." It should be noticed that *scola* also refers to a Jewish synagogue, but the term *Schola Judæorum* is applied by Matthew Paris to the House of Converts in London.

4. POOR PRIESTS' HOSPITAL, CANTERBURY

(6) HOMES FOR POOR CLERGY AND FOR LAY GENTLEFOLK

Diocesan clergy-homes were provided during the thirteenth century in most ecclesiastical centres. At Canterbury, the Archdeacon built (before 1225) the Poor Priests' hospital (Fig. 4). St. Richard of Chichester began a similar charity at Windeham in his diocese. Walter de Merton designed a small institution at Basingstoke for "ministers of the altar whose strength is failing," and incurables of Merton College. There were three beds for chaplains at St. Wulstan's, Worcester, and the Stratford gild intended to initiate a hospital for the diocesan clergy. To St. Giles', Lincoln, were admitted "needy ministers and servants and canons not able to work."

Similar retreats arose in the following century. The Bishop of Exeter built near his palace at Clist Gabriel a home for twelve blind, infirm, ancient or disabled priests, deacons and sub-deacons. The Dean of York maintained six infirm chaplains in St. Mary's, Bootham. Clergy-homes were usually founded by ecclesiastics ; but in 1329, a London layman, Elsyng by name, touched by the sufferings of the clergy in that time of scarcity, began his almshouse, ordaining that among the hundred pensioners, blind, paralytic and disabled priests should be specially cared for. The need is evident from a deed concerning St. Giles', Norwich (1340). The house had been founded for the poor " and principally to minister the necessaries of life to priests of the diocese of Norwich, who, broken down with age, or destitute of bodily strength, or labour-ing under continual disease, cannot celebrate divine service"; but the number of such priests and infirm persons "flocking to the hospital hath so grown and daily groweth" that assistance was urgently required. Although the priesthood was temporarily diminished by the pestilence of 1349, clerks acting as chantry priests were again numerous during the fifteenth century. These unbeneficed clergy, it was said, "when depressed by the weight of old age, or labouring under weak health . . .

PLATE IV

HOSPITAL OF ST. GILES, NORWICH

FOR AGED CHAPLAINS AND OTHER POOR

are by necessity compelled to wander about, begging miserably for food and raiment . . . to the displeasure of Him whose ministers they are." To put an end to this scandal, "the fraternity of St. Charity and St. John Evangelist" was founded in London (1442), and this clerical almshouse was commonly called "The Papey." Gregory, who was mayor in 1451, describes it in his note-book :—

"Pappy Chyrche in the Walle be twyne Algate and Beuysse Markes. And hyt ys a grete fraternyte of prestys and of othyr seqular men. And there ben founde of almys certayne prestys, both blynde and lame, that be empotent."

Persons of gentle birth who had suffered reverses of fortune often retreated into convents, or were received into hospitals with a semi-official position. During the fifteenth century one or two institutions arose to benefit those decayed gentlefolk who, as one has said, are of all people "most sensible of want." Staindrop College maintained a staff of priests and clerks, and certain gentle-men (*certi pauperes generosi*) and yeomen (*pauperes valecti*) who had been in the Earl of Westmorland's service. The "New Almshouse of Noble Poverty" (*Nova Domus Eleemosynaria Nobilis Paupertatis*), which Cardinal Beaufort intended to add to the original establishment of St. Cross, was never fully completed, but there are still four brethren of the professional class on the Cardinal's foundation.

(7) HOMES FOR WOMEN AND CHILDREN

One of the earliest permanent homes for women was St. Katharine's-by-the-Tower, London. The sisters of St. John's, Reading, are described as "certyn relygyous women, wydowes in chast lyuyngg in God's seruyce praying nygt and day." To provide for fatherless children and widows was part of the design of Holy Trinity, Salisbury. In two hospitals outside Lincoln this particular work was carried on. Originally served by the Gilbertine Order, they became entirely eleemosynary institutions under the care of lay-sisters. Many wills about the year 1400 allude to St. Katharine's asylum or hospital for widows, orphans, and bedemen. The daughter-house was a home for waifs and strays, namely, "certain orphans placed in danger through the negligence of their friends, and deserted, and brought into the hospital of St. Sepulchre, guarded and educated there."

A further reason for the adoption of children into the hospital family was this : that when women died in confinement, their infants were frequently kept and cared for. (See p. 9.) In connection with St. Leonard's, York, mention is made of "ministering to the poor and sick and to the infants exposed there." In 1280 there were twenty-three boys in the orphanage, with a woman in charge. Education was provided for them and for the thirty choristers. Two schoolmasters taught grammar and music. The Dean and Chapter were forbidden by the King on one occasion (1341) to meddle with the grammar school in the hospital. Among the expenses in 1369 is a gratuity to the bishop of the choir-boys. This shows, says Canon Raine, that there was a "boy-bishop" at St. Leonard's as well as in the Minster.

Nor was it uncommon thus to find young and strong side by side with aged and infirm inmates. Several almshouses maintained children. Bishop Grandisson carried out his predecessor Stapeldon's intention of adding twelve boys to the foundation of St. John's, Exeter, and Archbishop Chichele attached a boarding-school to his bedehouse at Higham Ferrers. There were children and adult pensioners in St. Katharine's, London, and in Knolles' almshouse, Pontefract.

Some hospitals had boarders or day-boarders whose studies were conducted in neighbouring schools. St. John's, Bridgwater, maintained thirteen scholars—such as were *habiles ad informandum in grammatica*—who were excused from full ritual that they might keep schools daily in the town (1298).[1] In some cases, like St. Giles', Norwich, food was provided for children who were getting free education elsewhere. At St. Cross, Winchester, seven choristers were boarded and instructed. Thirteen poor scholars from the Grammar School also received a substantial meal daily.

In other instances we find that instruction was provided without board and lodging. The lads taught in God's House, Exeter, were not inmates, like those of St. John's in that city. The master of the hospital was required to teach from three to nine boys, beginning with the alphabet and going on to the "great psalter of the holy David." In the almshouses of Ewelme and Heytesbury also there were non-resident pupils. Only the more advanced at Ewelme aspired to "the faculty of grammar." It was directed that should the school-master have no more than four "childer that actually lernes gramer, besides petettes [i.e. beginners] and reders," he should assist at matins and evensong. He must so rule his scholars that none be tedious, noisome, or troublous to the almspeople. Payment was forbidden at Heytes-

[1] Bishop Drokensford's Reg. p. 268.

bury except as a free gift, or by pupils whose friends
had a yearly income of over £10. Bishop Smyth, a
patron of learning, added a schoolmaster and usher to
his restored almshouse at Lichfield, where very poor
children were to be taught. The Grammar School connected with St. John's hospital, Banbury, became
famous.

Lastly, the development of these institutions must be
considered. Many of the almshouses built during the
twelfth and thirteenth centuries were intended from their
foundation for life-pensioners. In other cases, however,
on account of necessity or expediency, the permanent home
was evolved from one originally of a temporary character.
Charities underwent a change during the fourteenth and
fifteenth centuries. This may be attributed to various
social and economic causes—the decline of leprosy, legislation regarding vagrancy, and the redistribution of
wealth. As the number of lepers decreased, the alms
formerly bestowed upon them were available for other
necessitous persons, and some lazar-houses gradually
became retreats for aged invalids. This was chiefly
during the fifteenth century, but even about 1285 St.
Nicholas', York, is said to be "founded in the name of
lepers, and for the support of the old and feeble of the
city." Again, when it was realized that indiscriminate
hospitality encouraged vagrancy, the character of some
hospitals gradually altered. The Statute of 1388 helped
to develop local administration of charity by ordaining
that beggars unable to work must either remain in the
town where they found themselves or return to their birthplace and abide there for life.

The crying need for the permanent relief of genuine distress made itself heard. Langland, the poet of the people, called attention to the necessity of rebuilding hospitals. In his *Vision* "Truth" begs rich merchants to put their profits to good uses and "amenden meson-dieux" therewith. In 1410, and again in 1414, the Commons suggested that new almshouses might be

5. BEDE-HOUSE, STAMFORD

founded if some ecclesiastical property were confiscated. Although this was not done, many were provided through private liberality. By the redistribution of wealth and the rise of the middle classes, a fresh impetus was given to building. The chantry system also had an increasingly powerful influence upon the charity of this period. The newer foundations, even more explicitly than the older, were "bede-houses" or houses of prayer. All charitable foundations were to a certain extent chantries. Many, alas ! were solely on this account marked with the stigma of superstition, and fell under the two Acts for the dissolution of chantries : the plea of usefulness, however, happily prevailed in several cases.[1] For a time the work of building almshouses ceased, but revived after a while. In 1583 Philip Stubbes complained that although in some places the poor were relieved in hospitals, yet more provision was required :—

" For the supplie whereof, would God there might be in euerie parish an almes house erected, that the poore (such as are poore indeede) might be maintained, helped, and relieued. For until the true poore indeed be better provided for, let them neuer thinke to please God." [2]

[1] See Chapter XVI.
[2] Anatomie of Abuses, Pt. II, 43.

CHAPTER III

HOSPITALS FOR THE INSANE

"Hospitals . . . to maintain men and women who had lost their wits and memory." (Rolls of Parliament, 1414.)

LITTLE is known regarding the extent and treatment of insanity during the Middle Ages. Persons "vexed with a demon" were taken to holy places in the hope that the "fiends" might be cast out. An early thirteenth-century window at Canterbury shows a poor maniac dragged by his friends to the health-giving shrine of St. Thomas. He is tied with ropes, and they belabour him with blows from birch-rods. In the second scene he appears in his right mind, returning thanks, all instruments of discipline cast away. Even in the sixteenth century we read of pilgrimage by lunatics, especially to certain holy wells.

Formerly, all needy people were admitted into the hospital, mental invalids being herded together with those weak or diseased in body. From the chronicle of St. Bartholomew's, Smithfield, we learn that in the twelfth century mad people were constantly received as well as the deaf, dumb, blind, palsied and crippled. One young man lost "his resonable wyttys" on his journey to London. He wandered about running, not knowing whither he went. Arriving in London, he was brought to the hospital and "ther yn shorte space his witte

31

was recoueryd." Another patient was taken with the
"fallynge euill" [epilepsy], which is described as a
sickness hindering the operation of the senses. It
would seem that persons subject to fits were sometimes
placed in a lazar-house, for at St. Bartholomew's,
Rochester (1342), was one patient "struck with the
epilepsy disease."

The public did not make itself responsible for the
custody of the lunatic, whose own people were required
to guard him and others from harm. One of the
"Customs of Bristol" (1344) orders that the goods and
chattels of demented men be delivered to their friends
until they come to a good state of mind (*ad bonam
memoriam*). The sad condition of "lunatick lollers" is
described by Langland, who speaks compassionately of
this class of wanderers.

In London, the question of making special provision
for the insane came to the front about this time, for in
1369 one Denton intended to found a hospital "for poor
priests and others, men and women, who in that city
suddenly fell into a frenzy (*in frenesim*) and lost their
memory," but his plan was not carried out. Stow
mentions that the earliest asylum for distraught and
lunatic persons was near Charing Cross, "but it was said,
that some time a king of England, not liking such a kind
of people to remain so near his palace, caused them to be
removed farther off, to Bethlem without Bishopsgate."

St. Mary of Bethlehem was the most famous refuge for
the mentally disordered. In 1403 there were confined six
men deprived of reason (*mente capti*), and three other
sick, one of whom was a paralytic patient who had been
lying in the hospital for over two years. The good work

done in the institution was fully recognized. A bequest was made in 1419 to the sick and insane of St. Mary de Bedlam. A Patent Roll entry of 1437 speaks of "the succour of demented lunatics" and others, and of the necessity of cutting down these works of piety unless speedy help were forthcoming. The then town clerk, John Carpenter, recalled this need and remembered in his will (1441) "the poor madmen of Bethlehem." Another citizen, Stephen Forster, desired his executors to lay out ten pounds in food and clothing for the poor people "detained" there. Gregory, citizen and mayor, describes in his *Historical Collections* (about 1451) this asylum and its work of mercy, and it is satisfactory to hear that some were there restored to a sound mind :—

"A chyrche of Owre Lady that ys namyde Bedlam. And yn that place ben founde many men that ben fallyn owte of hyr wytte. And fulle honestely they ben kepte in that place ; and sum ben restoryde unto hyr witte and helthe a-gayne. And sum ben a-bydyng there yn for evyr, for they ben falle soo moche owte of hem selfe that hyt ys uncurerabylle unto man."

Probably the utterly incurable were doomed to those iron chains, manacles and stocks mentioned in the inventory of 1398 and quoted at the visitation of 1403 :

"Item. vj cheynes de Iren, com vj lokkes. Item iiij peir manycles de Iren. ij peir stokkys."[1]

In other parts of the country it was customary to receive persons suffering from attacks of mania into general infirmaries. At Holy Trinity, Salisbury, not only were sick persons and women in childbirth received, but mad people were to be taken care of (*furiosi custodiantur donec sensum adipiscantur*). This was at the

[1] Char. Com. Rep., xxxii. vi. 472.

close of the fourteenth century. In the petition for the
reformation of hospitals (1414) it is stated that they exist
partly to maintain those who had lost their wits and
memory (*hors de lour sennes et memoire*). Many alms-
house-statutes, however, prohibited their admission.
A regulation concerning an endowed bed in St. John's,
Coventry (1444), declared that a candidate must be "not
mad, quarrelsome, leprous, infected." At Ewelme "no
wood man" (crazy person) must be received; and an
inmate becoming "madd, or woode" was to be removed
from the Croydon almshouse.

Such disused lazar-houses as were inhabitable might
well have been utilized as places of confinement. This,
indeed, was done at Holloway near Bath. At what period
the lepers vacated St. Mary Magdalene's is not known,
but it was probably appropriated to the use of lunatics by
Prior Cantlow, who rebuilt the chapel about 1489. At
the close of the sixteenth century, St. James', Chichester,
was occupied by a sad collection of hopeless cripples,
among whom were found two idiots. A hundred years
later the bishop reported that this hospital was of small
revenue and "hath only one poor person, but she a
miserable idiot, in it."

Bethlehem Hospital was rescued by the Lord Mayor
and citizens at the Dissolution of religious houses and
continued its charitable work. In 1560 Queen Elizabeth
issued on behalf of this house an appeal of which a
facsimile may be seen in Bewes' *Church Briefs*. "Sume
be straught from there wyttes," it declares, "thuse be
kepte and mayntend in the Hospital of our Ladye of
Beddelem untyle God caule them to his marcy or to ther
wyttes agayne."

PLATE V

HARBLEDOWN HOSPITAL, NEAR CANTERBURY

ONCE USED FOR LEPERS

CHAPTER IV

THE LAZAR-HOUSE

" For the relief of divers persons smitten with this sickness and destitute and walking at large within the realm." [1] (Holloway, 1473.)

O N the outskirts of a town seven hundred years ago, the eye of the traveller would have been caught by a well-known landmark—a group of cottages with an adjoining chapel, clustering round a green enclosure. At a glance he would recognize it as the lazar-house, and would prepare to throw an alms to the crippled and disfigured representative of the community.

It is a startling fact that there is documentary evidence for the existence of over 200 such institutions in this country in the Middle Ages, though historians disagree in their conclusions on this subject, as they do on the extent and duration of the disease itself. To some, leprosy is a phantom playing upon the imagination of a terror-stricken nation; to others, an all-devouring giant stalking through the land. One writer surmises that all the *British* leper-hospitals together did not exceed fifty, for "there might have been a leper in a village here and there, one or two in a market-town, a dozen or more in a city, a score or so in a whole diocese." Another says that "the number of these lazar-houses, however great, was insufficient to accommodate

[1] Patent 12 Ed. IV, pt. II, m. 6.

more than a small proportion of those suffering from the disease. The rest flocked to the high roads, and exposed their distorted limbs and sores, and sought by attracting the notice of travellers to gain alms for their support."

Speaking broadly, one may say that leprosy raged from the eleventh to the middle of the thirteenth century, when it abated ; that it was inconsiderable after the middle of the fourteenth ; that, though not extinct, it became rare in the fifteenth ; and had practically died out by the sixteenth century, save in the extreme south-west of England.

It is commonly supposed that leprosy was introduced into this country by returning crusaders. "The leprosy was one epidemical infection which tainted the pilgrims coming thither," says Fuller ; "hence was it brought over into England—never before known in this island— and many lazar-houses erected." Voltaire makes this satirical epigram :—"All that we gained in the end by engaging in the Crusades, was the leprosy ; and of all that we had taken, that was the only thing that remained with us." This theory, however, is no longer accepted, and Dr. C. Creighton expresses an opinion that it is absurd to suppose that leprosy could be "introduced" in any such way. Geoffrey de Vinsauf, the chronicler who accompanied Richard I, says, indeed, that many perished from sickness of a dropsical nature. He was an eyewitness of the famine which led to the consumption of abominable food, but there is little proof that these wretched conditions engendered leprosy among the pilgrim-warriors. Only once is a leper mentioned in his *Itinerary*, and then it is no less a personage than Baldwin IV, the young prince who became seventh King of Jerusalem and victor over

Saladin. It is, moreover, an undeniable fact that there were lepers in Saxon and early Norman England. The Anglo-Saxon equivalent is found in the vocabulary attributed to Aelfric. Roger of Hoveden tells the story of a poor leper whom Edward the Confessor was instrumental in curing. Aelfward, Saxon Bishop of London, retired into a monastery because of this affliction; and Hugh d'Orivalle, Bishop of London, a Norman, died a leper in 1085. Finally, at least two lazar-houses were established within twenty years of the Conquest, and before the first Crusade.

(a) *Twelfth and Thirteenth Centuries*

Leprosy was rampant during the Norman period. By a happy providence, charity was quickened simultaneously by the religious movement which illuminated a dark age, so that the need was met. Two leper-houses were rivals in point of antiquity, namely, Rochester and Harbledown, both founded before 1100. These were followed (before 1135) by foundations at Alkmonton, Whitby, London, Lincoln, Colchester, Norwich, Newark, Peterborough, Oxford, Newcastle, Wilton, St. Alban's, Bury, Warwick. Within the next twenty years hospitals are mentioned at Canterbury (St. Laurence), Buckland by Dover, Lynn, Burton Lazars, Aylesbury, York, Ripon, and Northampton; there were also other early asylums at Carlisle, Preston, Shrewsbury, Ilford, Exeter, etc. The chief building period was before the middle of the thirteenth century. A glance at *Appendix B* will show how such houses multiplied. Moreover, many not specifically described as for lepers, were doubtless originally intended for them. (Cf. Lewes, Abingdon, Scarborough, etc.)

(b) *Fourteenth Century* (1300–1350)

During the first part of the fourteenth century, leprosy was widespread, but by no means as common as formerly. Directly or indirectly, testimony is borne to the fact of its prevalence by national laws, by hospital authorities and by the charitable public.

In the first place there is the witness of external legislation, which is two-fold. Schemes of taxation refer constantly to lepers (*Rolls of Parliament*, 1307–1324). Measures were repeatedly taken for their expulsion from towns. An ordinance was made in the Parliament of Lincoln (1315) commanding that houses founded for the infirm and lepers should be devoted to their use. The admission of other persons was now refused, as, for example, at St. Giles', London, and St. Bartholomew's, Oxford.[1]

There is, secondly, the phraseology of contemporary leper-house statutes, e.g. those drawn up by the Abbot of St. Alban's (1344), and by the Bishop of London for Ilford (1346). Here it is right to note a case where infected inmates were already in a minority. A summary of the history of St. Nicholas', Carlisle (1341), includes this definite statement :—"until by lapse of time the greater part of the lepers died, when . . . their places were filled by poor impotent folk."[2]

Thirdly, it is evident from the gifts of charitable persons that there were still many outcasts in need of assistance. Bishop Bitton of Exeter left money to lazars in thirty-nine localities within his diocese (1307). Practi-

---

[1] Pat. 8 Edw. II, pt. ii. m. 5.   Close 9 Edw. II, m. 18 *d.*
[2] Pat. 15 Edw. III, pt. i. m. 49, 48.

cally all the wills of the period allude to the presence of lepers in the neighbourhood. Although there already existed two asylums outside Rochester (St. Bartholomew's and St. Nicholas' at Whiteditch), to which bequests were continuously made until far into the next century,[1] St. Katherine's hospital was founded in 1316 for lepers and other mendicants :—

"if it happe anie man or woman of the cittie of Rouchester to be uisited with lepre, or other suche diseases that longe to impotence, with unpower of pouertie, there sholde be receaued."

If leper-houses were empty, the fact is largely accounted for by the mismanagement and poverty of charitable institutions at that period. This aspect of the subject has never received adequate attention. Destitute persons were ousted to make way for paying inmates. One thirteenth-century master of St. Nicholas', York, admitted thirty-six brethren and sisters, of whom four were received *pro Deo*, because they were lepers, but the rest for money. This practice was sadly common, and notorious instances might be cited from Lincoln (Holy Innocents'), London (St. Giles'), and Oxford (St. Bartholomew's).

Moreover, the leper would probably not be anxious for admission, because at this time, when hospitals were barely able to supply the necessaries of life, it meant restriction without the corresponding comfort which sometimes made it welcome. It is related that in 1315, the lepers of Kingston showed their independence by quitting the hospital and demolishing it. A Close Roll entry relating to St. Nicholas', Royston (1359), declares that the "lepers for a great while past have refused to come or to dwell

[1] J. Thorpe, *Custumale Roffense*, p. 39 et sq. ; *Reg. Roff.* p. 113.

there." About the year 1350 the chronicler of St. Alban's states that at St. Julian's hospital "in general there are now not above three, sometimes only two, and occasionally one." Possibly they had rebelled against the strict life enforced : in 1353 the master and lepers were made semi-independent by grant of the abbot and convent.[1]

In truth, hospitals were in great straits during this distressful century, and retrenchment was necessary. Leper-houses in particular were seldom on a sound financial basis. Even if they possessed certain endowments in kind there was rarely money to spend on the fabric, and buildings became dilapidated. Experience teaches the difficulty of maintaining old-established charities. Much of the early enthusiasm had passed away, and charity was at a low ebb.

It was indeed a poverty-stricken period. Heavy taxation drained the country's resources. War, famine and pestilence were like the locust, palmerworm and caterpillar devastating the land. These were cruel times for the poor, and also for houses of charity. The mediæval tale of Sir Amiloun shows that, so long as the land had plenty, the leper-knight and his companion fared well, but that when corn waxed dear, they were driven by hunger from town to town, and could barely keep themselves alive.

A few instances will show how charity suffered. At the Harbledown leper-house (1276), voluntary offerings were so diminished that inmates were come to great want, and it was feared the sick would be compelled to leave. In 1301 the authorities of the Stafford hospital were

[1] Pat. 27 Edw. III, pt. ii. m. 16.

said to be accustomed to receive lepers with goods and chattels, but they were not bound to support them, and the prior himself had been driven away by destitution. St. Giles', Hexham, was suffering from the Scotch wars. An inquiry ordered by the archbishop (1320) showed that the numbers were reduced, that none were admitted without payment, and that they had to work hard. The allowance of bread and beer from the priory was diminished, oxen were borrowed for ploughing, and there was scarcely enough corn to sow the land.[1] Wayfaring lepers had ceased to frequent St. Mary Magdalene's, Ripon (where they used to receive food and shelter), because applicants went away empty-handed (1317); and a later inquiry showed that none came there "because it was fallen down." In 1327, the Huntingdon lepers had barely sufficient to maintain their present company, admittance being refused to applicants solely on that account, and they were excused taxation in 1340, because if payment were made, they would have to diminish the number of inmates and disperse them to seek their food. Civil and ecclesiastical registers alike, in issuing protections and briefs for leprous men collecting alms for hospitals, tell a tale of utter destitution.

(c) *Fourteenth Century* (1350–1400)

Having discussed that portion of the century which preceded the fateful year 1349, we now inquire to what extent leprosy existed during the fifty years that followed. It is no longer mentioned in legislation, and there are indications that it had come to be regarded chiefly as a question for local government: the *Letter Books* of the

[1] Surtees Soc. 46, ii. 130.

Corporation of London record edicts of expulsion. There are other proofs that the number of sufferers was decreasing. If, for example, the language be compared of two Harbledown deeds, dated 1276 and 1371, an appreciable difference can be discerned. In the first it is declared that there "a hundred lepers are confined to avoid contagion," but a century later it is merely stated that "some of these poor are infected with leprosy." It was said at Maldon in 1402 that there had been no leper-burgesses for twenty years and more. The mention of burgesses is, however, inconclusive, for there may have been mendicant lazars who would gladly have accepted the shelter of St. Giles'; but the town was not bound to support them.

The gifts and bequests of this period testify to the fact that although there were lepers—notably in the vicinity of towns—yet the institutions provided for them were small in comparison with former asylums. A new lazar-house was built at Sudbury in 1373, to accommodate three persons. Shortly before 1384 a house for lepers and other infirm was founded at Boughton-under-Blean.[1] Richard II left money to complete two hospitals near London. The will of his uncle, John of Gaunt, who died the same year (1399), indicates the smallness of existing institutions within five miles of the city, for he bequeaths to every leper-house containing five *malades*, five nobles, and to lesser hospitals, three nobles each.

For a time, the pestilence of 1349 had brought financial ruin to houses dependent upon charity. In London, for example, in 1355, the full complement at St. Giles' should

[1] Cited Vict. Co. Hist. *Kent.*

have been fourteen—it had originally been forty—but the
authorities complained that they could not maintain even
the reduced number, for their lands lay uncultivated " by
reason of the horrible mortality." St. James' hospital—
which used to support fourteen—was empty, save for the
sole survivor of the scourge who remained as caretaker,
nor does it appear to have been reorganized as a leper-
asylum.

This diminution in numbers may be attributed to various
causes. An increase of medical knowledge with improved
diagnosis, together with the strict examination which now
preceded expulsion, doubtless prevented the incarceration
of some who would formerly have been injudiciously
classed as lazars. Possibly, too, the disease now took
a milder form, as it is apt to do in course of time. Again,
the Black Death (1349) had not merely impoverished
leper-hospitals, but must surely have been an important
factor in the decline of leprosy itself. If it reduced the
population by two-thirds, or even by one-half, as is computed, it also carried off the weakest members of society,
those most prone to disease. When the plague reached
a lazar-house, it found ready victims, and left it without
inhabitant. The same may be said of the terrible though
lesser pestilences which followed (1361–76). The attempt
to purify towns by sanitary measures contributed to the
improvement of public health. In Bartholomew's *De
Proprietatibus Rerum* (*circa* 1360) it is declared, among
divers causes of leprosy that :—" sometyme it cometh . . .
of infecte and corrupte ayre." Steps were taken in
London to improve sanitation (1388) because " many and
intolerable diseases do daily happen."

(d) *Fifteenth Century*

Having admitted that leprosy was steadily declining, so that by the year 1400 it was rare, we are not prepared to echo the statement that its disappearance "may be taken as absolute." Certain lazar-houses were, indeed, appropriated to other uses, as at Alkmonton (1406), Sherburn (1434), and Blyth (1446). In remembrance of the original foundation, accommodation was reserved at Sherburn for two lepers "if they could be found in those parts" [i.e. in the Bishopric of Durham] "or would willingly come to remain there," the place of the sixty-five lepers being now taken by thirteen poor men unable of their own means to support themselves.[1] This was a period of transition, and although ruins already marked the site of many a former settlement, yet there were places where a few lepers occupied the old habitations.

Leprosy certainly lurked here and there. The testimony of wills may not be considered wholly trustworthy evidence, yet they show that the public still recognized a need. In 1426 a testator left money for four lepers to receive four marks yearly for ten years. Bequests were made to lepers of Winchester (1420); to "eche laseer of man and woman or child within Bury" (1463); to "the leprous men now in the house of lepers" at Sandwich (1466). There were, perhaps, cases where testators had little personal knowledge of the charities. We cannot, however, doubt that a real need existed when the former mayor of Newcastle leaves forty shillings to "the lepre men of Newcastell" (1429), or when John Carpenter—

---

[1] One deed of reformation speaks of "the diminution of the means of the hospital and the small number of lepers who resort thither." (*Pap. Lett.* 1430–1.)

for over twenty years town-clerk of London—bequeaths money to poor lepers at Holborn, Locks and Hackney (1441).

In 1464, when confirming Holy Innocents', Lincoln, to Burton Lazars, Edward IV renewed Henry VI's stipulation that three leprous retainers should still be supported:— "to fynde and susteyn there yerely for ever, certeyn Lepurs of oure menialx Seruauntez and of oure Heires & Successours, yf eny suche be founde." The king relinquished some property near Holloway (Middlesex), in order to provide a retreat for infected persons. In the year 1480 there were a few lepers at Lydd, who were allowed to share in the festivities when the quarrels between Edward IV and Louis XI came to an end. The ships of the Cinque Ports had been requisitioned, including "the George" of Romney. The town-clerk of Lydd makes an entry of 4d. "Paid to the leperys, whenne the George was fette home fro Hethe."[1]

(e) *Sixteenth Century*

Cases of true leprosy were now of rare occurrence. Probably leper hospitals were in the main only nominally such, as a testator hints in 1519, bequeathing a legacy "to every Alms House called Lepars in the Shire of Kent." But although the social conditions of the country improved during the Tudor period, they were still low enough continually to engender pestilence. When Erasmus visited England, he was struck by the filthy habits which were prevalent; but the avengers of neglect of cleanliness were now plague and the sweating sickness. In some few cases old hospitals were

[1] Hist. MSS. 5th R. p. 527 a.

utilized for the sufferers. The plague having lately raged in Newcastle, it was recorded in the Chantry Certificate of St. Mary Magdalene's (1546) that it was once used for lepers, but "syns that kynde of sickeness is abated it is used for the comforte and helpe of the poore folks that chaunceth to fall sycke in tyme of pestilence."

The south-west corner of England was now the last stronghold of leprosy. St. Margaret's, Honiton, had been refounded about 1530. A new leper-hospital was built at Newton Bushell near Exeter in 1538 :—

"for the releff of powre lazar-people, whereof grete nomber with that diseas be now infectid in that partis, to the grete daunger of infection of moche people . . . for lacke of con- ueayent houses in the county of Devonshire for them."

Even in 1580, none were admitted to St. Mary Magdalene's, Exeter, except "sick persons in the disease of the leprosy." About the same time it was reported that "for a long time there had been a great company of lazar-people" at Bodmin.

A few of the old hospitals were kept up in different parts. In the first year of Edward VI (1547) it was enacted that all "leprouse and poore beddred creatures" who were inmates of charitable houses should continue in the places appointed, and be permitted to have proctors to gather alms for them. The Corporation MSS. of Hereford include a notification that year of the appoint- ment of collectors for "the house of leprous persons founded in the worship of St. Anne and St. Loye." Strype records similar licences granted to Beccles and Bury; and he also cites[1] "A protection to beg, granted to

[1] Ecclesiastical Memorials, II, 248.

the poor lazars of the house of our Saviour Jesus Christ
and Mary Magdalene, at Mile-end [in Stepney], and
J. Mills appointed their proctor " (1551).   The sixteenth-
century seal of this *Domus Dei et S. Marie Magd. de
Myle End* (figured below) shows a crippled leper and an
infirm woman of the hospital.   In 1553, £60 was given to
the lazar-houses round London on condition that inmates
did not beg to people's annoyance within three miles.

It has here been attempted to bring together some
notes touching the extent and duration of leprosy during
the Middle Ages, as affecting the provision and maintenance of leper-hospitals.   Into the nature of the disease
itself we have not endeavoured to inquire, that being
a scientific rather than an historical study.   Those who
would go further into the subject must gain access to
the writings of Sir James Simpson, Dr. C. Creighton,
Dr. George Newman and others.

6. SEAL OF THE LAZAR-HOUSE, MILE END

CHAPTER V

THE LEPER IN ENGLAND

*" From the benefactions and possessions charitably bestowed upon the hospital,
the hunger, thirst and nakedness of those lepers, and other wants and
miseries with which they are incessantly afflicted . . . may be relieved."*
(Foundation Charter of Sherburn.)

WE now turn from leper-asylums to consider the
leper himself—a sadly familiar figure to the wayfaring man in the Middle Ages. He wears a
sombre gown and cape, tightly closed ; a hood conceals
his want of hair, which is, however, betrayed by the
absence of eyebrows and lashes ; his limbs are maimed
and stunted so that he can but hobble or crawl ; his
features are ulcerated and sunken ; his staring eyes are
unseeing or unsightly ; his wasted lips part, and a
husky voice entreats help as he " extends supplicating
lazar arms with bell and clap-dish."

At the outset it is necessary to state that inmates of
lazar-houses were not all true lepers. Persons termed
*leprosi, infirmi, elefantuosi, languidi, frères malades,
meselles,* do not necessarily signify lepers in a strict sense.
Gervase of Canterbury, writing about 1200, speaks of
St. Oswald's, Worcester, as intended for " *Infirmi, item
leprosi*" ; and these words are used synonymously in Pipe
Rolls, charters, seals, etc. " Leprosy" was an elastic
term as commonly used. In the statutes of one hospital,

the patriarch Job was claimed as a fellow-sufferer—"who was so smitten with the leprosy, that from the sole of his foot to the crown of his head there was no soundness in him." A *lazar* was one "full of sores," and any person having an inveterate and loathsome skin-eruption might be considered infected. Disfiguring and malignant disorders were common. Victims of *scrofula, lepra, lupus, tuberculosis, erysipelas* (or "St. Anthony's fire") and persons who had contracted disease as the baneful result of a life stained with sin, would sometimes take advantage of the provision made for lepers, for in extremity of destitution this questionable benefit was not to be despised. In foreign lands to-day, some are found not unwilling to join the infected for the sake of food and shelter ; we are told, for example, that the Hawaiian Government provides so well for lepers that a difficulty arises in preventing healthy people from taking up their abode in the hospitals. On the other hand, it often happens that those who are actually leprous refuse to join a segregation-camp.

No one, however, can deny that leprosy was once exceedingly prevalent, and after weighing all that might be said to the contrary, Sir J. Y. Simpson and Dr. George Newman were convinced that the disease existent in England was for the most part true leprosy (*elephantiasis Græcorum*).

I. PIONEERS OF CHARITY

One practical outcome of the religious revival of the twelfth century was a movement of charity towards the outcast. The Lazarus whom Jesus loved became linked in pious minds with that *Lazarus ulceribus plenus* neglected by men, but now "in Abraham's bosom," and the thought took a firm hold of the heart and imagination. Abandoned by relatives, loathed by neighbours, the famished leper was now literally fed with crumbs of comfort from the rich man's table.

The work of providing for "Christ's poor," begun by the great churchmen Lanfranc and Gundulf, was carried into the realm of personal service by Queen Maud (about 1101), the Abbot of Battle (before 1171) and Hugh, Bishop of Lincoln (about 1186). Queen Maud is the brightest ornament of the new movement. Like St. Francis of Assisi a century later, she "adopted those means for grappling with the evil that none but an enthusiast and a visionary would have taken." Aelred of Rievaulx relates how Prince David visited her and found the house full of lepers, in the midst of whom stood the queen. She washed, dried and even kissed their feet, telling her brother that in so doing she was kissing the feet of the Eternal King. When she begged him to follow her example, he withdrew smiling, afterwards confessing to Aelred :—"I was sore afraid and answered that I could on no account endure it, for as yet I did not know the Lord, nor had His spirit been revealed to me." Of Walter de Lucy, the chronicler of Battle Abbey writes :—

"He especially compassionated the forlorn condition of those afflicted with leprosy and *elephantiasis*, whom he was so far from shunning, that he frequently waited upon them in person, washing their hands and feet, and, with the utmost cordiality, imprinting upon them the soothing kisses of love and piety."

St. Hugh used to visit in certain hospitals, possibly those at Peterborough and Newark connected with the

See or the Mallardry at Lincoln.[1] He would even dwell among the lepers, eating with them and ministering to them, saying that he was inspired by the example of the Saviour and by His teaching concerning the beggar Lazarus. On one occasion, in reply to a remonstrance from his Chancellor, he said that these afflicted ones were the flowers of Paradise, pearls in the coronet of the Eternal King.[2]

2. PUBLIC OPINION

These noble pioneers were doubtless important factors in moulding public opinion. They may often have out-stepped the bounds of prudence, but, as one has ob-served, "an evil is removed only by putting it for a time into strong relief, when it comes to be rightly dealt with and so is gradually checked." As long as possible the world ignored the existence of leprosy. The thing was so dreadful that men shut their eyes to it, until they were shamed into action by those who dared to face the evil. The Canon of the Lateran Council of 1179 acknowledged that unchristian selfishness had hitherto possessed men with regard to lepers. We need not suppose that the heroism of those who ministered to lepers was that which boldly faces a terrible risk, but it was rather that which overcomes the strongest repulsion for hideous and noi-some objects. There is no hint in the language of the chroniclers of encountering danger, but rather, expres-sions of horror that any should hold intercourse with such loathsome creatures. The remonstrances of Prince David and of William de Monte were not primarily on account of contagion.—"What is it that thou doest, O my lady?

[1] See p. 180.   [2] Chron. and Mem. 37, *Magna Vita*, pp. 162–5.

surely if the King knew this, he would not deign to kiss with his lips your mouth thus polluted with the feet of lepers!" "When I saw Bishop Hugh touch the livid face of the lepers, kiss their sightless eyes or eyeless sockets, I shuddered with disgust."—If St. Francis raised an objection to inmates wandering outside their precincts, it was because people could not endure the sight of them. The popular opinion regarding the contagious nature of the disease developed strongly, however, towards the close of the twelfth century. The Canon *De Leprosis* (Rome, 1179; Westminster, 1200) declares emphatically that lepers cannot dwell with healthy men. Englishmen begin to act consistently with this conviction. The Prior of Taunton (1174–85) separates a monk from the company of the brethren "in fear of the danger of this illness"; and the Durham chronicler mentions an infirmary for those "stricken with the contagion of leprosy."

3. CIVIL JURISDICTION

(a) *The Writ for Removal.*—The right to expel lepers was acknowledged before it was legally enforced. An entry upon the statute-book may be merely the official recognition of an established custom. The fact that where use and wont are sufficiently strong, law is unnecessary, is illustrated to-day in Japan, where public opinion alone enforces the separation of lepers. At length English civil law set its seal upon the theory of infection by the writ *De Leproso Amovendo*, authorizing the expulsion of lepers on account of manifest peril by contagion. An early instance of removal occurs in the Curia Regis Rolls (1220). It is mentioned that William, son of Nicholas Malesmeins, had been consigned with the assent of his friends to a certain Maladria in Bidelington, where he abode for two years. This was the leper-house near Bramber, mentioned four years previously in a Close Roll as "the hospital of the infirm of St. Mary Magdalene of Bidelington."

Legislation on this subject was chiefly local. The Assizes of London had proclaimed in 1276 that "no leper shall be in the city, nor come there, nor make any stay there." Edward III supplemented existing measures by an urgent local edict for London and Middlesex. The royal proclamation sets forth that many publicly dwell among the citizens, being smitten with the taint of leprosy; these not only injure people by the contagion of their polluted breath, but they even strive to contaminate others by a loose and vicious life, resorting to houses of ill-fame, "that so, to their own wretched solace, they may have the more fellows in suffering."[1] All persons proved leprous—citizens or others, of whatever sex or condition—are to quit the city within fifteen days, "and betake themselves to places in the country, solitary, and notably distant from the city and suburbs." This order, sent to the mayor, was followed by a proclamation to the sheriff of the county. Lepers are to abandon the highways and field-ways between the city and Westminster, where several such persons sit and stay, associating with whole men, to the manifest danger of passers-by.[2]

This social problem continued to vex municipal authorities. A precept was issued (1369) "that no leper beg in the street for fear of spreading infection." The porters of the eight principal gates of the city were sworn

---

[1] Riley, *Memorials of London*, 230.
[2] Close 1346 pt. i. m. 18 *d*, 14 *d*, and 1348 pt. i. m. 25 *d*.

to refuse them admittance. (That *barbers*—forerunners of the barber-chirurgeons—were included among the gate-keepers in 1310 and 1375, was perhaps due to their supposed capability of recognizing diseases.) If a leper tried to enter, he should forfeit his horse or his outer garment, and if persisting, be taken into custody. The foreman at "le loke" and an official at the Hackney lazar-house were also bound to prevent their entry into the city.

The "Customs of Bristol," written down by the recorder in 1344, declare "that in future no leper reside within the precincts of the town." Imprisonment was the penalty—a plan of doubtful wisdom. The measures ordained by the burgesses of Berwick-on-Tweed were summary :—

"No leper shall come within the gates of the borough ; and if one gets in by chance, the serjeant shall put him out at once. If one wilfully forces his way in, his clothes shall be taken off him and burnt, and he shall be turned out naked. For we have already taken care that a proper place for lepers shall be. kept up outside the town, and that alms shall be there given to them."[1]

It was comparatively easy for the civic authorities to control the ejection of lepers when the asylum was under their supervision, as it frequently was. At Exeter, ecclesiastical leniency permitted a continuance of the custom (which was already "ancient" in 1163) of allowing lepers to circulate freely in the town. In 1244 the bishop seems to have agreed with the mayor and corporation about the inadvisability of the practice ; and he resigned the guardianship of the lazar-house, accepting in its stead that of St. John's hospital.

---

[1] Toulmin Smith, *Gilds*, 241.

Municipal documents record the expulsion of lepers. In Gloucester (1273), Richard, Alice and Matilda gave trouble and would remain within the town "to the great damage and prejudice of the inhabitants." John Mayn, after repeated warnings to provide for himself some dwelling outside London, was sworn to depart forthwith and not return, on pain of the pillory (1372). A Leet Roll among the records of Norwich states that "Thomas Tytel Webstere is a leper, therefore he must go out of the city" (1375). In the following instances, the infected were consigned to hospitals. Margaret Taylor came before the keepers of Beverley in the Gild Hall, and asked by way of charity permission to have a bed in the lepers' house outside Keldgate Bar, which request was granted (1394). The town-clerk of Lydd makes an entry of ten shillings "Paied for delyvere of Simone Reede unto the howse of Lazaris" (*circa* 1460). The manorial court sometimes dealt with such cases. That of the Bishop of Ely at Littleport recorded (1321):—"The jurors say upon their oath that Joan daughter of Geoffrey Whitring is leprous. Therefore be she set apart."[1]

The law evidently had no power to touch a leper unless he made himself a source of public danger. No one interfered with him as long as he remained in a quiet hiding-place, quitting it, perhaps, only at night. Individuals, sheltered by the affection or self-interest of relatives, might never come under the ban of the law: in the Norwich records, for example, Isabella Lucas seems to have been allowed to remain at home (1391). Judge Fitz-Herbert, commenting on the writ of removal, observes

[1] Selden Soc., *Court Baron*, p. 134.

that it lies where a leper is dwelling in a town, and will come into the church or amongst his neighbours.[1] English legislation was never severe regarding lepers. We may believe that the tolerant spirit of a certain thirteenth-century Scottish canon prevailed throughout Great Britain. Lepers, it was declared, might well fulfil their parochial obligations, but "if they cannot be induced to do so, let no coercion be employed, seeing that affliction should not be accumulated upon the afflicted, but rather their misfortunes commiserated."[2] In France, however, upon one terrible occasion, Philip V was guilty of the abominable cruelty of burning lepers on the pretext that they had maliciously poisoned wells. Mezeray says :—"they were burned alive in order that the fire might purify at once the infection of the body and of the soul." The report of this inhuman act reached England and was recorded both in the Chronicle of Lanercost (under date 1318) and also by John Capgrave, who says :—

" And in this same yere [1318] the Mysseles [lepers] thorow oute Cristendam were slaundered that thei had mad couenaunt with Sarasines for to poison alle Cristen men, to put uenym in wellis, and alle maner uessels that long to mannes use ; of whech malice mony of hem were conuicte, and brent, and many Jewes that gave hem councel and coumfort."[3]

(b) *Property.*—The legal status of the leper must now be examined. When pronounced a leper in early days, a man lost not only his liberty, but the right to inherit or bequeath property. A manuscript Norman law-book

---

[1] *Natura Brevium*, ed. 1652 p. 584.
[2] Wilkins, *Concil. Mag.* i. 616.
[3] Chron. and Mem., 1. 186.

declares "that the mezel cannot be heir to any one."
In the days of Stephen, for example, Brien Fitz-Count
was lord of Wallingford and Abergavenny. "He had
two sons, whom, being lepers, he placed in the Priory
of Bergavenny and gave lands and tithes there to for
their support," bequeathing his property to other kinsmen. Again, two women of the Fitz-Fulke family
appeared in the King's Court (1203) in a dispute about
property at Sutton in Kent: Avice urged that Mabel,
having a brother, had no claim — "but against this
Mabel says that he is a leper."[1] Even a grant made by
such a person was void. In 1204 King John committed
the lands of William of Newmarch to an official who should
answer for them at the Exchequer, but "if he have given
away any of his lands after he fell sick of the leprosy,
cause the same to be restored to his barony."[2] This
illustrates Bracton's statement that "a leprous person
who is placed out of the communion of mankind cannot
give . . . as he cannot ask," and, again, "if the claimant
be a leper and so deformed that the sight of him is in-
supportable, and such that he has been separated . . .
[he] cannot plead or claim an inheritance."[3]

On the other hand, Lord Coke declares that "ideots,
leapers &c. may be heires," and he comments thus upon
Bracton and Britton:—"if these ancient writers be under-
stood of an appearance in person, I think their opinions
are good law; for [lepers] ought not to sue nor defend
in proper person, but by atturney."[4] Possibly the
Norman custom of disinheritance prevailed in England
at one time and then died out. The case of Adam

---

[1] Selden Soc., 3, No. 157.   [2] Rot. Litt. Claus. 6 John m. 21.
[3] Chron. and Mem., 70, i. 95 ; vi. 325.   [4] First Institutes, p. 8a., 135b.

de Gaugy proves that in 1278 this Northumbrian baron was not liable to forfeiture. He was excused, indeed, from appearing in the presence of Edward I, but was directed to swear fealty to an official. Although spoken of as his brother's heir, Adam did not long enjoy his property. He died the same year, childless, but leaving a widow (*Eve*), and the barony passed to a kinsman.[1]

The Norman maxim that the leper "may possess the inheritance he had before he became a leper" is illustrated by the story of the youthful heir of Nicholas de Malesmeins. Having attained full age, he left the hospital where he had been confined, appeared before his feudal lord, did homage, made his payment, and entered his fief.[2]

4. ECCLESIASTICAL JURISDICTION

Although leprosy was a penal offence, only laymen could be cited and dealt with by the king, mayor or feudal lord. Clerks in holy orders had to answer to their bishop. In the case of parochial clergy, the diocesan was responsible for their suspension from office, as stated by the Canon *De Leprosis*. Lucius III (1181–1185) decreed that they must serve by coadjutors and wrote to the Bishop of Lincoln on this subject.[3] The episcopal registers of Lincoln afterwards record the case of the rector of Seyton (1310). Several leprous parish priests are named in other registers, e.g. St. Neot, 1314 (Exeter), Colyton, 1330 (Exeter), Castle Carrock, 1357 (Carlisle). In the latter instance, the bishop having learned with sorrow that the rector was infected and unable to ad-

---

[1] Inquisition, cf. Rot. Curia Scacc. Abb., i. 33.
[2] Curia Regis Rolls, 72, m. 18 *d*.
[3] *Conciliorum Omnium*, ed. 1567, III, 700 (cap. 4).

minister the sacraments, cited him to appear at Rose with a view to appointing a coadjutor.[1] It was ordered by Clement III that when clergy were thus removed, they should be supported from the fruits of their benefices. Sir Philip, the leper-priest of St. Neot in Cornwall, was allowed two shillings a week, besides twenty shillings a year for clothing. He was permitted to keep the best room in his vicarage and the adjoining chambers, except the hall. The rest of the house was partitioned off for the curate, the door between them being walled up.[2]

5. EXAMINATION OF SUSPECTED PERSONS

The duty of reporting and examining cases fell to the clergy, doctors, civil officers or a jury of discreet men. (Cf. Fig. 7.) A curiously compli-cated lawsuit brought into the King's Court in 1220 relates how a certain man had custody of the children of Nicholas de Males-meins. When the eldest-born became a leper, his perplexed guardian took the young man to the King's Exchequer, and before the barons of the Ex-chequer he was adjudged a

7. LEPER AND PHYSICIAN

leper, and consigned to a hospital. (See pp. 52, 58.)

In ordinary cases, the leper would show himself to the parish priest as the only scholar. It was the village priest who helped the stricken maiden to enter "Badele Spital" near Darlington, and afterwards attested her

---

[1] Reg. Welton. Cited Vict. Co. Hist.
[2] Reg. Stapeldon, p. 342.

cure, as related by Reginald of Durham. (See p. 97.) The register of Bishop Bronescomb of Exeter declares that "it belongs to the office of the priest to distinguish between one form of leprosy and another." It was the duty of the clergy to take cognizance of cases, but it was not always politic to interfere. In 1433 the parson of Sparham endeavoured to get a parishioner, John Folkard, to withdraw from the company of other men because he was "gretely infect with the sekeness of lepre." The vicar advertised him to depart, for "his sekenes was contagious and myght hurte moche people." After much disputing, John went off to Norwich and took an action for trespass against the parson before the sheriffs. Whereupon the vicar had to appeal in chancery.[1]

The writ of removal ordered the careful investigation of cases in the presence of discreet and lawful men having the best knowledge of the accused person and his disease. Probably the best was not very good, for many judged by the outward appearance only. The Bishop of Lincoln, directing the resignation of a clergyman (1310), says that he is besprinkled with the spot of leprosy. The decree of 1346 condemns "all those who are found infected with leprous spots" to be removed. Anthony Fitz-Herbert, writing in 1534, points out that the writ is for those "who appear to the sight of all men that they are lepers," by their voice, disfigurement and noisome condition.

In medical treatises, great stress was laid on the necessity of investigation with pondering and meditation. The *Rosa Anglica* of John of Gaddesden (physician to Edward II) declares that "no one is to be adjudged a leper, and separated from intercourse of mankind, until

[1] P.R.O. Early Chancery Proceedings, Bundle 46, No. 158.

the figure and form of the face is actually changed."
The contemporary French doctor, Gordon, uses almost
the same words ; and, repeating his precautions, observes
that "lepers are at the present day very injudiciously
judged." A later writer, Guy de Chauliac (*circa* 1363)
says :—

"In the examination and judgement of lepers, there must be
much circumspection, because the injury is very great, whether
we thus submit to confinement those that ought not to be confined, or allow lepers to mix with the people, seeing the disease
is contagious and infectious."

Sir J. Simpson gives copious extracts from Guy's *Chi-*
rurgia, which has also been translated into modern French
(1890). Guy describes fully the examination of a suspected person, giving in detail all possible symptoms.
It may here be observed that Bartholomew *Anglicus*,
his contemporary, enumerates among the causes pre-
disposing to leprosy, dwelling and oft talking with leprous
men, marriage and heredity, evil diet—e.g. rotten meat,
measled hogs, flesh infected with poison, and the biting
of a venomous worm : "in these manners and in many
other the evil of *lepra* breedeth in man's body." Guy
advises the doctor to inquire if the person under examination comes of tainted stock, if he have conversed with
lepers, etc. He must then consider and reconsider the
equivocal and unequivocal signs of disease. After a
searching investigation—not to be confined to one day—
the patient must either be set free (*absolvendus*) with a
certificate, or separated from the people and conducted to
the lazar-house.

About the time that John of Gaddesden was professor
of medicine at Oxford (1307-1325), and was writing upon

leprosy, "experienced physicians" were summoned to examine a provincial magnate. The mayor and bailiffs of royal Winchester had been over-zealous "under colour of the king's late order to cause lepers who were amongst the healthy citizens to be expelled." It was surely a bitter hour to Peter de Nutle, late mayor of the grand old city, when his successor and former colleagues hounded him out! But there was justice for one "falsely accused"; and subsequently an order of redress was sent, not without rebuke to the civic authorities for their malicious behaviour towards a fellow-citizen :—

"as it appears, from the inspection and examination before our council by the council and by physicians expert in the knowledge of this disease, that the said Peter is whole and clean, and infected in no part of his body."

A few days later the sheriff of Hampshire was directed to make a proclamation to the same effect, so that Peter might dwell as he was wont unmolested.[1]

The royal mandate of 1346 reiterated the stipulation that men of knowledge should inquire into suspected cases. It therefore seems unlikely that a London baker ejected in 1372 was merely suffering from an inveterate eczema, as has been suggested. Careless as were the popular notions of disease, medical diagnosis was becoming more exact; four kinds of leprosy were distinguished, of which "leonine" and "elephantine" were the worst.

There is an interesting document extant concerning a certain woman who lived at Brentwood in 1468. She was indicted by a Chancery warrant, but acquitted on the

---

[1] Close 6 Edw. II, m. 21 d.

authority of a medical certificate of health. The neighbours of Johanna Nightingale petitioned against her,
complaining that she habitually mixed with them and
refused to retire to a solitary place, although "infected by
the foul contact of leprosy." A writ was therefore issued
by Edward IV commanding a legal inquiry. Finally,
Johanna appeared before a medical jury in the presence
of the Chancellor. They examined her person, touched
and handled her, made mature and diligent investigation,
going through over forty distinctive signs of disease. She
was at length pronounced "utterly free and untainted,"
and the royal physicians were prepared to demonstrate
this in Chancery " by scientific process." [1]

6. TREATMENT OF THE BODY

Alleviation was sometimes sought in medicinal waters.
Here and there the site of a hospital seems to have been
selected on account of its proximity to a healing spring,
e.g. Harbledown, Burton Lazars, Peterborough, Newark,
and Nantwich. In various places there are springs
known as the Lepers' Well, frequented by sufferers of
bygone days.

Tradition ascribes to bathing some actual cures of
"leprosy." Bladud the Briton, a prehistoric prince, was
driven from home because he was a leper. At length he
discovered the hot springs of Bath, where instinct had
already taught diseased swine to wallow : Bladud, too,
washed and was clean. The virtue of the mineral waters,
well known to the Romans, was also appreciated by the
Saxons; possibly the baths were frequented by lepers

[1] Close Roll, Rymer, ed. 1710, ix. 365. Translated, Simpson, *Arch.
Essays.*

from early days, for there was long distributed in Bath "an ancient alms to the poor and leprous of the foundation of Athelstan, Edgar and Ethelred." A small bath was afterwards set apart for their use, to which the infected flocked. Leland notes that the place was "much frequentid of People diseasid with Lepre, Pokkes, Scabbes, and great Aches," who found relief. A story similar to that of Bladud, but of later date, comes from the eastern counties: a certain man, sorely afflicted with leprosy, was healed by a spring in Beccles, near which in gratitude he built a hospital.

There was rivalry between the natural water of Bath and the miraculous water of Canterbury; the latter

8. ELIAS, LEPER MONK

consisted of a drop of St. Thomas' blood many times diluted from the well in the crypt of the cathedral.[1] William of Canterbury, a prejudiced critic, is careful to relate how a leper-monk of Reading, Elias by name, went with his abbot's approval to Bath desiring to ease his pain, and there sought earnestly of the physicians whatever he was able to gather from them. "He set his hope in the warmth of the sulphur and not in the wonder-working martyr," says William. After forty days in Bath, Elias set out for Canterbury, but secretly, pretending to seek medicine in London; because (adds the chronicler) the abbot honoured

[1] Chron. and Mem., 67, i. 416.

the martyr less than he ought to have done, and might
not have countenanced the pilgrimage. On his way,
Elias met returning pilgrims, who gave him some of the
water of St. Thomas (Fig. 8); he applied this externally
and internally and became well.[1] Lest any should doubt
the miracle, Benedict of Canterbury tells us that many
who were especially skilled in the art of medicine
used to say that Elias was smitten with a terrible leprosy,
and he proceeds to detail the horrible symptoms. In the
end, however, William declares that he who had been so
ulcerated that he might have been called another Lazarus,
now appeared pleasant in countenance, as was plain to all
who saw him. What the Bath doctors and Bath waters
could not do, that the miraculous help of St. Thomas
had achieved.

We see from the story of the monk Elias that the
ministrations of the physician and the use of medicine
were sought by lepers. Bartholomew says that the
disease, although incurable "but by the help of God"
when once confirmed, "may be somewhat hid and let,
that it destroy not so soon"; and he gives instructions
about diet, blood-letting, purgative medicines, plasters
and ointments. Efficacious too was (we are told) the
eating of a certain adder sod with leeks.

There is no information forthcoming as to the remedial
treatment of lepers in hospital. The only narrative we
possess is Chatterton's lively description of St. Bartholomew's, Bristol, the Roll of which he professed to find; it
satisfied Barrett, a surgeon, and a local, though uncritical,
historian. A father of the Austin Friary came to shrive
the lepers (for which he received ten marks) and to dress

[1] Id. ii. 242.

their sores (for which he was given fifty marks) saying,
"lette us cure both spryte and bodye." When barber-
surgeons came for an operation—"whanne some doughtie
worke ys to bee donne on a Lazar"—friars attended "leste
hurte ande scathe bee done to the lepers." The friars'
knowledge was such that barber-surgeons were willing to
attend "wythoute paye to gayne knowleche of aylimentes
and theyr trew curis."

7. TREATMENT OF THE SPIRIT

Disease was sometimes regarded as an instrument of
divine wrath, as in the scriptural case of Gehazi. Thus
Gilbert de Saunervill after committing sacrilege was smitten with leprosy, whereupon he confessed with tears that
he merited the scourge of God. The popular view that it
was an expiation for sin is shown in the romance of Cresseid false to her true knight. But except in signal cases
of wrong-doing this morbid idea was not prominent; and
the phrase "struck by the secret judgement of God" implies visitation rather than vengeance. Indeed, the use
of the expression "Christ's martyrs" suggests that the
leper's affliction was looked upon as a sacrifice—an attitude which illuminated the mystery of pain. St. Hugh
preached upon the blessedness of such sufferers : they
were in no wise under a curse, but were "beloved of God
as was Lazarus."

Those responsible for the care of lepers long ago
realized exactly what is experienced by those who carry
on the same extraordinarily difficult work to-day, namely,
that leprosy develops to a high degree what is worst in
man. Bodily torture, mental anguish, shattered nerves
almost amounting to insanity, render lepers wearisome

and offensive to themselves no less than to others. These causes, together with the absence of the restraining influences of family life, make them prone to rebellious conduct, irritability, ingratitude and other evil habits. Hope was, and is, the one thing to transform such lives, else intolerable in their wintry desolation. St. Hugh therefore bade lepers look for the consummation of the promise:—" Who shall change our vile body, that it may be fashioned like unto His glorious Body." [1]

Alleviation of the agonized mind of the doomed victim was undertaken first by the physician and afterwards by the priest. A recognized part of the remedial treatment advocated by Guy was to comfort the heart. His counsel shows that doctors endeavoured to act as physicians of the soul, for they were to impress upon the afflicted person that this suffering was for his spiritual salvation. The priest then fulfilled his last duty towards his afflicted parishioner :—

"The priest . . . makes his way to the sick man's home and addresses him with comforting words, pointing out and proving that if he blesses and praises God, and bears his sickness patiently, he may have a sure and certain hope that though he be sick in body, he may be whole in soul, and may receive the gift of eternal salvation."

The affecting scene at the service which followed may be pictured from the form in *Appendix A*. There was a certain tenderness mingled with "the terrible ten commandments of man." The priest endeavours to show the leper that he is sharing in the afflictions of Christ. For

---

[1] Compare the title of a modern leper-house at Kumamoto in Kiushiu, known as "The Hospital of the Resurrection of Hope": and in Japanese *Kwaishun Byōin*—"the coming again of spring."

his consolation the verse of Isaiah is recited :—"Surely He
hath borne our griefs and carried our sorrows, yet did we
esteem Him as a leper, smitten of God and afflicted."
The same passage from the Vulgate is quoted in the
statutes for the lepers of St. Julian's:—"among all infirmities the disease of leprosy is more loathsome than any
. . . yet ought they not on that account to despair or

9. A LEPER

murmur against God, but rather to praise and glorify Him
who was led to death as a leper."

After separation the fate of the outcast is irrevocably
sealed.   Remembering the exhortation, he must never
frequent places of public resort, nor eat and drink with
the sound ; he must not speak to them unless they are on
the windward side, nor may he touch infants or young
folk.   Henceforth his signal is the clapper, by which he
gives warning of his approach and draws attention to his

request. (Fig. 26.) This instrument consisted of tablets of wood, attached at one end with leather thongs, which made a loud click when shaken. In England, a bell was often substituted for this dismal rattle. Stow and Holinshed refer to the "clapping of dishes and ringing of bels" by the lazar. The poor creature of shocking appearance shown in Fig. 9 holds in his one remaining hand a bell. His piteous cry is "Sum good, my gentyll mayster, for God sake." This was the beggar's common appeal: in an *Early English Legendary*, a *mesel* cries to St. Francis, "Sum good for godes love."

Compelled to leave home and friends, many a leper thus haunted the highway—his only shelter a dilapidated hovel, his meagre fare the scraps put into his dish. To others, the lines fell in more pleasant places, for in the hospital pain and privation were softened by kindness.

CHAPTER VI

FOUNDERS AND BENEFACTORS

" Hospitals . . . founded as well by the noble kings of this realm and lords and ladies both spiritual and temporal as by others of, divers estates, in aid and merit of the souls of the said founders."

(Parliament of Leicester.)

AS our period covers about six centuries, some rough subdivision is necessary, but each century can show patrons of royal birth, benevolent bishops and barons, as well as charitable commoners. The roll-call is long, and includes many noteworthy names.

FIRST PERIOD (BEFORE 1066)

First, there is the shadowy band of Saxon benefactors. **Athelstan**, on his return from the victory of Brunanburh (937), helped to found St. Peter's hospital, York, giving not only the site, but a considerable endowment. (See p. 185.) Among other founders was a certain noble and devoted knight named **Acehorne**, lord of Flixton in the time of the most Christian king Athelstan, who provided a refuge for wayfarers in Holderness. Two Saxon bishops are named as builders of houses for the poor. To **St. Oswald** (Bishop of Worcester, died 992) is attributed the foundation of the hospital called after him ; but the earliest documentary reference to it is by Gervase of Canterbury (*circa* 1200). **St. Wulstan** (died 1094) pro-

70

vided the wayfarers' hostel at Worcester which continued
to bear his name. Wulstan, last of the Saxon founders,
forms a fitting link with Lanfranc, foremost of those
Norman "spiritual lords" who were to build hospitals
on a scale hitherto unknown in England.

SECOND PERIOD (1066–1272)

Lanfranc erected the hospitals of St. John, Canterbury,
and St. Nicholas, Harbledown; these charities remain
to this day as memorials of the archbishop. His friend
Bishop **Gundulf** of Rochester founded a lazar-house near
that city. In **Queen Maud**, wife of Henry I, the bishop
found a ready disciple. Her mother, Margaret of Scotland,
had trained her to love the poor and minister to them.
St. Margaret's special care had been for pilgrims, for
whom she had provided a hospital
at Queen's-ferry, Edinburgh. The
"holy Queen Maud," as we have
seen, served lepers with enthusiasm, and she established a home
near London for them. (Fig. 10.)
Henry I caught something of his
lady's spirit. "The house of
St. Bartholomew [Oxford] was
founded by our lord old King Henry, who married
the good queene Maud; and it was assigned for the
receiving and susteyning of infirme leprose folk,"
says Wood, quoting a thirteenth-century Inquisition.
Henry endowed his friend Gundulf's foundation at
Rochester, and probably also "the king's hospital"
near Lincoln, which had possibly been begun by Bishop
Remigius; that of Colchester was built by his steward

10. "THE MEMORIAL OF
MATILDA THE QUEEN"

Eudo at his command, and was accounted of the king's foundation. Matilda, daughter of Henry and Maud, left a benefaction to lepers at York.

King Stephen reconstructed St. Peter's hospital, York, after a great fire. (Cf. Pl. XXIV, XXV.) His wife, **Matilda of Boulogne,** founded St. Katharine's, London, which continues to this day under the patronage of the queens-consort. Henry II made considerable bequests for the benefit of lazars, but it is characteristic that his hospital building was in Anjou. **Richard I** endowed Bishop Glanvill's foundation at Strood. **King John** is thought to have founded hospitals near Lancaster, Newbury and Bristol. He is sometimes regarded as the conspicuous patron of lepers. Doubtless this may be partly attributed to the fact that at the outset of his reign the Church secured privileges to outcasts by the Council of Westminster (1200). There seems, however, to be some ground for his charitable reputation. Bale, in his drama *Kynge Johan*, makes England say concerning this king :—

" Never prynce was there that made to poore peoples use
  So many masendewes, hospytals and spyttle howses,
  As your grace hath done yet sens the worlde began."

. . . . . .

" Gracyouse prouysyon for sore, sycke, halte and lame
  He made in hys tyme, he made both in towne and cytie,
  Grauntynge great lyberties for mayntenaunce of the same,
  By markettes and fayers in places of notable name.
  Great monymentes are in Yppeswych, Donwych and Berye,
  Whych noteth hym to be a man of notable mercye." [1]

Indeed, as the Suffolk satirist knew by local tradition, King John did grant the privilege of a fair to the lepers of Ipswich.

[1] Camden Soc., 1838, pp. 82, 85.

PLATE VI

ST. BARTHOLOMEW'S, GLOUCESTER

ST. MARY'S, CHICHESTER

Henry III erected houses of charity at Woodstock, Dunwich and Ospringe, as well as homes for Jews in London and Oxford. He refounded St. John's in the latter city, and laid the first stone himself; he seems also to have rebuilt St. John's, Cambridge, and St. James', Westminster. The king loved Gloucester—the place of his coronation—and he re-established St. Bartholomew's, improving the buildings (Pl. VI) and endowment. The new hospitals of Dover and Basingstoke were committed to his care by their founders. Of Henry III's charities only that of St. James', Westminster, was for lepers; but St. Louis, who was with him while on crusade, told Joinville that on Holy Thursday (i.e. Maundy Thursday) the king of England "now with us" washes the feet of lepers and then kisses them. The ministry of the good queen Maud was thus carried on to the fifth generation.

If history tells how Maud cared for lepers and provided for them in St. Giles', London, tradition relates that **Adela of Louvain**, the second wife of Henry I, was herself a leper, and that she built St. Giles', Wilton. A Chantry Certificate reports that "Adulyce sometym quene of Englande" was the founder. The present inmates of the almshouse are naturally not a little puzzled by the modern inscription *Hospitium S. Egidii Adelicia Reg. Hen. Fund.* The local legend was formerly to be seen over the chapel door in a more intelligible and interesting form :—

"This hospitall of St. Giles was re-edified (1624) by John Towgood, maior of Wilton, and his brethren, adopted patrons thereof, by the gift of Queen Adelicia, wife unto King Henry the First. This Adelicia was a leper. She had a windowe and dore from her lodgeing into the chancell of the chapel, whence she heard prayer. She lieth buried under a marble gravestone."

Although in truth the widowed queen made a happy marriage with William d'Albini, and, when she died, was buried in an abbey in Flanders, she did endow a hospital at that royal manor—maybe to shelter one of her ladies, whose affliction might give rise to the tale of "the leprosy queen" and her ghost. When a person of rank became a leper, the terrible fact was not disclosed when concealment was possible. This is illustrated by another Wiltshire tradition—that of the endowment of the lazarhouse at Maiden Bradley by one of the heiresses of Manser Bisset, dapifer of Henry II. The story is as old as Leland's day; and Camden says that she " being herselfe a maiden infected with the leprosie, founded an house heere for maidens that were lepers, and endowed the same with her owne Patrimonie and Livetide." Margaret Bisset was certainly free from all taint of leprosy in 1237, when she sought and gained permission to visit Eleanor of Brittany, the king's cousin. She was well known at court at this time, and a Patent Roll entry of 1242 records that :—" At the petition of Margery Byset, the king has granted to the house of St. Matthew [sic], Bradeleg, and the infirm sisters thereof, for ever, five marks yearly . . . which he had before granted to the said Margery for life." Another contemporary deed (among the *Sarum Documents*) may support the legend of the leper-lady. It sets forth how Margaret Bisset desired to lead a celibate and contemplative life ; and therefore left her lands to the leper-hospital of Maiden Bradley on condition that she herself was maintained there.

Many famous churchmen, statesmen and warriors were hospital builders. Among the episcopal founders who figured prominently in public affairs were the following. **Ranulf Flambard**—"the most infamous prince of publicans" under William Rufus—founded Kepier hospital, Durham. The warlike **Henry de Blois**, half-brother of Stephen, erected St. Cross near Winchester. **Hugh de Puiset**, being, as Camden says, "very indulgently compassionate to Lepres," gathered them into his asylum at Sherburn, but it is hinted that his bounty was not altogether honestly come by. Again, "the high-souled abbot" **Sampson**—he who dared to oppose Prince John and also visited Richard in captivity—was the founder of St. Saviour's, at Bury St. Edmunds.

Even in the troublous days of Stephen there were barons who were tender towards the afflicted. **William le Gros**, lord of Holderness, was one of these. He was the founder of St. Mary Magdalene's, Newton-by-Hedon, for a charter speaks of "the infirm whom William, Earl of Albemarle, placed there." The *Chartulary of Whitby* relates how the earl—"a mighty man and of great prowess and power"—was wasting the eastern parts of Yorkshire. Nevertheless he "was a lover of the poor and especially of lepers and was accustomed to distribute freely to them large alms." Abbot Benedict therefore bethought him of a plan whereby he might save the threatened cow-pastures of the abbey from devastation : he permitted the cattle belonging to the Whitby hospital to join the herds of the convent ; consequently the earl was merciful to that place on account of the lepers, and the herds fed together henceforth undisturbed.

Another charitable lord was **Ranulf de Glanvill**—"jus-

ticiary of the realm of England and the king's eye "—who
with his wife Berta founded a leper-hospital at West
Somerton upon land granted to him by Henry II. His
nephew **Gilbert de Glanvill** built St. Mary's, Strood, near
his cathedral city of Rochester (*circa* 1193); the loyal
bishop declaring in his charter that it was founded
amongst other things " for the reformation of Christianity

11. THE TOMB OF RAHERE
(Founder and first prior of St. Bartholomew's)

in the Holy Land and for the liberation of Richard the
illustrious king of England." After the royal captive had
been freed, he endowed his faithful friend's foundation
with seven hundred acres of land. Among the leading
men of the day who built hospitals were Geoffrey Fitz-
Peter and William Briwere, Peter des Roches and Hubert
de Burgh, together with Hugh and Joceline of Wells.
Yet another distinguished bishop of this period must be

mentioned, namely, **Walter de Suffield,** who was very liberal
to the poor, especially in his city of Norwich. During
his lifetime he established St. Giles' and drew up its
statutes. He directed that as often as any bishop of the
See went by, he should enter and give his blessing to the
sick, and that the occasion should be marked by special
bounty. His will shows a most tender solicitude for
the welfare of the house, which he commended to his
successor and his executors.

Benefactors included not only men eminent in church
and state, but "others of divers estates," clerical and lay
commoners. Foremost of these stands **Rahere,** born of
low lineage, but court-minstrel and afterwards priest.
In obedience to a vision, he determined to undertake the
foundation of a hospital. He sought help from the
Bishop of London, by whose influence he obtained from
Henry I the site of St. Bartholomew's, Smithfield.
While many founders are forgotten, men delight to
honour Rahere. The chronicler, who had talked with
those who remembered him, records how he sympathized
with the tribulation of the wretched, how he recognized
their need, supported them patiently, and finally helped
them on their way. Rahere's character is delightfully
portrayed in the *Book of the Foundation :*—

"whoose prouyd puryte of soule, bryght maners with honeste
probyte, experte diligence yn dyuyne seruyce, prudent besynes
yn temperalle mynystracyun, in hym were gretely to prayse and
commendable."

Other clerical founders include William, Dean of Chichester (St. Mary's), Walter the Archdeacon (St. John's,
Northampton), Peter the chaplain (Lynn), Guarin the

chaplain (Cricklade), Walter, Vicar of Long Stow, etc. **Hugh the hermit** was reckoned the founder of Cockersand hospital, which grew into an abbey :—

" Be it noted that the monastery was furst founded by Hugh Garthe, an heremyt of great perfection, and by such charitable almes as [he] dyd gather in the countre he founded an hospitall."

The leading townsfolk of England have long proved themselves generous. **Gervase** of Southampton is in the forefront of a line of merchant-princes and civic rulers who have also been benefactors of the needy. Gervase "le Riche" was evidently a capitalist, and it is recorded that he lent moneys to Prince John. His responsible office was that of portreeve ; it may be that while exercising it, he witnessed sick pilgrims disembark and was moved to help them. Certainly, about the year 1185, Gervase built God's House (Pl. VII) beside the quay, and his brother Roger became the first warden. Leland's version is as follows :—

" Thys Hospitale was foundyd by 2 Marchauntes beyng Bretherne [whereof] the one was caullyd Ge[rvasius] the other Protasius. . . . These 2 Brethern, as I there lernid, dwellyd yn the very Place wher the Hospitale is now. . . . These 2 Brethern for Goddes sake cause[d] their House to be turnid to an Hospitale for poore Folkes, and endowed it with sum Landes."

Among other citizen-founders of this period may be named Walter and Roesia Brune, founders of St. Mary's, Bishopsgate, London ; Hildebrand le Mercer, of Norwich ; and William Prodom and John Long, of Exeter.

PLATE VII

GOD'S HOUSE, SOUTHAMPTON

THIRD PERIOD (1272-1540)

Few royal builders or benefactors can be named at this time. **Edward I,** who, from various motives, set his face like a flint against the Jews, was a beneficent patron to those who were prepared to submit to Baptism ; and he reorganized and endowed his father's House of Converts. His charity, however, was of a somewhat belligerent character and partook of the nature of a crusade. He was always extremely harsh towards the unconverted Jew; his early training as champion of the Cross in the Holy Land helped to make him zealous in ridding his own kingdom of unbelievers. But before finally expelling them, he did his best for their conversion, enlisting the help of the trained and eloquent Dominican brethren. Edward with justice ordained that as by custom the goods of the converts became the king's, he should hence- forth "provide healthfully for their maintenance"; and he granted them a moiety of their property when they became, by Baptism, "sons and faithful members of the Church." The chevage, or Jewish poll-tax, and certain other Jewish payments, were appropriated to the *Domus Conversorum*, over £200 being paid annually from the Exchequer. Edward took an interest in "the king's converts" and drew up careful regulations for them. **Eleanor,** his consort, was a benefactor of the royal hospital near the Tower, and she was also by tradition the founder of St. John's, Gorleston.

The unhappy **Richard II** desired in his will that five or six thousand marks should be devoted to the main- tenance of lepers at Westminster and Bermondsey.[1]

[1] Rolls of Parl. 1 Henry IV, vol. iii. 421.

The reference to "the chaplains celebrating before them for us" seems to imply that the king was the patron if not the founder; possibly one house was that of Knightsbridge. The will of **Henry VII** provided for the erection of three great charitable institutions. He was at least liberal in this, that he began in his lifetime the conversion of his palace of Savoy into a noble hospital. (Pl. XIV.) Its completion at the cost of 10,000 marks was the only part of his plan carried out, and of the 40,000 marks designed to be similarly expended at York and Coventry, nothing more is heard.

The great lords of this period who were founders are led by two distinguished kinsmen and counsellors of Edward III—each a **Henry of Lancaster** and Steward of England. The father, when he was becoming blind, erected St. Mary's at Leicester for fifty poor (1330), and his son doubled the foundation. **Richard, Earl of Arundel**—the victor of Sluys—began to found the Maison Dieu, Arundel, in 1380, but he was executed on a charge of treason; and the work ceased until his son, having obtained fresh letters-patent from Henry V (1423), set himself to complete the design. Several notable veterans of the French campaign may be mentioned as hospital builders, namely, **Michael de la Pole** (Kingston-upon-Hull), **Sir Robert Knolles** (Pontefract), **Walter, Lord Hungerford** (Heytesbury) and **William de la Pole** (Ewelme); when the latter became unpopular and was executed as a traitor, his wife Alice—called on her tomb *fundatrix*—completed the building and endowment of God's.House. (Pl. XVII.)

Although the benevolence of bishops now chiefly took the form of educational institutions, some well-known prelates

PLATE VIII

HOSPITAL OF ST. CROSS, WINCHESTER

GATEWAY AND DWELLINGS BUILT BY CARDINAL BEAUFORT

erected hospitals.   **Bubwith**—Treasurer of England under
Henry IV—planned St. Saviour's, Wells, but it was not
begun in his lifetime.   **Beaufort**—Lord Chancellor and
Cardinal—refounded St. Cross, but, owing to the York
and Lancaster struggle, the design was not fully carried
out.   His rival **Chichele**—the faithful Primate of Henry V
—built not only All Souls, Oxford, but the bede-house
at Higham Ferrers.   There is a tradition that while keeping the sheep by the riverside he was met by William
of Wykeham, who recognized his talents and provided
for his education.   He afterwards desired to found a college in the place where he was baptized, and of this
the almshouse formed part.   **William Smyth**—founder of
Brasenose—restored St. John's during his short episco-
pate at Lichfield.   When translated to Lincoln, he turned
his attention to St. John's, Banbury, and bequeathed
£100 towards erecting and repairing its buildings, in
addition to £60 already bestowed upon it.   "This man,"
says Fuller, "wheresoever he went, may be followed by
the perfume of Charity he left behind him."

It was undoubtedly townsfolk who were the principal
founders of the fourteenth and fifteenth centuries.   The
name of many an old merchant-prince is still a household
word in his native place, where some institution remains
as a noble record of his bounty.   St. John's, Winchester,
for example, was erected by an alderman, **John Devenish**,
its revenues being increased by another of the family and
by a later mayor; and the memory of benefactors was kept
fresh by a "love-feast and merry meeting" on the Sunday
after Midsummer Day.   **William Elsyng** established a
large almshouse near Cripplegate.   He was a mercer of
influential position, being given a licence to travel in the

king's service beyond seas with Henry of Lancaster; and
it may have been this nobleman's charitable work in
Leicester that inspired the foundation known as "Our
Lady of Elsyngspital."

A more famous London mercer, **Richard Whittington**,
proved himself the "model merchant of the Middle Ages";
Lysons records his manifold beneficent deeds.   Although
he did not live long enough to carry out all his schemes,
his executors completed them, and in particular, the almshouse attached to St. Michael Royal.   In a deed drawn
up after his death (1423) and now preserved in the Mercers'
Hall, is a fine pen-and-ink sketch which depicts the passing of this "father of the poor." (Pl. IX.)   John Carpenter
and other friends stand round the sick man; nor are we
left in doubt as to the significance of the group at the foot
of the bed—evidently twelve bedemen, led by one who
holds a rosary in token of his intercessory office—it being
recorded in the document that :—

"the foresayde worthy and notable merchaunt, Richard
Whittington, the which while he leued had ryght liberal and
large hands to the needy and poure people, charged streitly on
his death bed us his foresayde executors to ordeyne a house of
almes, after his death . . . and thereupon fully he declared his
will unto us."[1]

The same benefactor not only repaired St. Bartholomew's,
but added a refuge for women to St. Thomas', Southwark,
as is set forth by William Gregory, one of Whittington's
successors in the mayoralty :—

" And that nobyl marchaunt Rycharde Whytyngdon, made a
new chamby[r] with viij beddys for yong weme[n] that hadde
done a-mysse in truste of a good mendement.   And he com-

[1] T. Brewer, *Carpenter's Life*, p. 26.

PLATE IX

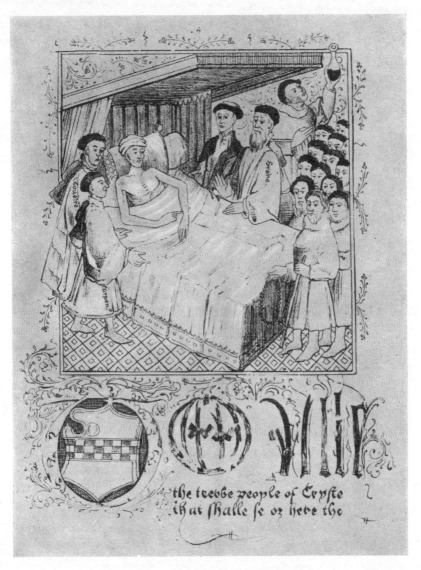

the trewbe people of Cryste
that shalle se or here the

THE DEATH OF RICHARD WHITTINGTON

maundyd that alle the thyngys that ben don in that chambyr shulde be kepte secrete with owte forthe, yn payne of lesynge of hyr leuynge ; for he wolde not shame no yonge women in noo wyse, for hyt myght be cause of hyr lettyng of hyr maryage."

"Verily," we exclaim with Lysons, "there seems to be no end to the good deeds of this good man."

Nor were other places without their public-spirited townsmen.   Unlike "Dick" Whittington who died child-less, **Thomas Ellis** left twenty-three sons and daughters : nevertheless this large-hearted draper provided an alms-house for his poorer neighbours in Sandwich.

The wealth of **William Browne** of Stamford and of **Roger Thornton** of Newcastle-upon-Tyne was proverbial when Leland visited those industrial centres and saw the charities which they had established.   Browne, founder of the bede-house (Fig. 5), "was a Marchant of a very wonderful Richeness."   Thornton, a very poor man, reported to have been a pedlar, who rose to be nine times mayor, was remembered as "the richest Marchaunt that ever was dwelling in Newcastelle."   While in this way many that were rich made offerings of their abundance, there were those, too, who gave of their penury.   Such was "**Adam Rypp**, of Whittlsey, a poor man, who began to build a Poor's Hospital there, but had not sufficient means to finish it."   His work was commended to the faithful by briefs from Bishop Fordham of Ely (1391-4).

TOMBS OF FOUNDERS AND BENEFACTORS

Many benefactors associated themselves so closely with their bedemen that they desired to be buried within the precincts of the hospital.   Robert de Meulan, one of the

Conqueror's lords, is said to have founded and endowed Brackley hospital, where his heart was embalmed. His descendant, Roger, Earl of Winchester, a considerable benefactor in the time of Henry III, "ordered a measure

12. JOHN BARSTAPLE
(Burgess of Bristol)

to be made for corn in the shape of a coffin, and gave directions that it should be placed on the right side of the shrine, in which the heart of Margaret his mother lay intombed," providing that it should be filled thrice in a year for ever for the use of the hospital.[1] The chapel

[1] Bridges' *History*, I, 146.

continued to be a favourite place of interment, for Leland says:—"There ly buryed in Tumbes dyvers Noble Men and Women." Bishop Suffield directed that if he should die away from Norwich—as he afterwards did—his heart should be placed near the altar in the church of St. Giles' hospital. The blind and aged Henry of Lancaster and Leicester was buried in his hospital church, the royal family and a great company being present (1345); and there likewise his son was laid. Few founders' tombs remain undisturbed in a spot still hallowed by divine worship, but some have happily escaped destruction. Rahere has an honoured place at St. Bartholomew's. The mailed effigy of Sir Henry de Sandwich—lord warden of the Cinque Ports—remains in the humbler St. Bartholomew's near Sandwich. The fine alabaster monument of Alice, Duchess of Suffolk, is in perfect preservation at Ewelme. The rebuilt chapel of Trinity Hospital, Bristol, retains a monumental brass of the founder (Fig. 12) and his wife.

AIMS AND MOTIVES OF BENEFACTORS

It is sometimes asserted that the almsgiving of the Middle Ages was done from a selfish motive, namely, that spiritual benefits might be reaped by the donor. Indeed it is possible that the giver then, like some religious people in every age, was apt to be more absorbed in the salvation of self than in the service of others; but the testimony of deeds and charters is that the threefold aim of such a man was to fulfil at once his duty towards God, his neighbour, and himself. That he was often imbued with a true ministering spirit is shown by his personal care for the comfort of inmates.　Doubtless the hidden springs of charity were as diverse as they are now : not every name on a modern subscription list represents one that "considereth the poor."　No one could imagine, for instance, that Queen Maud and King John had a common motive in their charity to lepers ; or that the bishops Wulstan and Peter des Roches were animated by the same impulse when they provided for the wants of wayfarers.

The alleged motives of some benefactors are revealed in documents.　Henry de Blois, Bishop of Winchester, refers to St. Cross—"which I for the health of my soul and the souls of my predecessors and of the kings of England have founded . . . that the poor in Christ may there humbly and devotedly serve God."　Herbert, Bishop of Salisbury, in making a grant to clothe the lepers of a hospital in Normandy, says that :—"Among all Christ's poor whom a bishop is bound to protect and support, those should be specially cared for whom it has pleased God to deprive of bodily power," and these poor inmates "in the sorrow of fleshly affliction offer thanks to the Lord for their benefactors with a joyous mind."　Matthew Paris writes of Henry III that "he being touched with the Holy Ghost and moved with a regard to pity, ordained a certain famous hospital at Oxon."

In the case of Rahere, the foundation of St. Bartholomew's was an act of gratitude for deliverance from death, and the practical outcome of a vision and a sick-bed vow. While Rahere tarried at Rome,

" he began to be uexed with greuous sykenesse, and his douloures, litill and litill, takynge ther encrese, he drew to the extremyte of lyf. . . . Albrake owte in terys, than he auowyd yf helthe God hym wolde grawnte, that he myght lefully returne to his contray, he wolde make and hospitale yn recreacion of poure men, and to them so there i gaderid, necessaries mynystir, after his power."

Now and again a benefactor evinces deep religious feelings, as shown in the charter of Bishop Glanvill at the foundation of St. Mary's, Strood :—

" Bearing in mind the saying of the Lord : ' I was an hungred, and ye gave Me meat ; I was thirsty, and ye gave Me drink ; I was a stranger, and ye took Me in ; ' . . . And seeing that the Lord takes upon Himself the needs of those who suffer . . . we have founded a hospital in which to receive and cherish the poor, weak and infirm."

Another founder showed the zeal of Apostolic days ; a layman of Stamford, Brand by name, made an offering to God and held nothing back.   This we learn from a papal document (*circa* 1174) :—

" Alexander the bishop to his beloved son Brand de Fossato, greeting . . . we having been given to understand . . . that you, guided by divine inspiration, having sold all you did possess, have erected a certain hospital and chappel . . . where you have chose to exhibit a perpetual offering to your creator." [1]

The meritorious aspect of almsgiving was sometimes uppermost.   Hugh Foliot, Bishop of Hereford, in founding his hospital at Ledbury, sets forth the importance and advantage of exercising hospitality.   He illustrates the point by the case of the patriarchs, who were signally rewarded for their hospitality :—

"Bearing in mind therefore that . . . almost nothing is to be preferred to hospitality, and that so great is its value that Lot and

[1] F. Peck's *Annals of Stanford*, v. 15.

Abraham who practised it were counted worthy to receive angels for guests . . . we have built a certain hospital for strangers and poor people."

The Church continued to teach the imperative duty of almsgiving. It is stated in the will of Henry VII that in the one act of establishing a hospital the Seven Works of Mercy might be fulfilled :—

" And forasmuch as we inwardly consideir, that the vij. workes of Charite and Mercy bee moost profitable, due and necessarie for the saluation of man's soule, and that the same vij. works stand moost commonly in vj. of theim ; that is to saye in uiseting the sik, mynistring mete and drinke and clothing to the nedy, logging of the miserable pouer, and burying of the dede bodies of cristen people. . . . We therefor of our great pitie and compassion . . . have begoune to erecte, buylde and establisshe a commune Hospital in our place called the Sauoie . . . to the laude of God, the weale of our soule, and the refresshing of the said pouer people, in daily, nightly and hourely exploytyng the said vj. works of Mercy, Pitie, and Charity."

To the hospital which he had provided, the founder looked not only for spiritual and temporal profit in this life, but above all for help to his soul in the world to come. The desire for the prayers of generations yet unborn was a strong incentive to charity.   The bede-houses testify to a purposeful belief in the availing power of intercession. Thus the patrons of Ewelme speak in the statutes of " prayoure, in the whiche we have grete trust and hope to oure grete relefe and increce of oure merite and joy fynally."   The same faith is expressed by the action of the merchants and mariners of Bristol in 1445.   Because

" the crafte off maryners is so auenturous that dayly beyng in ther uiages ben sore vexed, trobled and deseased and distried, the which by gode menys of the prayers and gode werkes might be graciously comforted and better releced of such trobles,"

they wished to found a fraternity to support, within the old hospital of St. Bartholomew (Fig. 13), a priest and

13. ST. BARTHOLOMEW'S HOSPITAL, BRISTOL
(Called in 1387 *the Domus Dei dy Fromne Bridge*)

twelve poor seamen who should pray for those labouring on the sea, or passing to and fro into their port.

An earnest desire to make the world better is shown in one foundation deed, dating probably from the middle of the fourteenth century. It concerns Holy Trinity, Salisbury, erected by Agnes Bottenham on a spot where a house of evil repute had existed "to the great perils of souls " :—

"The founders, by means of the inspiration of the Holy Spirit, have ordained thirty beds to the sustentation of the poor and infirm daily resorting thither, and the seven works of charity are there fulfilled. The hungry are fed, the thirsty have drink, the naked are clothed, the sick are comforted, the dead are buried, the mad are kept safe until they are restored to reason, orphans and widows are nourished, lying-in women are cared for until they are delivered, recovered and churched."

The aim of pious benefactors was indeed the abiding welfare of their bedemen. The hard-headed, warm-hearted business men of Croydon and Stamford, no less than the ladies of Heytesbury and Ewelme, expressed a hope that the *Domus Dei* on earth might be a preparation for the eternal House of God. In the words of the patrons of Ewelme, they desired the poor men so to live :—

"that aftyr the state of this dedely [mortal] lyf they mowe come and inhabit the howse of the kyngdome of heven, the which with oure Lordes mouth is promysed to all men the which bene pore in spirit. So be yt."

CHAPTER VII

HOSPITAL INMATES

*" To the master and brethren of the hospital of St. Nicholas, Scarborough.—
Request to admit John de Burgh, chaplain, and grant him maintenance
for life, as John has been suddenly attacked by the disease of leprosy, and
has not wherewith to live and is unable through shame to beg among
Christians."* (Close Roll, 1342.)

THOUGH a visit to a modern infirmary calls forth in
us, doubtless, passing thoughts of admiration for
the buildings and the arrangements, what draws
most of us thither is the bond of brotherhood. It is the
inmates of the wards who are to us the centre of attrac-
tion. Looking upon the sufferers, we desire to know
their circumstances, their complaints, their chance of
cure. Nor is it otherwise in studying the history of
ancient institutions. The mere site of an old hospital
may become a place of real interest when we know something of those who once dwelt there, when we *see* the
wayworn pilgrim knocking at the gate, the infirm man
bent with age, the paralysed bedridden woman, and the
stricken leper in his sombre gown, and realize what
our forefathers strove to do in the service of others.

In many cases the link between the first founder and
first inmate was very close, being the outcome of personal
relations between master and servant, feudal lord and
tenant. It was so in the case of Orm, the earliest hospital inmate whose name has been handed down to us.

This Yorkshireman, who lived near Whitby eight hundred years ago, "was a good man and a just, but he was a leper." The abbot, therefore, having pity on him, founded a little asylum, in which Orm spent the rest of his days, receiving from the abbey his portion of food and drink. In the same way Hugh Kevelioc, Earl of Chester, built a retreat outside Coventry for William de Anney, a knight of his household, which was the origin of Spon hospital for the maintenance of such lepers as should happen to be in the town.

(i) PERSONS MIRACULOUSLY CURED

In dealing with mediæval miracles it may not unnaturally be objected that we are wandering from the paths of history into the fields of fiction; but it is absolutely necessary to allude to them at some length because they played so important a part in the romantic tales of pilgrim-patients. We shall see that sufferers were constantly being carried about in search of cure, and in some cases were undoubtedly restored to health. This was an age of faith and therefore of infinite possibilities. It would appear that "marvels" were worked not only on certain nervous ailments, but on some deep-seated diseases. It is a recognized fact that illness caused by emotion (as of grief) has oftentimes been cured by emotion (as of hope). Possibly, too, not a few of the persons restored to health were suffering from hysteria and nervous affections, which complaints might be cured by change of scene and excitement. In the *Book of the Foundation* is the story of a well-known man of Norwich who would not take care of his health, and therefore "hadde lost the rest of slepe," which alone keeps the nature sound and whole. His in-

somnia became chronic, and by the seventh year of his
misfortune he became very feeble, and so thin that his
bones could be numbered.   At length he betook himself
to the relics of St. Bartholomew; there, grovelling on the
ground, he multiplied his prayers and began to sleep —
"and whan he hadde slepte a grete while he roys up
hole."

On the other hand the conviction is forced upon us that
many, perhaps most, of the so-called miracles were not
genuine.   Some diseases might have been feigned by
astute beggars.   Although experienced doctors and
skilled nurses to-day are quick to detect cases, cleverly
simulating paralysis, epilepsy, etc., the staff in a mediæval hospital would probably not discover the deception.
When one such person became the hero of a dramatic
scene of healing, the officials would joyfully acknowledge
his cure, without intention of
fraud.   The narratives come
down to us through monk-
chroniclers, whose zeal for
their home-shrines made them
lend a quick ear to that which
contributed to their fame.   In
those days people were uncritical and were satisfied without minute investigation.

There is, indeed, little information about early hospital
inmates unless they were for-
tunate enough to receive what
was universally believed in
those days to be miraculous

14. ST. BARTHOLOMEW
(Twelfth-century seal)

healing. Startling incidents are related by contemporary writers, whose vivid and picturesque narratives suggest that they had met witnesses of the cures related. The twelfth-century chronicler of St. Bartholomew's, Smithfield, gives us eyes to see some of the patients of that famous hospital.

(1) *Patients of St. Bartholomew's.*—The cripple Wolmer, a well-known beggar who lay daily in St. Paul's, was a most distressing case. He was so deformed as to be obliged to drag himself along on all fours, supporting his hands on little wooden stools. (Cf. Pl. XX.) His story is extracted from Dr. Norman Moore's valuable edition of the faithful English version of the *Liber Fundacionis*, dating about the year 1400.

"There was an sykeman Wolmer be name with greuous and longe langoure depressid, and wrecchid to almen that hym behylde apperyd, his feit destitute of naturall myght hyng down, hys legges cleuyd to his thyis, part of his fyngerys returnyd to the hande, restynge alwey uppon two lytyll stolys, the quantite of his body, to hym onerous, he drew aftir hym. . . ."

For thirty winters Wolmer remained in this sad condition, until at length he was borne by his friends in a basket to the newly-founded hospital of St. Bartholomew, where his cure was wrought by a miracle as he lay extended before the altar in the church :—

". . . and by and by euery crokidness of his body a litill & litill losid, he strecchid un to grownde his membris & so anoon auawntynge hym self up warde, all his membris yn naturale ordir was disposid. . . ."

The scene of this incident was, presumably, that noble building which we still see (Fig. 11), and which was then fresh from the hand of the Norman architect and masons.

Aldwyn, a carpenter from Dunwich, once occupied a place in St. Bartholomew's. His limbs were as twisted and useless as those of Wolmer; his sinews being contracted, he could use neither hand nor foot. Brought by sea to London, the cripple was "put yn the hospitall of pore men," where awhile he was sustained. Bit by bit he regained power in his hands, and when discharged was able to exercise his craft once more.

Again the veil of centuries is lifted and we see the founder himself personally interested in the patients. A woman was brought into the hospital whose tongue was so terribly swollen that she could not close her mouth. Rahere offered to God and to his patron prayer on her behalf and then applied his remedy :—

"And he reuolvynge his relikys that he hadde of the Crosse, he depid them yn water & wysshe the tonge of the pacient ther with, & with the tree of lyif, that ys with the same signe of the crosse, paynted the tokyn of the crosse upon the same tonge. And yn the same howre all the swellynge wente his way, & the woman gladde & hole went home to here owne."

Perhaps the most startling cure was that of a maid deaf, dumb, blind of both eyes and crippled. Brought by her parents to the festival of St. Bartholomew in the year 1173, she was delivered from every bond of sickness. Anon she went "joyfull skippyng forth"; her eyes clear, her hearing repaired, "she ran to the table of the holy awter, spredyng owte bothe handys to heuyn and so she that a litill beforne was dum joyng in laude of God perfitly sowndyd her wordes "; then weeping for joy she went to her parents affirming herself free from all infirmity.

In the foregoing narratives it will be , noticed that hospital and shrine were adjacent. This convenient combination not being found elsewhere, incurable patients were carried to pilgrimage-places. Two of the chief wonder-workers were St. Godric of Finchale and St. Thomas of Canterbury, who both died in 1170. Reginald of Durham narrates the cure by their instrumentality of three inmates from northern hospitals.[1]

(2) *The Paralytic Girl and the Crippled Youth.*—A young woman who had lost the use of one side by paralysis, was brought from the hospital of Sedgefield (near Durham) to Finchale, where the same night she recovered health. The poor cripple of York was not cured so rapidly. Utterly powerless, his arms and feet twisted after the manner of knotted ropes, this most wretched youth had spent years in St. Peter's hospital. At length he betook himself as best he could to Canterbury, where he received from St. Thomas health on one side of his body. It grieved him that he was not worthy to be completely cured, but learning from many witnesses the fame of St. Godric, he hastened to his sepulchre ; falling down there, he lay in weakness for some time, then, rising up, found the other side of his body absolutely recovered. The lad returned home whole and upright, and this notable miracle was attested by many who knew him, and by the procurator of the hospital.

(3) *A Leper Maiden.*—The touching tale of a girl who was eventually released from the lazar-house near Darling-

[1] Surtees Soc., Vol. 20, pp. 376, 432-3, 456-7.

ton (Bathelspitel) is also related by Reginald, and transcribed by Longstaffe.

"There is a vill in the bishopric called Hailtune [Haughton-le-Skerne] in which dwelt a widow and her only daughter who was grievously tormented with a most loathsome leprosy. The mother remarried a man who soon began to view the poor girl with the greatest horror, and to torment and execrate her. . . . She fled for aid to the priest of the vill, who, moved with compassion, procured by his entreaties the admission of the damsel to the hospital of Dernigntune [Darlington], which was almost three miles distant, and was called Badele."

There the maiden remained three years, growing daily worse. After describing her horrible symptoms and wasted frame, the chronicler narrates her marvellous cure at Finchale. Thrice did the devoted mother take her thither until the clemency of St. Godric was outpoured and "he settled and removed the noxious humours." When at length the girl threw back the close hood, her mother beheld her perfectly sound. The scene of this pitiful arrival and glad departure was that beautiful spot at the bend of the river Weir, now marked by picturesque ruins. The complete recovery was attested by all, including the sheriff and the kind priest, Normanrus. We reluctantly lose sight of the delivered damsel, wondering whether the cruel step-father received her less roughly when she got home. It is simply recorded that never did the disease return, and that she lived long to extol the power given by God to His servant Godric.

(4) *A Taunton Monk.*—Seldom do we know the after-life of such patients, but a touching picture shows us one cleansed of his leprosy, serving his former fellow-inmates. This was John King, a monk of Taunton Priory. Prior

Stephen tells how he was smitten with terrible and manifest leprosy, on which account he was transferred to a certain house of poor people, where he stayed for more than a year among the brethren. The prior's letter, after declaring how the fame of St. Thomas was growing throughout the world, refers to divers miracles, by one of which John was completely cured. Returning from Canterbury, he was authorized to gather alms for his former companions :—

"We . . . earnestly implore your loving good will for the love of God and St. Thomas, that you listen to the dutiful prayer of our brother John, wonderfully restored to health by God, if you have power to grant it. For he earnestly begs you to help by your labour and your alms the poverty of those sick men whose company he enjoyed so long." [1]

Two similar instances of service are recorded. Nicholas, a cripple child cured at St. Bartholomew's, was sent for a while to serve in the kitchen,—"for the yifte of his helth, he yave the seruyce of his body." In the same way a blind man who had been miraculously cured by the merit of St. Wulstan (1221), afterwards took upon himself the habit of a professed brother in the hospital of that saint in Worcester. He had been a pugilist and had lost his sight in a duel, but having become a peaceable brother of mercy, he lived there honourably for a long while. [2]

(ii) CROWN PENSIONERS

Leaving the chronicles, and turning to state records, we find that the sick, impotent and leprous were recipients of royal favour. An early grant of maintenance was

---

[1] Chron. and Mem., 67, i. 428–9.
[2] Chron. and Mem., 36, iv. p. 413.

made in 1235 to Helen, a blind woman of Faversham whom Henry III caused to be received as a sister at Ospringe hospital. Similar grants were made from time to time to faithful retainers, veteran soldiers or converted Jews (who were the king's wards).

Old Servants, Soldiers, etc.—The most interesting pensioners were veterans who had served in Scotland and France. The year of the battle of Bannockburn (1314), a man was sent to Brackley whose hand had been inhumanly cut off by Scotch rebels.[1] There are several instances of persons maimed in the wars who were sent for maintenance to various hospitals. One of the many grants of Richard II was made—"out of regard for Good Friday "—to an aged servant, that he should be one of the king's thirteen poor bedemen of St. Giles', Wilton. Another of Richard II's retainers, a yeoman, was generously offered maintenance at Puckeshall by Henry IV.[2]

Jewish Converts.—The House of Converts was akin to a modern industrial home for destitute Jewish Christians, inmates being kept busily employed in school and workshop. During the century following the foundation of these "hospitals," many converts are named, *Eve*, for instance, was received at Oxford, and *Christiana* in London. Usually admitted after baptism, they were enrolled under their new names. *Philip* had been baptized upon St. Philip and St. James' Day, and *Robert Grosseteste* was possibly godson of the bishop. Converts were brought from all parts. We find John and William of Lincoln, Isabel of Bristol and her boy, Isabel of Cam-

---

[1] Close 8 Edw. II, m. 35 *d*.
[2] Pat. 8 Ric. II, pt. ii. m. 22 ; 9 Hen. IV, pt. ii. m. 14.

bridge, Emma of Ipswich, etc.[1] A century later pensioners must have been immigrants, since all Jews resident in England had been expelled in 1290. A Flemish
Jew, baptized at Antwerp in the presence of Edward III,
was granted permission to dwell in the London institution
with a life-pension of 2d. a day :—

"Inasmuch as our beloved Edward of Brussels has recently
abandoned the superstitious errors of Judaism . . . and
because we rejoice in Christ over his conversion, and lest he
should recede from the path of truth upon which he has entered,
because of poverty . . . we have granted to him a suitable
home in our House of Converts."

Theobald de Turkie, "a convert to the Catholic Faith,"
was afterwards received, together with pensioners from
Spain, Portugal, France, and Italy. A chamber was
granted to Agnes, an orphan Jewess of tender age and
destitute of friends, the child of a convert-godson of
Edward II. A later inmate, of whose circumstances we
would fain know more, was Elizabeth, daughter of Rabbi
Moyses, called "bishop of the Jews" (1399). Converts
frequently had royal sponsors. Henry V stood godfather
to Henry Stratford, who lived in the *Domus Conversorum*
from 1416-1441. There was a certain risk in being called
after the sovereign, nor was it unknown for the king's
converts to change their names. As late as 1532 Katharine of Aragon and Princess Mary stood sponsor to two
Jewesses.

(iii) INMATES OF SOME LAZAR-HOUSES

(1) *Lincoln Invalids.*—Near Lincoln is a spot still
pointed out as the "Lepers' Field." Formerly it was
known as the Mallardry or as Holy Innocents' hospital.

[1] Close Rolls *passim.*

Had one visited this place in the days of Edward I, ten of the king's servants—lepers or decrepit persons—would have been found there, together with two chaplains and certain brethren and sisters. Thomas, a maimed clerk, was one of the staff, but after thirty years he incurred the jealousy of his companions, who endeavoured to ruin his character while he was absent on business. Brother Thomas appealed to the king, and justice was administered (1278). Some time afterwards the household became so quarrelsome that the king issued a writ, and a visitation was held in 1291 to set matters straight. In 1290 William le Forester was admitted to the lepers' quarters, his open-air life not having saved him from disease. Dionysia, a widow, took up her abode as a sister the same year, and remained until her death, when another leper was assigned her place. An old servant of the house past work was admitted as pensioner, and also a blind and aged retainer whose faithfulness had reduced him to poverty, he having served in Scotland and having moreover lost all his horses, waggons and goods in the Welsh rebellion. But strangest of all the residents in the hospital of Holy Innocents was the condemned criminal Margaret Everard. She was not a leper, but had once been numbered among the dead. Mistress Everard, of Burgh-by-Waynflete, was a widow, convicted of "harbouring a thief, namely, Robert her son, and hanged on the gallows without the south gate of Lincoln." Now the law did not provide interment for its victims, but it seems that the Knights Hospitallers of Maltby paid a yearly sum to the lepers for undertaking this work of mercy at Canwick.[1] On this memorable

[1] P.R.O. Chanc. Misc. Bundle 20, No. 10.

occasion, however, the body being cut down and already removed near the place of burial—the lepers' churchyard —the woman "was seen to draw a breath and revive." We learn from a Patent Roll entry (1284) that pardon was afterwards granted to Margaret "because her recovery is ascribed to a miracle, and she has lived two years and more in the said hospital."

(2) *The Lancastrian falconer and Yorkist yeoman.*—A certain Arnald Knyght, who had been falconer to Henry IV, Henry V, and Henry VI, caused a habitation to be built for himself on the site of the hospital by the Whiteditch, near Rochester, in order that there he might spend his days in divine service. In consideration of his age and of his infirmity of leprosy, Henry VI granted to Arnald and Geraldine his wife not only the building recently erected, but the lands and rents of St. Nicholas' hospital. Edward IV afterwards granted a parcel of land between Highgate and Holloway to a certain leper-yeoman " to the intent that he may build a hospital for the relief of divers persons smitten with this sickness and destitute." This man—half-founder, half-inmate—soon succumbed, for a record four years later states that "the new lazarhouse at Highgate which the king lately caused to be made for William Pole . . . now deceased" was granted for life to another leper, Robert Wylson, a saddler, who had served well "in divers fields and elsewhere."[1]

(3) *The Mayor of Exeter.*—Shortly before 1458, St. Mary Magdalene's, Exeter, had a prominent inmate in the sometime mayor, Richard Orenge. In 1438 Richard

[1] Pat. 21 Hen. VI, pt. i. m. 35, pt. ii. m. 16; 12 Edw. IV, pt. ii. m. 6; 17 Edw. IV, pt. i. m. 1.

William, *alias* Richard Orenge, is mentioned as a tailor ; he is also described as being a man of French extraction and of noble family. Once he had been official patron of the asylum, but when the blow fell, he threw in his lot with those to whom he had formerly been bountiful. There, Izacke says, he finished his days and was buried in the chapel.

(4) *Two Norfolk lepers.*—We learn incidentally through a lawsuit that about the year 1475 the vicar of Foulsham, Thomas Wood, was in seclu-sion in a London lazar-house:— "and nowe it is said God hathe visited the seid parsone with the sekenes of lepre and is in the Spitell howse of knygtyes brygge beside Westminster."[1] Why the priest came up from the country to Knightsbridge does not appear ; it would seem, however, that the Nor-folk manor was temporarily in the king's hands, so that pos-sibly the crown bailiff procured his removal. One of the latest leper-inmates whose name is recorded ended his days at

15. SEAL OF KNIGHTSBRIDGE HOSPITAL

Walsingham. The patron of the Spital-house left it in 1491 to John Ederyche, a leper of Norwich, and Cecily his wife, stipulating that after their decease, one or two lepers—"men of good conversation and honest disposi-tion "—should be maintained there.

[1] P.R.O., Early Chancery Proceedings, Bundle 60, No. 93.

(iv) SOLITARY OUTCASTS

It must not be supposed that there were no lepers save those living in community. To use the old phrase, there was the man who dwelt in a several house and he who was forced to join the congregation without the camp. To lepers "whether recluses or living together" the Bishop of Norwich bequeathed five pounds (1256). Hermit-lazar and hospital-lazar alike fulfilled the legal requirement of separation. It may be noticed that the service at seclusion implies that the outcast may dwell alone. In early records, before the king habitually imposed "corrodies" on charitable institutions, pensioners are named who were not inhabiting lazar-houses. Philip the clerk was assigned a tenement in Portsmouth, which was afterwards granted to God's House on condition that Philip was maintained for life, or that provision was made for him to go to the Holy Land (1236). Long afterwards, in 1394, Richard II pensioned a groom of the scullery from the Exchequer, but provided for one of his esquires in a hospital.[1]

In hermitage and hospital alike service was rendered to the leper in his loneliness. The little cell and chapel at Roche in Cornwall is said to have been a place of seclusion for one "diseased with a grievous leprosy." Since no leper might draw from a spring, his daughter Gundred fetched him water from the well and daily ministered to his wants.

Mediæval poems tell of solitary or wandering lepers as well as of those residing in communities. In the romance *Amis and Amiloun*, the gentle knight is stricken with

---

[1] Pat. 20 Hen. III, m. 13; 17 Ric. II, pt. ii. m. 14.

leprosy. His lady fair and bright expels him from his own chamber. He eats at the far end of the high table until the lady refuses to feed a *mesel* at her board—" he is so foule a thing." His presence becoming intolerable, a little lodge is built half a mile from the gate. The child Owen alone is found to serve Sir Amiloun, fetching food for his master until he is denied succour and driven away. Knight and page betake themselves to a shelter near a neighbouring market-town, and depend for a time upon the alms of passers-by. The next stage is that of wandering beggars.[1]

In the *Testament of Cresseid* the leper-heroine begged to go in secret wise to the hospital, where, being of noble kin, they took her in with the better will. She was conveyed thither by her father, who daily sent her part of his alms. But Cresseid could not be resigned to her affliction, and in a dark corner of the house alone, weeping, she made her moan. A leper-lady, an old inmate, tries in vain to reconcile her to her fate—it is useless to spurn herself against the wall, and tears do but double her woe —but in vain :—

> "Thus chiding with her dreric destenye,
> Weiping scho woik the nicht fra end to end."

This "Complaynt of Cresseid" is affecting in its description of the lamentable lot of a woman whose high estate is turned into dour darkness : for her bower a leper-lodge ; for her bed a bunch of straw ; for wine and meat mouldy bread and sour cider. Her beautiful face is deformed, and her carolling voice, hideous as a rook's. Under these sad conditions, Cresseid dwells for the rest of her life in the spital.[2]

---

[1] H. M. Weber, *Metrical Romances*, II, 269.
[2] R. Henryson, *Testament of Cresseid* (Bannatyne Club).

CHAPTER VIII

HOSPITAL DWELLINGS

"He" [Lanfranc] "built a fair and large house of stone, and added to it several habitations for the various needs and convenience of the men, together with an ample plot of ground." (Eadmer's History.)

THE Canterbury monk mentions the foundation of Archbishop Lanfranc's two hospitals. The lepers' dwellings on the hill-side at Harbledown were merely wooden houses. The architecture of St. John's was more striking: *lapideam domum decentem et amplam construxit.* The edifice (*palatium*) was divided in two parts, to accommodate men and women. As Eadmer was living until 1124, he saw the hospital shortly after its erection. He may even have watched the Norman masons complete it, and the first infirm occupants take up their abode.

Before considering the plan of hospital buildings, it will be of interest to learn how they impressed men of those days. The twelfth-century writer of the *Book of the Foundation* betrays his unfeigned admiration of St. Bartholomew's. The hospital house was at a little distance from the church, which was "made of cumly stoonewerke tabylwyse." The traditional commencement of the work was that Rahere playfully acted the fool, and thus drew to himself a good-natured company of children and servants : "with ther use and helpe stonys and othir thynges profitable to the bylynge, lightly he gaderyd to

gedyr," until at length "he reysid uppe a grete frame."
When all was finished and he had set up the sign of the
cross "who shulde not be astonyd, ther to se, constructe
and bylyd thonorable byldynge of pite."

Matthew Paris gives sketches and brief descriptions
of three hospitals in his *Chronica Major*.[1] St. Giles',
near London—"the memorial of Matilda the Queen"—
seems to consist of hall and chapel with an eastern tower

16. HOSPITAL OF ST. JOHN, EXETER   17. HOSPITAL OF ST. ALEXIS, EXETER

and another small tower at the south-west (Fig. 10); of
the *Domus Conversorum*, London, he says, "Henry built
a decent church, fit for a conventual congregation, with
other buildings adjoining" (Fig. 3); St. John's, Oxford,
he calls *quoddam nobile hospitale*. (Fig. 1.) The chronicler
died in 1259, and these sketches were probably made
about ten years previously, when the two latter houses
were newly built.

Two thirteenth-century seals depict hospitals at Exeter.
Mr. Birch describes that of St. John's as "a church-like

[1] Chron. and Mem., 57, iii. 262-3.

building of rectangular ground-plan, with an arcade of three round-headed arches along the nave, roof of ornamental shingles, and crosses at the gable-ends." The artist contrives to show not only one side, but one end, apparently the west front, with entrance. (Fig. 16.) The other seal is that of the neighbouring hospital of St. Alexis "behind St. Nicholas." (Fig. 17.) The beautiful seal of St. John's, Stafford (reproduced by the kindness of the Society of Antiquaries) shows architectural features

18. ST. JOHN'S, STAFFORD

of the transition period between the Early English and Decorated styles. The windows are triple-lancets with a delicately-pierced trefoil above; and an arcade runs round the base. (Fig. 18.)

Casual references to building in progress occur in records, but they give little information. As early as 1161-3 Pipe Rolls mention works going on at the houses of the infirm at Oxford; there is one entry of over £8 spent on repairs. In 1232 timber was being sent to Crowmarsh to make shingles for the roof of the hospital church. Land was granted to St. Bartholomew's, Gloucester, for the widening of their chancel (1265); it is of interest to compare this fact with the elegant Early English work shown in Lysons' view. (Pl. VI.) There occurs on another roll a licence to lengthen the portico of the Maison Dieu, Dover (1278).

The arrangement of most of these buildings is unknown, for frequently not a vestige remains. In many cases they grew up with little definite plan. A private dwelling was adapted, further accommodation being added as funds permitted. The domestic buildings were usually of wood and thatched, which accounts for the numerous allusions to fire. Even St. John's, Canterbury, which was chiefly of stone, was burnt in the fourteenth century, but some traces of Norman work remain. (Pl. III.)

In time of war, houses near the Border or on the South Coast suffered. The buildings of God's House, Berwick-on-Tweed, were cast down by engines during a siege. The master and inmates implored aid in their sore extremity, declaring that in spite of all efforts to repair the buildings, the work was unfinished, and that they could not endure the winter without being utterly perished.[1] The same year (1333) the destroyed hospital at Capelford-by-Norham was being rebuilt. St. Nicholas', Carlisle, was levelled to the ground more than once, and Sherburn was partly demolished at the time of the Battle of Neville's Cross. The same story of attack and fire comes from houses at Southampton and Portsmouth.

Before proceeding to any classification of buildings, some of the component parts may be mentioned. The precincts were often entered by a gateway beneath a

[1] Cal. of Documents relating to Scotland, III, p. 199.

tower. (Pl. VIII, XVI.) Sometimes, as at Northallerton, there was a hospice near the gate, especially intended for wayfarers who were too feeble to proceed; and an almonry, as at St. Cross, for the distribution of out-relief.

The mode of life in different hospitals affected their architectural arrangement. The warden and professed members of the staff were expected to live in community. The master of St. John's, Ely, was charged not to have delicate food in his own chamber, but to dine in the refectory. In most houses the rule was relaxed, and the warden came to have private apartments, and finally, a separate dwelling. (Pl. XVI, XXI.) In large institutions, the dining-hall was a fine building. The "Brethren Hall" at St. Cross (about 36 × 20 feet) consists of four bays, and has a handsome chestnut ceiling. (Pl. X.) The beautiful refectory at St. Wulstan's, Worcester (48 feet × 25 feet 8 inches), adjoins another long, narrow hall; these buildings present interesting features—such as the screen, a coved canopy over the dais, and a loft from which reading was given during meals. The screen, gallery and oriel are reproduced in *Domestic Architecture during the Tudor Period.* The title of "minstrels' gallery," given by J. H. Parker to the screen at the western end of the hall, has been called in question; but as the same name is found at St. Cross it may be remarked that in such institutions minstrels were called in to perform on festal days, for the account rolls of St. Leonard's, York (1369), and St. John's, Winchester[1] (1390), allude to it. The hospital was a semi-secular house, and such halls were occasionally used for public affairs. Permission was granted in 1456 that the hall and kitchen of St. Katherine's Maison Dieu,

[1] The original hall stands west of the chapel, and is let as a public dining-hall.

PLATE X

HALL OF ST. CROSS, WINCHESTER

Newcastle, might be used by young couples for their
wedding dinner and the reception of gifts, because at
that time houses were not large.   Leland notes that Thornton "buildid St. Katerines Chapelle, *the Towne Haulle*, and
a Place for poor Almose Menne."   If the above-mentioned
kitchen was as magnificent as that of St. John's, Oxford
(now incorporated into Magdalen College), a wedding-
feast or civic banquet might well take place there.

The transaction of business was conducted in the chap-
ter-house or in an audit-room.   At Ewelme, for example,
there was a handsome chamber above the steps leading
from the almshouse into the church, and the audit-room
at Stamford is still in use.

The development of hospital buildings has been admir-
ably dealt with by F. T. Dollman.   In his earlier work
(*Examples of Domestic Architecture*, 1858), he illustrates
in great detail seven ancient institutions; a reprint with
additions followed (1861).   The subject calls for a more
exhaustive study, which is now being undertaken by a
competent architect.   In this chapter nothing is attempted
beyond a brief indication of the prevalent styles.   Frequently, however, the original construction can be barely
conjectured, for only a part is left, and that has probably
suffered from alteration.   Dollman distinguishes four
principal modes of arrangement :—

(i) Great hall—infirmary or dormitory—with chapel at
    the eastern end.

(ii) As above, with chapel detached, and entered from
    without.

(iii) Suite of buildings, usually quadrangular; chapel
    apart.

(iv) Narrow courtyard.

i. HALL WITH TERMINATING CHAPEL

(a) *Infirmary.*—The early form of a hospital was that of a church. A picturesque fragment of St. James', Lewes, is figured in *Beauties of Sussex;*[1] the foundations remained within memory, consisting, apparently, of nave, aisles and chancel, the dimensions of the latter being about 34 × 15 feet. From an ancient deed in the Record Office, this building is shown to have been the sick-ward with its chapel ; it refers to the "sick poor in the great hall of the hospital of Suthenovere." Mention is frequently made of chapels "within the dormitory" or "in the infirmary,"and of beds "in the hospital on the west of the church." The statutes of Kingsthorpe show how this arrangement met the patients' spiritual wants :—

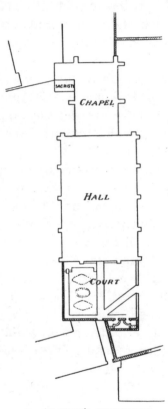

19. ST. MARY'S, CHICHESTER

"In the body of the house adjoining the chapel of the Holy Trinity there should be three rows of beds joined together in length, in which the poor and strangers and invalids may lie for the purpose of hearing mass and attending to the prayers more easily and conveniently."

[1] J. Rouse, 1825, Pl. 76.

The finest remaining example of such an infirmary is St. Mary's, Chichester. (Pl. XVIII.) It is now a great hall of four bays, and seems originally to have been longer by two bays. (See Ground-plan, Fig. 19.) The hall measures

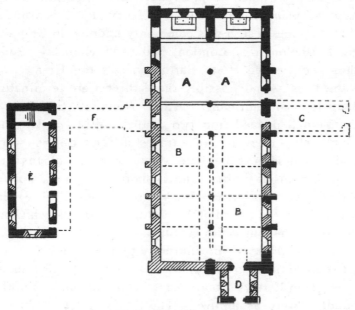

20. ST. NICHOLAS', SALISBURY

Black.	Extant remains (xiii. cent.).
Tint.	Site of destroyed walls.
Dotted lines.	Probable arrangement of original buildings.
AA.	The Chapels.
C.	Latrines.
E.	Old Hospital.

BB.	Cubicles.
D.	Porch.
F.	Covered way.

over 84 feet, and opens into a chapel 47 feet in length. A wide and lofty roof with open timbers spans the whole building, the pitch of the roof being such that the north and south walls are unusually low. (Pl. VI.) The Domus

Dei, Portsmouth, was of similar construction. Its thirteenth-century chapel still exists as the chancel of the Royal Garrison Church, the nave and aisles of which replace the infirmary, or " Nurcery " as it is called in one document.

The early French hospitals were usually of three wings, as at St. Jean, Angers, built by Henry II. It is probable that the same design was commonly adopted in England. St. Bartholomew's, London, had three chapels—besides those now called "St. Bartholomew's the Great" and "the Less"—and possibly these three were terminating chapels of an infirmary. At St. Nicholas', Salisbury, a double-hall opened into two chapels. (Fig. 20, Ground-plan.) Here there are some traces of Early English work, which can almost be dated, for an entry of 1231 records a grant of timber,[1] and Bishop Bingham completed the hospital before 1244. Buckler's sketches (Pl. XV) give some idea of the charm of the existing buildings, which are mainly of the fourteenth century.

(b) *Almshouse.*—The infirmary-plan became a model for some of the later almshouses. A fine example remains at Higham Ferrers (about 1423). The dimensions of this building were as follows:—Hall, 63 × 24 feet ; Chapel, 17 feet, 10 inches × 20 feet. Wooden screens subdivided the dormitory ; and the statutes directed that each bedeman should join in evening prayers at his chamber door. Although not so secluded as the separate-tenement type, the early arrangement was good, for inmates had the benefit of air from the spacious hall, with its fine and lofty oak ceiling. Modern examples of this cubicle-system are still seen at Wells, St. Mary's, Chichester, and St. Giles', Norwich. In the latter case, the dormitory forms

---

[1] Close 16 Hen. III, m. 17.

PLATE XI

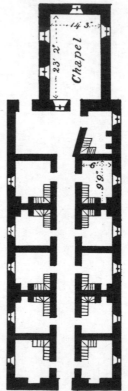

ST. MARY MAGDALENE'S, GLASTONBURY

(*a*) VIEW FROM THE WEST.   (*b*) GROUND-PLAN

part of a church adapted for the purpose ; the compartments communicate with a corridor-hall and are open above to the panelled ceiling of St. Helen's church with its heraldic devices. The early fifteenth-century Maison Dieu at Ripon was not unlike that of Higham Ferrers. The ruined chapel exists, with the arch which led into the domicile. By means of a partition, four men, four women and two casual guests were accommodated, and the priest had apartments at the west end.

St. Saviour's, Wells, was a contemporary foundation. Leland remarks :—"The Hospitale and the Chapelle is buildid al in lenghth under one Roofe." This interesting old dwelling-place still exists, but has lost its former character, as has also the Glastonbury almshouse for men, of which a view and ground-plan are shown on Plate XI.

Slightly different again was the plan of a two-storied block, having a chancel-like chapel with a roof of lower pitch. Sherborne almshouse (Dorset) was built thus. It opens to both stories of the adjoining domicile ; this is done on the upper floor, by means of a gallery in which the women sit during service.

Later, it was customary for the chapel to extend to the height of the whole building under one roof, as at Browne's hospital, Stamford. (Fig. 5.) Although the lofty chapel corresponded in height to both stories, only the lower one—which in this case was the dormitory—communicated with it. This block formed part of a suite ranging round a quadrangle. A ground-plan and views of this imposing almshouse, with descriptions of its architectural features, are found in Wright's history. There is a striking similarity of construction between it and

Wigston's hospital, Leicester (figured by Nichols[1]). Both were good specimens of the domestic Perpendicular style.

The earlier almshouse in Leicester, called the "Newark" (afterwards known as Trinity) was a large building. Nichols' view (1788)[2] shows a range of dwellings below, others above with dormer windows in the roof, clumsy chimneys, a bell-cote, and at one end a chancel-like extension. There must originally have been extensive buildings to accommodate the hundred poor. Leland says: "The large Almose House stondith also withyn the Quadrante of the Area of the College"; and of the church associated with it Camden says that "the greatest ornament of Leicester was demolished when the religious houses were granted to the king." Bablake hospital, Coventry (*circa* 1508), which was somewhat similar to the Leicester almshouse, still exists. This "Hospitall well builded for ten poore Folkes," as Leland reports, formed a simple parallelogram; below, ambulatory, hall, dining-room, and kitchen; above, dormitories.

ii. HALL WITH DETACHED CHAPEL

Of a great hall with separate chapel, Dollman cites one instance, St. John's, Northampton. Here the hospital was a parallelogram, the chapel touching it at one corner, but not communicating with it; another detached building, sometimes called the Master's House, was probably the refectory. (Plan and details, Dollman; see also T. H. Turner, *Domestic Architecture*, Vol. III.) From the engraving (Frontispiece) it would seem that the Maison

---

[1] Leicestershire, Vol. I, pt. ii. 495.
[2] Bibliographica Top. Brit., viii. facing p. 718.

PLATE XII

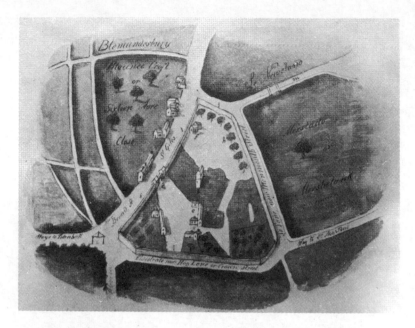

PLAN OF THE LEPER HOSPITAL OF ST. GILES, LONDON

(*a*) GATE. (*b*) CHAPEL AND PARISH CHURCH. (*c*) HOSPITAL MANSION. (*d*) POOL CLOSE. (*e*) ORCHARD.
(*f*) COTTAGES. (*g*) HOUSES, ETC., OF DR. BORDOY. (*h*) GARDENS. (*i*) WALLS. (*l*) GALLOWS

THE CHURCH OF ST. GILES IN THE FIELDS

(*a*) PARISH CHURCH. (*b*) HOSPITAL CHURCH. (*c*) BELL TOWER. (*d, e*) ALTARS.
(*f*) ST. MICHAEL'S CHAPEL. (*g*) SCREEN DIVIDING CHURCHES. (*h*) WESTERN ENTRANCE

Dieu, Dover, was similarly designed; at the north-east angle is the chapel, three bays of which may still be seen. The various apartments existing in 1535 are mentioned in the Inventory.[1] "The Great Chamber called the Hoostrye" (hostelry or guest-hall) was probably the common-room and refectory, but besides trestle-tables, settle and seats, the furniture included a great bedstead and a little one; this hall contained an inner room. There were four other small bed-chambers, a *fermery* (infirmary) with accommodation for fifteen persons, besides day-room, kitchens, etc.

iii. GROUP OF BUILDINGS AND CHAPEL

(a) *Leper-house.*—Although originally lepers had a common dormitory, the plan began to be superseded as early as the thirteenth century, when a visitation of St. Nicholas', York, shows that each inmate had a room to himself. The rule at Ilford was that lepers should eat and sleep together "so far as their infirmity permitted." The dormitory afterwards gave place to tenements. The Harbledown settlement in the eighteenth century is shown in Pl. II, the buildings being named by Duncombe, master and historian of the hospital. Facing the "hospital-chapel" were the "frater-house" and domestic quarters. The chantry-house by the gateway was, doubtless, the residence of the staff. (See p. 147.) The original dwellings must have been more extensive, for they sheltered a hundred lepers. The view of Sherburn (Durham) may reproduce the later mediæval design. (Fig. 21.) In some cases a cloister ran round the buildings. The statutes of St. Julian's leper-hospital ordained "that there be no standing in the corridor (*penticio*), which extends in

[1] M. E. C. Walcott, *Arch. Cant.*, VII, pp. 273-80.

length before the houses of the brothers in the direction of the king's road."

The Winchester leper-house was quadrangular. It existed until 1788, and was drawn and described in *Vetusta Monumenta*. (Fig. 22, Pl. XXI.) A row of habitations ex-

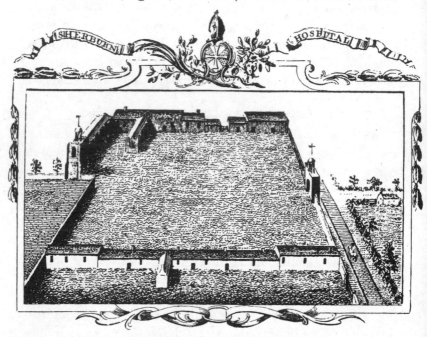

21. SHERBURN HOSPITAL, NEAR DURHAM

tended east and west, parallel to them was the chapel ; the master's house connected the two ; the fourth side being occupied by a common hall. Probably St. Bartholomew's, Oxford, was of a similar character. (Pl. XXII.) The long building which remains north of the chapel has four windows above and four below, as though to accommodate the eight brethren. When dwellings ranged round an enclosure, it was usual to have a well in the centre. Such "lepers' wells" may still be seen on the site of St. Mary Magdalene's, Winchester, and at Lyme Regis.

The lepers' chapel was almost invariably a detached building. Sherburn had a fair-sized church, which is

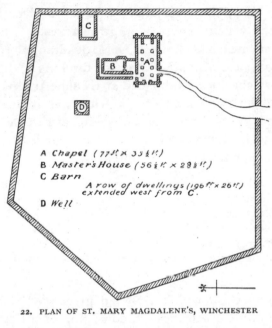

A *Chapel (77 ft. × 35½ ft.)*
B *Master's House (56½ ft. × 29½ ft.)*
C *Barn*
      A row of dwellings (196 ft. × 26 ft.)
      extended west from C.
D *Well*

22. PLAN OF ST. MARY MAGDALENE'S, WINCHESTER

still in use, besides two chapels, one of which communicated with the quarters of the sick (*capella interior infra domum infirmorum*). The above were large institutions; but at St. Petronilla's, Bury St. Edmunds—which might be described as a cottage-hospital for lepers—the chapel and hall were under one roof. The projection on the right (more clearly seen in Yates' engraving) was the refectory. The window of the chapel shown in Pl. XXVIII still exists, though the ruin is not *in situ*.

(b) *Almshouse.*—The modern design of almshouse, consisting of cottages each with its own fireplace and offices, developed during the fifteenth century. Thus about the year 1400, Grendon's new charity in Exeter became known as the "Ten Cells." It was directed by the founder at Croydon (1443) that every inmate have "a place by himsilf in the whiche he may ligge and reste." Some of these tenement almshouses were quadrangular, whilst others consisted of a simple row of dwellings. The contemporary charities established at Ewelme and Abingdon illustrate the two variations of what was in reality the same type. The picturesque almshouse at Ewelme, dating about 1450, is shown in Pl. XVII. The founder's intention was thus expressed in the statutes :—

"We woll and ordeyne that the minister . . . and pore men have and holde a certeyn place by them self within the seyde howse of almesse, that is to sayng, a lityl howse, a celle or a chamber with a chemeney and other necessarys in the same, in the whiche any of them may by hym self ete and drynke and rest, and sum tymes among attende to contemplacion and prayoure."

The buildings (of which Dollman gives views, ground-plan, etc.) were quadrangular, consisting of sitting-rooms below, with bedrooms above.

Formerly, inmates gathered round an open hearth (compare Pl. X) or in a capacious ingle-nook, like that in use at St. Giles', Norwich. The chimney—which originally signified fireplace—is a new feature indicating a change of life. At Ludlow, for example, Hosyer's almshouse was constructed with thirty-three chambers

PLATE XIII

FORD'S HOSPITAL, COVENTRY

and in every chamber a chimney. Those at St. Cross are slender and unobtrusive, but the later erections at St. John's, Lichfield, are oppressive in size.

Of the simple row of tenements, a beautiful example remains at Abingdon. (Pl. XXVI.) It was founded by the Gild of the Holy Cross for thirteen impotent men and women. The present hospital consists of fourteen dwellings (with a central hall reconstructed in Jacobean times); the timbered cloister has recently been carefully repaired. The Spital Almshouse near Taunton, rebuilt by Abbot Beere about 1510, consists of a simple two-storied row of cottages, with a covered way in front.

iv. NARROW COURTYARD

Ford's hospital at Coventry (Pl. XIII) is placed in a class by itself. This half-timbered house is a perfect gem of domestic architecture. The oaken framework, the elaborately-carved verge-boards of the gables, the varied tracery of the windows, the slender pinnacled-buttresses, alike call for admiration. Entering the doorway, a narrow court (39 × 12 feet) is reached, perhaps the most beautiful part of the building. Each dwelling communicates with the bed-chamber above, and at either end were the chapel and common hall. Dollman gives the ground-plan, etc.; Garner and Stratton's recent work on Tudor Domestic Architecture also contains lovely plates of the western front, courtyard and rich details.

v. CRUCIFORM PLAN

The ground-plan of the great Savoy hospital was cruciform, which is unusual. It would appear from the following extract from Henry VII's will, that he himself superintended the architectural design :—

"We have begoune to erecte, buylde and establisshe a commune Hospital . . . and the same we entende with Godd's grace to finish, after the maner, fourme and fashion of a plat which is devised for the same, and signed with our hande."

When completed, this was one of the most notable things of the metropolis. In 1520, some distinguished French visitors were entertained at a civic banquet. "In the afternoon, inasmuch as they desired amonge other things to see the hospital of Savoy and the king's chapell at the monastery of Westminster, they were conueyed thither on horseback."[1] The engraving (Pl. XIV) shows an imposing pile of buildings.

Hospital buildings were good of their kind, and the chapels were of the best that could be provided. In Leland's eyes Burton Lazars had "a veri fair Hospital and Collegiate Chirch"; Worcester could show "an antient and fayre large Chappell of St. Oswald"; St. John's, Bridgwater, was "a thing notable" even to that insatiable sight-seer. Of the finest examples, most have vanished. At St. Bartholomew's the Great, Smithfield, however, a portion survives of those "honourable buildings of pity" which astonished twelfth-century onlookers; and the noble church and quadrangles of St. Cross, Winchester (Pl. VIII), show the scale upon which some were designed. The church of the Dunwich leper-house (Pl. XXVIII) was 107 feet in length. (Groundplan, *Archæologia*, XII.) Part of the apse remains, showing a simple arcade of semicircular arches, the

[1] B.M., MS. Calig. D. vii. f. 240.

PLATE XIV

A VIEW, of the SAVOY from the River Thames

In the Year 1145 PETER Earl of SAVOY built a Palace in the STRAND, and gave it to the Fraternity of MONTJOY, of whom it was purchased by ELEANOR Queen to King HENRY III, for her Son EDMUND Earl of LANCASTER.
It was afterwards repaired, or rather new built, by HENRY Duke of LANCASTER at the expence of 52000. Marks.
In 1357 JOHN the French King was imprisoned there, and in 1363 came over again as a Visitor, and there died.
K. 36th that Palace being burnt down by the Rebels of KENT, and ESSEX, lay in Ruins till the Reign of King HENRY VII, when it was rebuilt in a beautiful manner for an Hospital to relieve poor Pilgrims, Strangers, and Children, and dedicated to the Honor of St. JOHN about the Year 1509. But that Hospital being afterwards suppressed by King EDWARD VI, it was again founded by Queen MARY in 1557.
Upon the Erection of Queen ELIZABETH the Chapel was converted into a Church, for the Use of the Parish.

SAVOY HOSPITAL, LONDON
(a) HOSPITAL BUILDINGS   (c) CHAPEL

chancel being ornamented with intersecting arches. A treatise of Queen Mary's time describes this church as "a great one, and a fair large one, after the old fashion . . . but now greatly decayed."[1]

The most ancient, and, from an architectural point of view, one of the most interesting chapels remaining, is that of St. Bartholomew, Rochester; the domed apse with its own arch, writes the chaplain, is rare even in the earliest Norman churches. (Ground-plan, see *Journal Arch. Assoc.*, XI.) Norman work may be seen in chapels at Sherburn, Gloucester and Stourbridge, and in the fine hospital-hall at High Wycombe. Beautiful specimens of the Early English style remain at St. Bartholomew's, Sandwich; the Domus Dei, Portsmouth; and St. Edmund's, Gateshead. The latter chapel, built by Bishop Farnham about 1247, is still in use, for the graceful ruin drawn by Grimm (Pl. XXX) has been restored. It is described in Boyle's *Guide to Durham*:—"The west front has a deeply-recessed central doorway, flanked by two tiers of arcades, whilst over these is an upper arcade, the alternative spaces of which are pierced by lancet lights", etc. The chapel at Bawtry has a fine Early English window and a handsome niche at the eastern end.

Among disused or misused chapels may be named St. Mary Magdalene's, Gloucester; St. Laurence's, Crediton; Stourbridge; Poor Priests', Canterbury; St. Mary Magdalene's, Durham; some, like the last-named, are beyond restoration. St. Bartholomew's, Oxford, and St. James', Tamworth, long desecrated or deserted, are now being restored as houses of prayer. St. Katherine's,

[1] Weever, *Funeral Mon.*, ed. 1767, p. 459.

Exeter, has recently been given to the Church Army, for the use of the destitute poor resorting to the Labour Home.

Ancient chapels remain attached to almshouses in the following places :—

> Bawtry ; Bristol (Three Kings of Cologne) ; Canterbury (St. John, St. Thomas) ; Chichester ; Gloucester (St. Margaret) ; Honiton ; Ilford ; Lichfield ; Oakham ; Ripon (St. John Baptist, St. Mary Magdalene) ; Rochester ; Salisbury ; Sandwich ; Sherborne ; Sherburn ; Stamford ; Wimborne ; Winchester (St. John's) ; Glastonbury (2) ; Leicester (Trinity) ; Tiverton ; Wells.

23. CHAPEL OF ABBOT BEERE'S ALMSHOUSE, GLASTONBURY
(For interior see Fig. 25)

Those of Wilton (St. John), Taddiport near Torrington, and Holloway near Bath, are now chapels-of-ease ; that of St. John and St. James, Brackley, is used in connection with Grammar School and Parish Church ; Roman Catholics worship in St. John's, Northampton, and French Protestants use the Anglican liturgy in

St. Julien's, Southampton ; the chapel of the Domus Dei, Portsmouth, is part of the Garrison Church ; St. Mark's, Bristol, is the Lord Mayor's Chapel ; St. Edmund's, Gateshead (Holy Trinity), and St. Cross, Winchester, are Parish Churches.

CHAPTER IX

THE CONSTITUTION

"It is agreed amongst men of religion that order be observed, because without order there is no religion." (Rules of St. John's, Nottingham.)

WE now turn to the inner working of the hospital and inquire how the lives of inmates were ordered.

Early charitable institutions were under a definite rule, either that of the diocesan bishop or of the monastic order with which they were in touch. In the Constitutions of Richard Poore of Sarum (*circa* 1223), one clause is headed : "Concerning the Rule of Religion, how it is lawful to found a *xenodochium*." Persons desiring so to do shall receive a form of government from the bishop, "since too great diversity of forms of religion brings in confusion to the church of God." Laymen therefore applied for an episcopal constitution ; the burgesses of Nottingham, for instance, charged Archbishop Gray with the drawing up of an "Ordination" for St. John's (1231–4). Even when a community was under a monastic house, the diocesan was often asked to compile statutes, as Grossetête did for Kingsthorpe and Bishop Stratford for Ilford ; but the abbot of St. Albans drew up his own code for St. Julian's. There was apparently a definite Anglican Rule, for "The Statutes of St. James' according to the Use of the Church of England" were promulgated at Canterbury in 1414.

Founders and patrons also had a voice in the matter, sometimes drawing up the rule and submitting it to their Father in God; thus the Ordinances of St. Mark's, Bristol, made by the patron and "exhibited to the Bishop" (1268) are entered in the registers.

Most hospitals followed a definite system, at least in theory, as to admission, observation of regulations and penalties for disobedience.

I. NOMINATION AND ADMISSION

(*a*) Appointments to all offices were usually in the patron's hands. In a few privileged houses (e.g. Dover, Gloucester, Oxford, Cambridge, Norwich) the staff brothers had licence to elect their superior from amongst themselves, and to nominate him to the patron. Officials and inmates alike were admitted by a religious ceremony, of which the vow formed a prominent part. At St. Katherine's, Bedminster, the following oath was taken before induction by the master :—

"I, ——, promise perpetual observance of good morals, chastity, and denial of property . . . according to the rule of the Hospital St. Katherine, near Bristol, in the diocese of Bath and Wells, which I henceforth profess as ordained by the holy fathers . . . and I will lead my life according to regular discipline."

The selection of honorary workers on the hospital staff is dealt with in one of the deeds of St. Mary's, Chichester (formerly preserved at University College, Oxford, but now in the Bodleian) :—

"If any one seeks the Hospital of St. Mary, at Chichester, let the Warden examine whether he is in sound or in infirm health. If in sound health, whether male or female, let the

Warden consider whether he is a person of good conversation, of honest life and character, likely to be useful to the House, whether in serving or labouring for the poor. If he should be found such, the Warden shall first point out to him the poverty of the House, the poorness of the food, the gravity of the obedience, and the heavy duties, which may possibly deter him and induce him to recall his purpose. But if he perseveres in knocking, then with the counsel of the Lord Dean and the brethren of the House, he may be received in the name of the Lord, without the intervention of any money or any compact, unless he has any property of his own and is disposed to resign it into the hands of the Warden. But if the character of the man who seeks admission be insufficient he must be repelled entirely."[1]

A brother or sister being admitted to St. John Baptist's, Reading, was professed in the adjoining church. *Veni Creator* and certain prayers were said as the candidate knelt before the altar ; after the sprinkling with holy water he or she then received the habit or veil, a kiss of charity being bestowed by the rest of the household. A discourse followed upon the rules and benefits of the society. The Office for the admission of members to the staff of St. John's, Nottingham, is given in the *Records of the Borough*. One prayer, at the benediction of the religious habit, shows the spirit in which hospital officials were expected to enter upon their duties :—

" O Lord Jesus Christ, who didst deign to put on the covering of our mortality, we beseech the immense abundance of Thy goodness, that Thou mayst so deign to bless this kind of vestment, which the holy fathers have decreed should be borne by those who renounce the world, as a token of innocence and humility, that this Thy servant, who shall [use it], may deserve to put on Thee," etc.

[1] Sussex Arch. Coll., 24, pp. 41-62.

PLATE XV

HOSPITAL OF ST. NICHOLAS, SALISBURY
(*a*) SOUTH-EAST VIEW. (*b*) WEST VIEW

As the brother changed his dress, the Scripture was repeated concerning putting off the old man and putting on the new in righteousness. The versicles "Our help is in the name of the Lord," "Save Thy servant," etc., were also used, together with prayers for the Gift, for increase of virtue, for light and life.

(*b*) Almsmen, too, were usually admitted by a solemn oath. That taken at Oakham is typical :—

"I. —— the which am named into a poor man to be resceyued into this Hospital after the forme of the Statutes and ordanacions ordeyned . . . shall trewly fulfille and obserue all the Statutes . . . in as moche as yey longen or touchen me to my pour fro hensuorthwardys . . . without ony fraude soe helpe me God and my Holydom and by these holy Euangelies the whiche y touche and ley my honde upon."

At Sandwich, after being sworn in, the person was introduced by the mayor to the rest of the fraternity, and was saluted by them all ; and after paying the customary gratuities, the new inmate was put in possession of his chamber.

The ancient form of admission to St. Nicholas', Salisbury, contains such injunctions as :—

"N. thu shalt be trewe and obedient to the maistre of this place.

"Item. thu shalt kepe pees yn thy self, and do thy deuoyrs that euery brother and sustre be in parfyte pees, loue and charite, eche with othre."

Few foundations have retained their religious and social life with less change than this hospital, of which Canon Wordsworth has given us a complete history. Following the old traditions, the present inmates give a new member the right hand of fellowship when he is duly installed.

(c) Lepers, like other paupers, were admitted either at the patron's will or at the warden's discretion. The custody of the Crown hospital at Lincoln was at one time committed to the sheriffs, who were charged to notify a vacancy to the king or his chancellor " so that he might cause a leper to be instituted in place of the deceased, in accordance with the ancient constitution." Later it was stated that they were admitted of the king's gift, or by the presentation of the mayor. In some instances the right of nomination was held jointly. There were eight beds in the Hexham Spital, four being open to poor leper-husbandmen born within the Liberty, whilst the archbishop and prior might each appoint two tenants.

A patron or donor often kept the nomination to one bed or more. Thus the founder of St. Sepulchre's lazar-house, Hedon, reserved the right to present one man or woman, whole or infirm ; he even made prudent provision to sustain any afflicted object allied to the patron within the fourth degree of blood. As early as 1180, a subscriber to St. Nicholas', Carlisle, stipulated that two lepers from Bampton should be received. According to some statutes the candidate had also to be approved by his future companions ; " without the consent and will " of the Colchester lepers, no brother could gain entrance, and the same rule obtained at Dover. The little Sudbury hospital maintained three lepers ; when one died or resigned, his comrades chose a third ; if they disagreed, the mayor was informed, and the selection devolved upon the vicar. An examination by the warden into the candidate's condition and circumstances was sometimes ordered, as at Dover. At Harbledown sufficient knowledge of the simple formulas of the faith was required.

To enter a leper-hospital in early days practically involved the life of a "religious," especially in hospitals attached to monastic houses. The vow of an in-coming brother at St. Julian's is given in the Appendix to Matthew Paris :—

"I, brother B., promise, and, taking my bodily oath by touching the most sacred Gospel, affirm before God and all His saints . . . that all the days of my life I will be subservient and obedient to the commands of the Lord Abbot of St. Albans and to his archdeacon ; resisting them in nothing, unless such things should be commanded, as would militate against the Divine pleasure. I will never commit theft, nor bring a false accusation against any one of the brethren, nor infringe the vow of chastity."

He goes on to promise that he will not hold or bequeath anything without leave ; he will be content with the food, and keep the rules on pain of punishment, or even expulsion. The oath at St. Bartholomew's, Dover, is found in the register :—

"I, ——, do promise before God and St. Bartholomew and all saints, that to the best of my power I will be faithful and useful to the hospital, . . . to be obedient to my superior and have love to my brethren and sisters. I will be sober and chaste of body ; and a moiety of the goods I shall die possessed of, shall belong to the house. I will pray for the peace of the church and realm of England, and for the king and queen, and for the prior and convent of St. Martin, and for the burgesses of Dover on sea and land, and especially for all our benefactors, living and dead."

After making this vow, the brother was sprinkled with holy water and led to the altar, where he received the warden's blessing on bended knees. The form of general benediction was prescribed (with special collects if the candidate were a virgin or a widow), and a prayer was said at the consecration of the habit.[1]

2. REGULATIONS

The general rule of poverty, chastity and obedience was supplemented by detailed statutes.

(a) *Rules concerning Payment and Property.*—There are some instances of compulsory payment by statute. If the candidate at Dover satisfied the warden's inquiries, he might be received into the community after paying 100 shillings, or more if he could. Even then gratuities were expected; half a mark was offered to the warden and half a mark distributed among the brethren and sisters. The entrance fee sounds prohibitive, but the *Liber Albus* records a similar custom in London under the title *Breve de C solidis levandis de tenemento Leprosorum*. This edict authorized the levying of 100*s.* from lepers' property to be delivered to their officers for their sustenance.

Sometimes hospital statutes provided against this practice. Thus the chancellor's ordinances for St. Nicholas', York (1303), forbade the admission of any one by custom or by an agreement for money or goods, but without fear of simony the property of an in-coming brother might be received if given spontaneously and absolutely. The statutes are of special interest because evidently framed to reform abuses recently exposed; and the details of the cross-questioning by the jury and the replies of witnesses in that visitation are recorded. We learn, for example, that most of the inmates had been received for money "each for himself 20 marks more or less"; one, indeed,

---

[1] *Lieger Book*, Bodl. Rawl. MS. B. 335.

with the consent of the community, paid 23 marks (£15. 6s. 8d.), a considerable sum in those days. Under special circumstances the patron sometimes countenanced a bargain. Thus when a healthy candidate for admission to St. Bartholomew's, Oxford, promised repairs to the chapel, the timber of which was decayed, he was received contrary to rules by the king's express permission (1321).

The question of the property of the warden, officials and inmates now comes before us. The staff were frequently under the three-fold vow which included poverty. The rule at St. John's, Nottingham, was as follows :—

"And no one shall be a proprietor, but if any one have any property, he shall resign it to the warden or master before seven days . . . otherwise he shall be excommunicated. . . . But if it shall be found that any one has died with property, his body shall be cast out from Christian burial, and shall be buried elsewhere, his property being thrown upon him by the brethren, saying, 'Thy money perish with thee.'"

The same enactment is found at St. Mary's, Chichester, unless, indeed, the offender make a death-bed confession. But poor people sojourning there retained their possessions, and could dispose of them by will :—

"If he has anything of his own let the warden take charge of it and of his clothes, until he is restored to health ; then let them be given to him without diminution, and let him depart, unless, of his own accord, he offer the whole, or part, to the house. If he die, let his goods be distributed as he hath disposed of them. If he die intestate, let his property be kept for a year, so that if any friend of the deceased shall come and prove that he has a claim upon it, justice may not be denied to him. If no one claim within the year, let it be merged into the property of the hospital."

A total renunciation of personal goods was required of the inmates of leper-hospitals in early days. Alms received by the wayside went into the common chest, as did money found within the enclosure; if picked up outside, the finder might keep it. The lepers of St. Julian's might not appropriate or bequeath anything without the consent of the community. A singular article in the oath of admission was this:—"I will make it my study wholly to avoid all kinds of usury, as a monstrous thing, and hateful to God." In the Dover statutes trading and usury were strictly forbidden.

The leper's clothing and furniture were all that he could call his own. In the disposal of such meagre personal effects, a precedent was found in the *heriot*—the best chattel of a deceased man due to the feudal lord. An ancient French deed relating to St. Margaret's, Gloucester, ordains that "when a brother or sister is dead, the best cloth that he hath the parson shall have in right of heriot." At Lynn, the bed in which he died, and his chest, if he had one, were appropriated by the hospital, as well as his best robe and hood. These rules indicate that the leper furnished his own apartment. The Office at seclusion enumerates the clothing, furniture and other articles necessary. (*Appendix A.*)

One of the questions asked by the official visitor of St. Mary Magdalene's, Winchester, was whether the goods of deceased inmates went to the works of the church after the settlement of debts. In some hospitals, the rule of poverty was not held, or it was relaxed as time went on. By the will of William Manning, *lazer*, of the house of Monkbridge, York (1428), he requests that half a pound of wax be burnt over his coffin; he leaves 6*d.* to the works going on at the Minster, 6*d*. to the Knaresburgh monks, and the residue to his wife. In the old Scottish version of Troylus and Cresseid, the latter makes her testament before dying in the spital-house. She had lived in poverty, but a purse of gold had lately been thrown to her in alms. Her cup and clapper and her ornament and all her gold the leper folk should have, when she was dead, if they would bury her. The ruby ring, given her long ago by her lover, was to be carried back to him by one of her companions.

Pensioners of the better class were expected to provide all necessary articles, and to contribute what they could to the funds. Money acquired during residence was divided, a portion being retained by the individual; at his death, either half his goods or the whole belonged to the community. The Heytesbury statutes directed :—

"that euery poreman in his first Admyssion all such moueable goodes as he hath, pottis, pannys, pewter vessel, beddyng, and other necessaries, if he haue eny such thynges, to bryng hit within into the hous. And if he haue eny quycke catell, that hit be made monay of. And halfe the saide monay to be conuerted to yᵉ use of yᵉ hous, and yᵉ other halfe to yᵉ poreman to haue to his own propre use."

The goods of a deceased member were distributed to those who should "happe to overlyve," whether "gownes, hodys, cotys, skertys, hosyn or shone." It was ordained at Higham Ferrers that when an almsman died, his goods were taken into the storehouse, and either dealt out to the other poor men, or sold to a new inmate for the benefit of the rest.

(b) *Rules of Conduct.*—Social intercourse within the house and with the outside world was clearly defined. Among habited brethren and sisters, the sexes were rigidly separated, excepting at worship or work. In the case of inmates who were not professed, men and women seem to have lived a common life, meeting in refectory, day room, etc.

As to the intercourse of lepers with the outside world, there was a curious admixture of strictness and laxity. The ordinances of early lazar-houses show that the theory of contagion had little place in their economy. They recognized that the untainted need not be harmed by slight communication with the infected. When visitors came from a distance to Sherburn they were permitted to stay overnight. The lepers of St. Julian's were allowed to see friends—"if an honest man and true come there, for the purpose of visiting an infirm brother, let him have access to him, that they may mutually discourse on that which is meet"—but no woman was admitted except a mother, sister or other honest matron. The general public was protected, inmates not being permitted to frequent the high-road or speak to passers-by (1344). At the time of seclusion, the leper was forbidden henceforth to enter church, market or tavern. At St. Julian's, the mill and bakehouse were likewise forbidden. The statutes of Lynn required that the infirm should not enter the quire, cellar, kitchen or precincts, but keep the places assigned in church, hall and court. So long as they did not eat or drink outside their own walls, lepers might roam within a defined area. The Reading lepers might never go out without a companion. At Harbledown they might not wander without permission, which was granted for useful business, moderate recreation, and in the event of the grievous sickness or death of parents and friends.

Such rules were more a matter of discipline than of public health. It was not merely lepers who were required to keep within bounds, for ordinary almsmen had similar restrictions. At Croydon they were forbidden to walk or gaze in the streets, nor might they go out of sight of home, excepting to church.

The rules of St. Katherine's, Rochester, were drawn up by the innkeeper Symond Potyn. He stipulates that if the almsmen buy ale,. it shall be consumed at home :—

"also that none of them haunt the tauerne to go to ale, but when theie have talent or desier to drynke, theire shall bye theare drynke, and bringe yt to the spitell ;
"also that none of them be debator, baretor, dronkelew, nor rybawde of his tounge." [1]

If any thus offend, the prior with twain good men of Eastgate shall go to the Vicar of St. Nicholas' and the founder's heirs, who "shall put them oute of the same spittle for cuermore, withoute anie thing takinge with them but theare clothinge and their beddc."

(c) *Supervision.*—In ecclesiastical hospitals, the approved method of maintaining order was by weekly chapter, at which correction was to be justly administered without severity or favour. The injunctions at St. John's, Nottingham, were as follows :—

"They shall meet at least once in each week in chapter, and excesses shall be there regularly proclaimed and corrected by warden or master ; and the chapter shall be held without talking or noise, and those who have transgressed shall humbly and obediently undergo canonical discipline."

[1] Hist. of Rochester, ed. 1817, p. 215.

At stated periods of a month or a quarter, the statutes were openly recited, usually in the vulgar tongue. After the revision of the ordinance of St. Nicholas', York, it was ordered that the keepers should read the articles aloud in their church on the eve of St. Nicholas.

Internal authority was vested in the warden, whose power was sometimes absolute; but in the case of hospitals dependent upon a religious house, grave offences were taken to head-quarters. For external supervision, the hospital was dependent upon the patron or his agents, who were supposed to inspect the premises, accounts, etc., yearly. This civil visitation was frequently neglected, especially that of the chancellor on behalf of the Crown. Abuses were apt to accumulate until a royal commission of inquiry and reformation became obligatory. Where an institution was under the commonalty, their representatives acted as visitors. At Bridport (1265), the town administered the endowment of the manorial lord ; the provosts conducted a yearly investigation whether the brethren and lepers were well treated and the chaplains lived honestly. In London, there were officials who daily inspected the lazar-houses ; these " overseers " and " foremen " seem to have been busy citizens who undertook this work on behalf of the corporation (1389). As late as 1536 a gentleman was appointed to the office of visitor of "the spyttel-howses or lazar cotes about thys Citye."

3. PENALTIES

The punishments inflicted by the warden were chiefly flogging, fasting and fines, but he could also resort to the stocks, suspension and expulsion. The regulations of

St. Mary's, Chichester, show the discipline suggested for offenders :—

"If a brother shall have a quarrel with a brother with noise and riot, then let him fast for seven days, on Wednesdays and Fridays, on bread and water, and sit at the bottom of the table and without a napkin. . . . If a brother shall be found to have money or property concealed from the warden, let the money be hung round his neck, and let him be well flogged, and do penance for thirty days, as before."

The rules were particularly rigorous in lazar-houses. Among the lepers of Reading, if a brother committed an offence, he was obliged to sit during meals in the middle of the hall, fasting on bread and water, while his portion of meat and ale was distributed before his eyes. The penalties to which Exeter lazars were liable were fasting and the stocks. Punishment lasted one day for transgressing the bounds, picking or stealing ; three days for absence from chapel, malice, or abusing a brother ; twelve days for reviling the master ; thirty days for violence. At Sherburn the prior did not spare the rod. "After the manner of schoolboys" chastisement was to be meted out to transgressors, and the lazy and negligent awakened. "But if any shall be found to be disobedient and refractory, and is unwilling to be corrected with the rod, let him be deprived of food, as far as bread and water only." Equally severe was the punishment at Harbledown for careless omission of appointed prayers. Delinquents made public confession the following Friday, and received castigation. "Let them undergo sound discipline, the brethren at the hands of the prior, and the sisters from the prioress." The following day the omitted devotions were to be repeated twice.

In the case of almsmen of a later period corporal punishment was never practised. If a poor pensioner at Heytesbury, after instruction, could not repeat his prayers properly, he must be put to "a certayne bodely payne, that is to say of fastyng or a like payne." In most fifteenth-century almshouses, however, the inmates were no longer boarded, but received pocket-money, which was liable to forfeiture. An elaborate system of fines was worked out in the statutes of Ewelme. The master himself was fined for any fault "after the quality and quantitye of his crime." The fines were inflicted not only upon those who were rebellious, or neglected to clean up the courtyard and weed their gardens, but also upon those who arrived in church without their tabards, or were unpunctual :—

"And if it so be that any of theym be so negligent and slewthfull that the fyrst psalme of matyns be begon or he come into his stall that than he lese i*d.*, and yf any of thayme be absent to the begynnyng of the fyrst lesson that thanne he lese ii*d.* ; And for absence fro prime, terce, sext and neynth, for ich of thayme i*d.* Also if any . . . be absent from the masse to the begynnyng of the pistyll . . . i*d.*, and yf absent to the gospell . . . ii*d.*" etc.

Industry, punctuality and regularity became necessary virtues, since the usual allowance was but 14*d.* weekly.

The rules of the contemporary almshouse at Croydon were stringent. After being twice fined, the poor man at his third offence was to be utterly put away as " incorrectable and intolerable." When convicted of soliciting alms, no second chance was given :—" if man or woman begge or aske any silver, or else any other good . . . let him be

expellid and put oute at the first warnyng, and never be
of the fellowship."

Expulsion was usually reserved for incorrigible persons. "Brethren and sisters who are chatterboxes, conten-
tious or quarrelsome," sowers of discord or insubordinate,
were ejected at the third or fourth offence. Summary
expulsion was the punishment for gross crimes. The
town authorities of Beverley discharged an inmate of
Holy Trinity for immorality. The ceremony which preceded the expulsion of an Ilford leper is described by a
writer who obtained his information from the leger-book
of Barking Abbey :—

"The abbesse, beinge accompanyed with the bushop of
London, the abbot of Stratford, the deane of Paule's, and
other great spyrytuall personnes, went to Ilforde to visit the
hospytall theere, founded for leepers ; and uppon occacion of
one of the lepers, who was a brother of the house, having
brought into his chamber a drab, and sayd she was his sister.
. . . He came attyred in his lyvery, but bare-footed and bare-
headed . . . and was set on his knees uppon the stayres
benethe the altar, where he remained during all the time of
mass. When mass was ended, the prieste disgraded him of
orders, scraped his hands and his crown with a knife, took
his booke from him, gave him a boxe on the chiek with the end
of his fingers, and then thrust him out of the churche, where
the officers and people receyved him, and putt him into a carte,
cryinge, *Ha rou, Ha rou, Ha rou,* after him."[1]

This public humiliation, violence and noise, although
doubtless salutary, are a contrast to the statute at
Chichester, where pity and firmness are mingled :—

"If a brother, under the instigation of the devil, fall into
immorality, out of which scandal arises, or if he be disobedient

[1] Hearne, *Curious Discourses,* ed. 1775, i. 249.

to the Superior, or if he strike or wound the brethren or clients
. . . then, if he prove incorrigible, he must be punished
severely, and removed from the society like a diseased sheep,
lest he contaminate the rest. But let this be done not with
cruelty and tempest of words, but with gentleness and compassion."

PLATE XVI

THE WARDEN'S HOUSE, SHERBURN

HOSPITAL OF ST. GILES, KEPIER

CHAPTER X

THE HOUSEHOLD AND ITS MEMBERS

" No more brethren or sisters shall be admitted than are necessary to serve the infirm and to keep the goods of the house." (St. John's, Nottingham.)

THE hospital family varied widely in size and in the arrangement of its component parts, but this chapter, like the preceding, is concerned chiefly with the type of institution which had a definite organization. The establishments for infected persons will first be considered.

(i) THE LEPER HOUSEHOLD

(a) *The Master.*—"The guidance of souls is the art of arts," says St. Gregory : particularly difficult is the guidance of souls in ailing bodies. Lanfranc realized that men of special gifts should be selected for the care of his Harbledown lepers. He not only arranged to supply all they might need on account of the nature of their illness, but appointed men to fulfil this work "of whose skill, gentleness and patience no one could have any doubt." The Oxford statutes ordained that the master be "a compassionate priest of good life and conversation, who shall reside personally and shall celebrate mass daily, humbly and devoutly." He was required to visit the infirm, to console them as far as possible, and confer upon them the Sacraments of the Church.[1] The priest

[1] Close 9 Edw. II, m. 18 *d.*

serving lepers was permitted to dispense rites which did not pertain to other unbeneficed clergy ; thus the Bishop of London commanded the lepers' chaplain at Ilford to hear their confessions, to absolve the contrite, to administer the Eucharist and Extreme Unction. The ideal man to fill the unpleasant post of lepers' guardian as pictured in foundation deeds and statutes was hard to find : men of the type of St. Hugh and Father Damien—separated indeed by seven centuries, but alike in devotion—are rare. Two Archbishops of Canterbury witness to the scarcity in a deed referring to Harbledown (1371, 1402). After stating that clergy are required to celebrate the divine offices in St. Nicholas' Church, the document declares:—

"It may be at present, and very likely will be in future, difficult to find suitable stipendiary priests who shall be willing to have intercourse in this way with the poor people, especially as some of these poor are infected with leprosy ; and this hospital was founded especially for sick persons of this sort."

The master might himself be a leper. An inquisition of 1223 showed that at St. Leonard's, Lancaster, it had formerly been customary for the brethren to elect one of the lepers as master.[1] In 1342 the prior of St. Bartholomew's, Rochester, was a leper. The regulations at Ilford provided for a leper-master and secular master, but those of Dover merely said that the master may be a leper. Although the law offered privileges to communities governed by a leper-warden (see p. 196), it does not appear to have been a common custom to appoint one. In hospitals dependent upon a monastery, some monk was selected to superintend the lazar-house.

(b) *The Staff.*—It has been said that leper-hospitals

[1] Cited Vict. Co. Hist. *Lancs.* ii. 165.

were "heavily staffed with ecclesiastics." There were indeed three at Lincoln, Ilford and Bolton to minister to ten or twelve men, but they conducted the temporal as well as spiritual affairs of the society. At Bolton, for example, the priests had to administer the manor which was held by the hospital. It was more usual to have only one chaplain in a household of thirteen. This was a favourite number, the figure being regarded with reverence as suggestive of the sacred band of Christ and His Apostles: "for thirteen is a convent as I guess," writes Chaucer. There were to be at Sherburn "five convents of lepers, that is of the number of sixty-five at the least"; five priests ministered to them, of whom one acted as confessor, and used also to visit the bedridden and read the Gospel of the day to them.

The collection of alms also fell upon the staff, for as it was said at Bridport "lepers cannot ask and gather for themselves." The procurator or proctor therefore transacted their business. It was ordained at St. Bartholomew's, Oxford, that the clerk serving in the chapel should collect alms and rents and act as proctor. The staff sometimes included other untainted persons. Two healthy brethren at this Oxford leper-house were to be skilled agricultural labourers, able also to make enclosures and cover houses.

(c) *Attendants.* Domestic and farm service was also done by paid attendants. There were female-servants in the Sherburn leper-house, who undertook laundry and other work, and one old woman cared for the bedridden.

(d) *Leper Inmates.*—Among the larger asylums, the approximate accommodation was as follows:—Harbledown 100, Sherburn 65, St. Giles', London 40, St. Nicholas',

York 40, Thaning*ton* near Canterbury 25, Dover 20, Plymouth 20, Bodmin 19, Winchester 18. There were 13 beds at Carlisle, Exeter, Gloucester, Reading, etc. In some towns there were several small hospitals. Numbers were of course liable to fluctuation, and often apply to a company of infected and healthy persons, as at St. Nicholas', York. "They used to have, and ought to have, forty brethren and sisters, as well lepers as others; now they have thirty-two only." (1285.) By an inquisition taken in 1291, it was reported that a former master had admitted thirty-six, of whom four were received *pro Deo* because they were lepers, but the rest for money. The king commanded that henceforth none should be received without special mandate, inasmuch as the funds scarcely sufficed for the multitude already maintained. The same abuse is noticeable a century earlier, for in 1164 Pope Alexander III forbade the patrons of St. James', Thanington, to admit into the sisterhood any who were not infected, for healthy women had been importunately begging admission.[1] It was complained in 1321, that St. Bartholomew's, Oxford, was occupied by healthy and sturdy men; and that at St. Leonard's, Lancaster, there were six whole and three lepers (1323). Both were originally intended solely for the diseased, the inmates of St. Leonard's being called by Henry III "our lepers of Lancaster."

It has been represented, as a proof that isolation was non-existent, that lepers and untainted persons lived a common life, eating and sleeping together. This was evidently not the case. The sheriff of Lincoln received orders that at Holy Innocents' "the chaplains and brethren are to reside in one house, the lepers by them-

[1] Chron. and Mem., 85, pp. 75–6.

selves and the sisters by themselves."[1] The statutes at
Ilford and Dover give similar directions. The priests at
Sherburn slept apart in a chamber adjoining the church,
but the Harbledown staff lacked such accommodation until
in 1371 it was ordained that they should henceforth dwell
in a clergy-house—"a home separate from the sick persons and near to them."

When both sexes were admitted, they lived apart,
a woman with the title of prioress being selected to rule
the female community. Some
houses were set apart for women,
e.g. Alkmonton, Thanington,
Bristol (St. Mary Magdalene),
Newbury (St. Mary Magdalene),
Bury (St. Petronilla), Woodstock,
Clattercot, Hungerford, Arundel,
Westminster, whilst one left behind it the name of "Maiden"
Bradley. It sometimes happened
that a married couple contracted
the disease. A clerk smitten
with leprosy and his wife with the
same infirmity were seeking admission to St. Margaret's, Hunting-

24. SEAL OF THE LEPER-
WOMEN OF WESTMINSTER

don, in 1327. By the Ilford statutes, no married man was
admitted unless his wife also vowed chastity. On no
account was a married person received at Dover without
the consent of the party remaining *in seculo*, and then only
upon similar conditions. In this connection a passing
reference may be made to the marriage laws. Although
by the laws of the Franks leprosy was a valid reason for

[1] Pat. 12 Edw. I, m. 16.

divorce, later Norman laws considered separation un-
justifiable; this latter was the attitude of the Church,
which is given fully in the Appendix to the Lateran
Council of 1179.[1] Yet the pathos of the leper's lot is
suggested by the declaration of Amicia, a woman of
Kent in 1254—that in truth at one time she had a certain
Robert for husband, but that now he had long been a
leper and betook himself to a certain religious house, to
wit, the leper-hospital at Romney.[2]

For many reasons the leper-household was most difficult
to control : it is small wonder that abuses crept in.   Men
forcibly banished were naturally loth to submit to rigorous discipline.   They were persons who would never have
dreamed of the religious life save by pressure of circumstances ; moreover, the nature of their infirmity caused
them to suffer from bodily lassitude, irritability and a
mental depression bordering upon insanity ; in the life of
St. Francis is a description of his ministry to a leper so
froward, impious, abusive and ungrateful that every one
thought him possessed by an evil spirit.   London lepers
were evidently not less refractory.   From early days the city
selected two men as keepers and overseers at St. Giles', the
Loke and Hackney ; these officials, who were accustomed
to visit the lazar-houses daily and to chastise offenders,
were granted exemption from inquests, summonses,
etc., on account of this "their meritorious labour, their
unpleasant and onerous occupation." (1389.) The London
edict of 1346 confirms the undoubted fact that lepers are
specially tempted to a loose life.   Banished from the
restraining influences of home and public opinion, they

---

[1] Cap. 2, 3, *vide Conciliorum Omnium*, ed. 1567, III, 700.
[2] Assize Roll No. 361, 39 Hen. III, m. 28.

were found in haunts of vice. The master of the lazar-house had no means of enforcing control. If the leper escaped and fell into evil habits none could prevent it : indeed, this did but ensure the liberty he craved, for the ultimate punishment of inmates was expulsion.

(ii) THE HOUSEHOLD OF THE INFIRMARY AND ALMSHOUSE

(a) *The Master* or Warden, who was also known as prior, *custos*, keeper or rector, was usually a priest, but occasionally a layman. One of the early masters of St. Mark's, Bristol, was a knight, Henry de Gaunt, whose mailed effigy remains in the chapel. Crown hospitals were often served by chaplains and clerks, but the appointment of "king's servants," yeomen or knights, is noticeable during the fourteenth century.

It is rarely recorded that the custodian of the sick was a physician, but the absence of the title *medicus* in no way proves that he and his helpers were ignorant of medicine. In early days, indeed, it was only the clergy, religious or secular, who were trained in the faculty, and the master and his assistants must have acquired a certain intimacy with disease ; they would have a knowledge of the herbals, of the system of letting blood, and other simple remedies. An important medical work, *Breviarium Bartholomæi*, was written late in the fourteenth century by John Mirfield of St. Bartholomew's, Smithfield. He acknowledges that it is a compilation for the benefit of those who could not afford to buy the treatises whence it was derived ; but he adds that part had been personally communicated to him and was supported by the experience of others. The fine manuscript copy in Pembroke

College, Oxford, includes a list of medical ingredients, herbs, etc.[1]

In some instances the warden *is* described as a physician. When the chaplain of St. John's, Bridport, was incapacitated, Master John de Brideport, physician, was deputed to act for him (1265). The Duke of Lancaster presented his foreign doctor, Pascal de Bononja, to the Preston hospital (1355). "Louis the physician," who held St. Nicholas', Pontefract (1399–1401), may be identified with Louis Recouchez, king's physician, who was then appointed to the hospital at Westminster. It is possible that visiting doctors and barber-surgeons attended hospitals. In an inventory of Elsyng Spital a debt of xxxvij*s*. ij*d*. was due to Robert the leech, and of x*s*. to Geoffrey the barber. One of the inquiries at the Dissolution of religious houses was :—"Whether the maister of the house doo use his brethren charitably when they be syke and diseased ; and whether, in tyme of their sykenes, he doo procure unto them physicions."

The duties—and temptations—of a warden are suggested by the "Articles of Inquisition touching the Savoy" (1535). Not only was inquiry made whether the master visited the poor at least twice a week, and the sick twice daily, but also :—

"Whether he be mercifull, beningne and louyng to the poore ; and not skoymys [squeamish] or lothesome to uisite theym or to be among theym.

"Whether he or his ministers by his sufferance do take in suche as they reken moste clene of the poore, and repell theym that they reken most sore or deseased, for auoydyng of their owne lothesomenes or contagion."

[1] Hist. MSS., 6th R. 550.

PLATE XVII

GOD'S HOUSE, EWELME

The qualifications and duties of the head of an alms-house are defined in the minute regulations of fifteenth-century founders. The master of Ewelme must be an able and well-disposed person in body and soul, one who could counsel and exhort the poor men to their comfort and salvation. He had to conduct frequent services, and was warned to omit none—not even "for plesaunce of lorde or lady"—save "if he be let by sekenesse or prech-yng of the worde of God, or by visitacion of Fadyre and modir." The master of God's House, Exeter, might not be absent more than once or twice a year, his recess never exceeding three weeks and three days. At Wells, a chap-lain of commendable life, manners and learning was sought—one "circumspect and expert in spiritual and temporal things, and free from all infamous vice." The ale-house and hunting were forbidden to the warden of Heytesbury, as well as "inhonest playes, as of the Dees, cartes or of the hande-ball." He must never be absent at night, nor for long by day, although it was lawful for recreation to walk a mile or two at certain times. He had, indeed, little leisure, for he conducted certain services both in the chapel and parish church, and kept school, besides ruling the almshouse.

The model master did not exist only in the imagination of founders, although he occurred rarely. Among good men who are not forgotten where they fulfilled their duty, mention must be made of John de Campeden, warden and benefactor of St. Cross. His friend William of Wyke-ham placed him in charge of that despoiled and dilapidated institution. He ruled wisely and spent large sums upon restoration. After a faithful stewardship of twenty-eight years, his death occurred in 1410. His memorial brass retains its place before the altar. The brasses of several wardens are also preserved at Greatham.

(b) *The Staff: Brethren and Sisters.*—These offices became in some cases mere honorary posts ; there was no salary attached to them, but officials were supplied with food and clothing. The sisterships at St. Katharine's-near-the-Tower used to be given by the queen to her ladies. Of the eight sisters at St. Leonard's, York, some were workers (see p. 154), but others lived apart from the rest in a place built for them near the hospital, and were mere pensioners enjoying provision of food, clothing, fuel and bedding. Unprotected women were often glad to relinquish some little property by arrangement, and be settled for life. " Brothers " might be priests, monks or lay-brethren. The staff of St. John's, Oxford, consisted of three Augustinian chaplains—one being elected master —with six lay-brethren and six sisters. At Lechlade two brothers distinguished for kindness and courtesy were selected to exercise hospitality with charity and cheerfulness, and to watch over the sick.[1] Of thirteen brethren at Kepier, six were chaplains, and the rest acted as steward, keeper of the tannery, miller, etc. The brethren of St. John's, Ely, were forbidden to play with dice, or to be present at such play, but were to give themselves to contemplation and study of Scripture, one or two being deputed to wait upon the infirm. Each lettered brother of St. Leonard's, York, was directed to study at his desk in the cloister two or three times a day.

The "proctor" was the financial agent of the community. He held an important post, and had occasionally an official seal. It was sometimes his duty to deliver a

[1] Bishop Giffard's Register, ii. 391.

charity-sermon—"to preach and to collect alms." When the traffic in indulgences began, the proctor became a "pardoner." (See p. 189.) Spurious agents abounded, for the post was lucrative. A man was arrested as feigning himself proctor of St. Thomas', Canterbury; another was convicted of receiving money, beasts, legacies and goods ostensibly for that house.[1] The collector received gifts in kind, and the following appeal was put forward by St. John's, Canterbury :—"if any one wishes to give . . . ring, brooch, gold, silver, cows, heifer, sheep, lamb or calf, let him send and deliver it to our proctor." Sister Mariana Swetman was licensed to collect alms on behalf of that hospital (1465), an interesting instance of a woman virtually holding the office of proctor.

Ministering women have long laboured in our infirmaries for the benefit of the sick, carrying on their works of mercy side by side with men. "The lay sisters shall observe what we have above ordained to be observed by the brethren, as far as befits their sex," decreed Archbishop Gray for St. John's, Nottingham (1241). One of the men, corresponding to the monastic *infirmarer*, was responsible for the sick ward; thus a brother of Northallerton held the office of *procurator infirmorum in lectulis*, whilst two sisters watched by the sick, especially at night, and a third attended to household affairs. At Bridgwater, women "not of gentle birth but still fit for the purpose" assisted in nursing; they lodged in a chamber adjoining the infirmary and were to be always careful and ready both by night

[1] Pat. 6 Edw. II, pt. i. m. 15. Pat. 17 Edw. II, pt. i. m. 10. Compare inscription upon Watts' Almshouse, Rochester (1579); poor people to be sheltered " provided they be not rogues nor proctors." The law authorizing proctors was repealed in 1597. Cf. *Fraternity of Vagabonds*.

and day to help the sick and to minister to them in all things."

The work of women among the sick developed further during the fifteenth century; they evidently took a prominent part in the management of the larger infirmaries. A lady, corresponding perhaps to the matron of to-day, was in authority at York. By a will of 1416, money was bequeathed for distribution among the helpers and inmates of St. Leonard's at the discretion of Alice *materfamilias*. Long before (1276) the officers had included not only a brother called Gamel *de Firmaria*, but a sister named Ann *medica;*[1] and in 1385 the principal sister was known as Matilda *la hus-wyf*.[2] In some institutions there were already distinct ranks among nursing women. The pious poet Gower remembers in his will (1408) the staff and patients of four London hospitals; he leaves sums of money not only to the master and priests of St. Thomas', Southwark, but "to every sister professed" and "to each of them who is a nurse of the sick."

Woman's sphere in hospital life was confined to work by the bedside and domestic duties. Occasionally they were found to undertake what was not fitting. The prior of Christchurch, Canterbury, made a visitation of the daughter-hospital of St. James, Thanington, after which he issued a deed of reformation (1414). A curious clause occurs in these statutes :—

"We command that no one of the sisters . . . or any other woman soever while divine service is being celebrated in the chapel should stand or sit in any way round or near the altars or should presume to serve the priests celebrating the

---

[1] Chron. and Mem., 71, *Historians of York*, iii. 202-3.
[2] *Arch. Journ.* 1850.

divine offices or saying the canonical hours, since, according to the first foundation of the said hospital its chaplains or priests ought to have a clerk who ought to officiate in the aforesaid matters."

In addition to regular brethren and sisters, there were under-officials. The staff of the larger institutions included clerks in minor orders, who assisted in worship and work. In almshouses where there was no resident master, a trustworthy inmate held a semi-official post. Thus at Donnington there were thirteen pensioners, and "one at their head to be called God's minister of the poor house." When the "tutor" at Croydon went out of doors, he ordained "oon of his fellawes moost sadde [serious] and wise to occupy his occupacion for him till he come ageyne."

(c) *Attendants*, etc. Serving men and women were employed to wait upon the infirm and upon the staff. Lanfranc ordered that the poor of St. John's, Canterbury, should have careful servants and guardians, lest they should need anything. When the poll-tax was levied in Oxford (1380), there were twelve servants, artisans and farm-labourers working at St. John's. In the immense establishment at York there were sixteen male and female servants, besides a host of other stipendiaries—two or three cooks, bakers, brewers, smiths and carters, a ferrywoman, twelve boatmen, etc. Working-class officials called the "man harbenger" and "woman harbenger" were employed to attend to beggars passing the night at St. John's, Sandwich. At the Maison Dieu, Dover, two women made the beds, served the poor and washed their clothes. The position of the female attendant in an almshouse is well described by the name

"sister-huswiff" used at Heytesbury.   The ideal woman
to hold the post is pictured in the statutes of Higham
Ferrers ; of good name and fame, quiet and honest, no
brawler or chider, she should be "glad to please every
poor man to her power."   She had minute directions as
to housekeeping and other duties which would fill the
day, and in illness she must visit the patients at night.
The keeper of the five married couples at Ford's hospital,
Coventry, was required "to see them clean kept in their
persons and houses, and for dressing their meats, washing
of them, and ministering all things necessary to them."

(d) *The Sick and Infirm.*—Having described the officials,
it will be well to form some idea of the number of the
infirm to whom they ministered.   The largest establishment of this kind was St. Leonard's, York; and at Easter
1370, there were 224 sick and poor in the infirmary,
besides 23 children in the orphanage.   About the same
time there were 100 brothers and sisters at St. John's,
Canterbury.   A large number of patients were cared for
in the London hospitals of St. Bartholomew, St. Thomas
and St. Mary.   St. Giles', Norwich, accommodated 30
poor besides 13 aged chaplains, and 40 persons were
maintained at Greatham.   The majority of permanent
homes were smaller, thirteen beds being a usual number.
Many hospitals were obliged to reduce the number of
patients as the revenues diminished.   In the year 1333,
St. Bartholomew's, Gloucester, supported 90 sick, lame,
halt and blind ; but two centuries later Leland notes that
it once maintained 52, but now only 32.

Of pilgrim, patient and pensioner, little can be recorded.
Temporary inmates came and went, receiving refreshment
and relief according to their needs.   Some of the resident

poor were chronic invalids, but others were not too infirm
to help themselves and assist others.

The frequent attendance at prayers certainly gave the
almsfolk constant occupation, and they were required to
be busy at worship or work. The poor men of Croydon
were charged "to occupy themsilf in praying and in
beding, in hering honest talking, or in labours with
there bodies and hands." Inmates at Ewelme must be
restful and peaceable, attending to prayer, reading or
work ; their outdoor employment was to "kepe clene the
closter and the quadrate abowte the welle fro wedis and all
odyr unclennesse." (Pl. XVII.) It was directed at Higham
Ferrers that in springtime each poor man should help to
dig and dress the garden, or if absent, give the dressers a
penny a day. In the same way, at Sandwich, an inmate's
allowance was stopped if he failed to render such service
as he could. Those brothers at Ewelme who were "holer in
body, strenger and mightier" were commanded to "fauer
and soccour and diligently minister to them that be seke
and febill in all behofull tyme."

CHAPTER XI

THE CARE OF THE SOUL

" The brothers and sisters must pray continually, or be engaged in work, that the devil may not find them with nothing to do."
(Statutes of St. Mary's, Chichester.)

THE daily life in a hospital was essentially a religious life. From warden to pauper, all were expected to pay strict attention to the faith and give themselves to devotion. "The brethren and sisters serving God" were fully occupied with prayer and work. "A representation of a mediæval hospital shows the double hall, the priest is administering the last rites of the Church to one patient, the sisters are sewing up the body of another just dead, mass is being sung at the altar, a visitor is kneeling in prayer."[1]

I. THE SERVICES

The offices consisted of mass and the canonical hours. All who could rise attended the chapel on bended knees, the bedridden worshipping simultaneously. Even sick people could join in the intercessions; thus the master of St. John Baptist's, Bath, agreed that the name of a late canon of Wells should be daily recited before the brethren, sisters and poor in the infirmary (1259).

(a) *The Staff.*—In regular hospitals helpers were directed to keep the canonical hours unless reasonably hindered,

[1] Besant, *London, Med. Ecc.*, p. 256.

PLATE XVIII

ST. MARY'S HOSPITAL, CHICHESTER

each being expected to pray according to his powers and education. The lettered repeated the *Hours* and *Psalter* of the Blessed Virgin, *Placebo* and *Dirige*, penitential psalms and litany. Those who did not know the offices said *Paternoster, Ave Maria, Gloria Patri*, and *Credo*. The brethren rose early for mattins; after prime and tierce, mass was celebrated; sext and none followed. They then gave themselves to household duties, until the day closed with vespers and compline. Attendance at the night offices sometimes caused them to fall sick with the cold, on which account the brethren of St. John's, Bridgwater, asked the bishop for relief (1526). Accordingly they were allowed to hold their first service at 5 a.m. in summer and 6 a.m. in winter, provided that they first rang a bell to waken travellers, workmen and others, that they might attend mass and ask God's blessing before going about their work.[1]

(b) *Lepers.* When a leper was solemnly set apart, he was counselled to say devoutly every day *Paternoster, Ave Maria, Credo in Deum, Credo in Spiritum;* he was to say often *Benedicite* and protect himself with the sign of the Cross. In most leper-houses inmates were required to hear mass daily and keep the canonical hours. At Dover, they were instructed not only to say their two hundred *Paternosters* and *Aves* by day, but as many at night; one brother roused the slumbering by ringing the dormitory bell, and the prayers were repeated sitting erect in bed. At St. James', Chichester, a similar custom was confirmed in 1408 ; the first hour after midnight, the brethren (unless too feeble) had to rise together from their cubicles and say the night office. The prayers included not only

[1] W. Hunt, *Diocesan Hist.*, pp. 158-9.

the Creed, Lord's Prayer and Salutation, but intercessions for the Catholic Church, king and queen and benefactors; if omitted, they must be said next day. Bishop Stratford of London, in compiling regulations for Ilford (1346) writes :—

"We also command, that the lepers omit not attendance at their church . . . unless prevented by grievous bodily infirmity : they are to preserve silence there, and hear mattins and mass throughout, if they are able; and whilst there, to be intent on prayer and devotion, as far as their infirmity permits them."

At Sherburn those unfit to leave their beds were to raise themselves at the sound of the bell and join in worship, or in extreme weakness, to lie still and pray.

(c) *Almsmen.*—Inmates of almshouses were frequently under a solemn vow regarding religious exercises. By the oath upon admission to St. Bartholomew's, Sandwich, (Pl. XIX) each individual bound himself to

"be obedient wᵗ hooly deuocyon prayyng for the founder of this place . . . and in especiall I shall be at the bedys [bedes] in the churche, and at matynys, and atte messe, and euensong and complyne, as the custome of maner is and usage—so help me God, and all holy dome, and all seints of heuen."

The offices were sometimes grouped into morning and evening worship. Potyn directed that his almsmen at Rochester should say at a certain hour morning and evening "our ladie sawter." As this Psalter of the Blessed Virgin was the standard form of worship for the unlettered, a knowledge of it was required before admission to a hospital. At Heytesbury, the examination was conducted after entrance :—"and if he cannot perfitely, we wull that he be charged to cunne [learn] sey

PLATE XIX

ST. BARTHOLOMEW'S HOSPITAL, SANDWICH
(*a*) CHAPEL. (*b*) GATEWAY

y⁰ said Sawter, his Pater Noster, Ave and Credo, as well
as he canne." The keeper was to teach the ignorant,
and if he were still found defective in repetition, penance
was prescribed until his knowledge were amended.

" We wull also that euerich of y⁰ poremen other tymes of y⁰
day when they may beste entende and have leyser, sey for y⁰
state and all y⁰ sowlis abovesaide, iij sawters of y⁰ most glorious
Virgyne Mary. Every sawter iii times, 50 aues, with xv paternosters & iii credes. . . . And furthermore, that thei say
euery day onys our Lady Sawter for all Christen soulis."

After supper when the household attended chapel, all
that could joined in *De Profundis* " with y⁰ versicles and
orisons accustomed to be saide for dede men." At the
close a bedeman said openly in English the bidding
prayer.

The almsmen of Ewelme after private prayer by their
bedside, attended mattins and prime soon after 6 a.m.,
went at 9 a.m. to mass, at 2 p.m. to bedes, at 3 p.m.
to evensong and compline. About 6 o'clock the final
bidding prayer was said around the founders' tombs :—

"God have mercy of the sowle of the noble prince Kyng
Harry the Sext and of the sowles of my lord William sum
tyme Duke of Suffolke, and my lady Alice Duchesse of Suffolke
his wyfe, oure fyrst fownders, and of theyr fadyr and modyr
sowles & all cristen sowles."

The ministry of intercession was fostered in hospital
chapels. A collect, breathing humble and trustful petitions, was drawn up by Wynard, Recorder of Exeter, who
built God's House in that city :—

"O Lord Jesu Christ, Son of the Living God, have mercy
upon Thy servant William founder of this place, as Thou wilt
and as Thou knowest best ; bestow upon him strong hope,

right faith and unshadowed love, and grant to him a good end, which is a gift above all others. *Amen.*"

The bidding prayer directed for the use of almsmen at Lichfield included petitions for the founder and for the royal family :—

"O God, who by the grace of the Holy Spirit, the Comforter, pourest the gifts of charity into the hearts of the faithful, grant to Thy servant William the bishop, our founder, and grant to Thy servants and to Thy handmaids, for whom we implore Thy clemency, health of mind and of body ; that they may love Thee with all their strength, and with all joyfulness perform such things as please Thee, through Christ our Lord. *Amen.*"

The pious custom of remembering benefactors is continued at Lambourn. The little almshouse was founded in 1501 by John Isbury, who is buried in the adjoining church. Every morning at 8, the senior almsman repeats the prayer for the soul of the founder, after which the pensioners attend mattins. The vicar recently recovered a part of the original prayer (in brass) from off the tomb.

2. THE CHAPEL

The life of the community centred in the chapel. Of the chaplains at St. John's, Chester, two served in the church and "the third in the chapel before the poor and feeble sustained in the said hospital." There were three chapels in St. Leonard's, York (Pl. XXV), including "St. Katherine in the sick hospital" and "St. Michael in the infirmary." Henry III was present at the dedication of the Maison Dieu, Dover,[1] and again long afterwards when an altar was consecrated to St. Edmund by Richard

[1] Charter Roll 16 Hen. III, m. 19.

of Chichester. Every hospital had one or more altars. Portable super-altars were occasionally kept, these being probably used when the infirmary did not adjoin the chapel.

In order to gain an idea of the external side of worship, some account of the accessories of a chapel, such as lights, decoration and ornaments, must be given. Lights were kept burning day and night before the altar. For this purpose oil lamps with rush wicks, and wax tapers were required. The two Sandwich hospitals obtained their supply of tapers thus. When the mayor and townsmen came in procession to St. Bartholomew's on the patronal festival, many bore wax lights which they left in the chapel for use during the year. St. John's hospital, not being equally favoured, arranged otherwise, for the inmates agreed that if any one reviled another with vicious language, brawling in ungodly fashion, he should pay four lb. of wax to the light of the church. The altar expenses at Holy Trinity, Bristol, included payments for standards, candlesticks and lamps. The wax-maker received 5s. 10d. for ten lb. of new wax for the Sepulchre light, and 8½d. for a "wachyng tapir for the Sepulcre" (1512).[1]

The chapel was adorned with paintings and carvings. The figure of St. Giles now preserved in Lincoln Cathedral was brought there from the hospital of that name. When St. Mary Magdalene's chapel, Durham, was being rebuilt, the sum of 15s. 1d. was paid for painting an image of the patron-saint. Alabaster heads of the Baptist were kept at St. John's, Exeter, and Ewelme. The inventory and valuation of Holy Trinity, Beverley,

[1] MS. in Municipal Charities Office.

enable one to picture the appearance of the sanctuary. The ornaments included an alabaster representation of the Trinity with painted wooden tabernacle, a well-carved and gilded image of the Blessed Virgin and Child (worth 40s.) with sundry small pictures and crucifixes.

Books, plate and vestments were frequently the gift of benefactors by will. The founder bequeathed to St. Giles', Norwich, "the gilt cup which was the blessed Saint Edmund's" (i.e. probably the Archbishop's); he left a Bible to the hospital and a missal to the master. Office-books were costly, the manual and missal at Holy Trinity, Beverley, being valued at £4 each. A master of Sherburn bequeathed to that house a richly-illuminated New Testament (*Argenteus Textus*), besides cloths of gold and brocade. John of Gaunt gave to his Leicester foundation "his red garment of velvet embroidered with gold suns." When festal services were held at St. Mary's, Newcastle (Pl. XXVII), three gold chalices were seen upon the altar, whilst the celebrant wore one of the beautifully-embroidered garments of the hospitals, which included one wrought with peacocks, another bordered with roses, and "one entire vestment of bloody velvet, woven about with a golden fringe."

Many valuables fell a prey to dishonest wardens. Frequent allusions are made to defects in the books, jewels, etc., of hospital chapels and of their being withdrawn, put into pledge, or sold. The treasures had often dwindled considerably before the final pillage, which partly accounts for entries in Chantry Surveys, etc., "plate and ornaments none." But as late as the sixth year of Edward VI, some traces remained of ornate services. St. John's,

Canterbury, possessed ecclesiastical robes of black velvet, red velvet and white fustian, and a cope of Bruges satin. Some of these were removed, but amongst articles left for the ministration of divine service were " one cope of blewe saten of bridgs, one cope of whytt fustyan."

25. ANCIENT HOSPITAL ALTAR, GLASTONBURY

The fittings of such chapels have seldom survived, but original altar-stones remain in two hospitals at Ripon, as well as at Stamford and Greatham ; the ancient slab found in the floor at Trinity Hospital, Salisbury, has this year been restored to its place. The altar (Fig. 25) in the women's almshouse at Glastonbury (Fig. 23) has a recess in the masonry under the south end of the altar-slab. At

Chichester and Stamford sedilia and stalls with misericords may be seen.   Wall-paintings remain at Wimborne, and fragments of ancient glass at St. Cross; St. Mark's, Bristol; St. Mary Magdalene's, Bath; Trinity, Salisbury; Sherborne; and Stamford.

CHAPTER XII

THE CARE OF THE BODY

" Let there be in the infirmary thirteen sick persons in their beds, and let them be kindly and duly supplied with food and all else that shall tend to their convalescence or comfort." (Statutes of Northallerton.[1])

IN considering the provision for material comfort in hospitals, one must distinguish between residents and sojourners. Board and clothing had to be found for the leper or the almsman, and the sick needed food and shelter for a time. Travellers either called for doles in passing, or required supper, bed and breakfast. Upon every pilgrim, sick or well, spending the night at St. Thomas', Canterbury, four-pence was expended from the goods of the hospital. Bodily necessaries of life may be classified under the headings food, fuel, baths, bedding and clothes.

1. FOOD

(a) *Food for resident pensioners.*—There was of course a wide difference between the lot of the ill-fed lazar who lodged in some poor spital dependent upon the chance alms of passers-by, and that of the occupant of a well-endowed institution. At the princely Sherburn hospital, each person received daily a loaf (weighing five marks) and a gallon of beer ; he had meat three times a week, and on other days eggs, herrings and cheese, besides

[1] Surtees, Vol. 56. Gray's Register, p. 181.

butter, vegetables and salt. The statutes laid stress upon the necessity of fresh food, and it was forbidden to eat the flesh of an animal which had died of disease. This was wise, for the constant consumption in the Middle Ages of rotten meat, decayed fish and bread made from blighted corn predisposed people to sickness and aggravated existing disease. Forfeited victuals were granted to the sick in hospitals at Oxford, Cambridge, Sandwich, Maldon, etc. The Forest law directed that if any beast were found dead or wounded, the flesh was to be sent to the leper-house if there were one near, or else be distributed to the sick and poor; Dr. Cox in his *Royal Forests* cites instances of the lepers of Thrapston and Cotes benefiting by this statute.

Salt meat was largely consumed, but it was insufficiently cured on account of the scarcity of salt. Bacon was a most important article of food; one of the endowments of St. Mary Magdalene's, Winchester, consisted of four flitches annually. About Christmas-tide, according to the "Customal of Sandwich," each person at St. Bartholomew's received a hog with the inwards and all its parts. The lepers at St. Albans had a similar custom, but they made their own selection for the salting-tub at Martinmas:—"we desire that the pigs may be brought forward in their presence . . . and there each, according to the priority of entering the hospital, shall choose one pig."

In some households, a meat-allowance was given to each person, perhaps two-pence a week, or a farthing a day. There were vegetarians among the residents at Southampton, for the account-rolls mention Sister Elena who for a time "ate nothing that had suffered death,

and Sister Joan, "who does not eat flesh throughout the year." In those days of murrain they were
prudent, for it is recorded that an ox was killed for
consumption in the house "because it was nearly
dead."

In the later almshouses the inmates received wages and
provided their own victuals, which were cooked by the
attendant. It was directed at Higham Ferrers :—

> "That every poor man shall buy his meat upon the Saturday
> . . . and deliver it to the woman, and she shall ask them
> which they will have against Sunday, and the rest she shall
> powder up against Wednesday ; she shall upon Sunday set
> on the pot and make them good pottage, and shall give
> every man his own piece of meat and a mess of pottage in
> his dish, and the rest of the pottage shall be saved until
> Monday."

The remainder was served up on Wednesday by the
careful housewife, who was directed to buy barm on
Fridays for the bread-making.

Baking was done once a fortnight at St. Bartholomew's,
Sandwich, the allowance to each person being seven penny
loaves. The exact provision of brown and white bread
is sometimes given in regulations. Oats "called La
Porage" was provided for the poor in the Leicester almshouse, where there was a porridge-pot holding sixty-
one gallons. Ancient cooking utensils are preserved at
St. Cross, Winchester, at St. John's, Canterbury, and
at Harbledown.

In most hospitals there was a marked difference between
daily diet and festival fare. Festal days, twenty-five in
number, were marked at Sherburn by special dinners.
St. Cuthbert was naturally commemorated ; his festival

in March and the day of his "Translation" in September
were two-course feasts ; but the first falling in Lent, Bishop
Pudsey provided for the delicacy of fresh salmon, if pro-
curable. Both at Sherburn, and at St. Nicholas', Pontefract, there was a goose-feast at Michaelmas, one goose
to four persons. The "Gaudy Days" at St. Cross were
also marked by special fare.

(b) *Food for casuals.*—Out-door relief was provided in
many hospitals. St. Mark's, Bristol, was an almonry
where refreshment was provided for the poor. Forty-five
lb. of bread made of wheat, barley and beans, was given
away among the hundred applicants; the resident brethren
"each carrying a knife to cut bread for the sick and impotent " ministered to them for two or three hours daily. A
generous distribution of loaves and fishes took place at
St. Leonard's, York, besides the provision of extra dinners
on Sundays.

Special gifts were also provided occasionally, on
founders' days or festivals. At St. Giles', Norwich, on
Lady Day, one hundred and eighty persons had bread
and cheese and three eggs each. Maundy Thursday was
a day for almsgiving, when all lepers who applied at the
Lynn hospital were given a farthing and a herring.
"Obits" were constantly celebrated in this way. The
eve of St. Peter and St. Paul, being the anniversary of
Henry I's death, was a gala-day for lepers within reach
of York ; bread and ale, mullet with butter, salmon when
it could be had, and cheese, were provided by the Empress
Matilda's bounty, in memory of her father. The ancient
glass reproduced on Pl. XX depicts hungry beggars to
whom food is being dealt out.

The Maison Dieu, Dover, kept the memorial days of

PLATE XX

THE BEGGARS' DOLE

Henry III and of Hubert de Burgh and his daughter. The fare and expenses on such occasions are recorded, *viz.* :—

> "Also in the daye of Seynt Pancre yerely for the soule of Hughe de Burgo one quarter of whete   vj. viij*d*.
> Also the same daye if it be flesshe day one oxe and if it be fisshe day ij barells of white heryng   xx*s*."[1]

Probably the annual distribution of three hundred buns at St. Bartholomew's Hospital, Sandwich, is handed down from some ancient custom on the patronal festival, but almost all these charities came to an end at the Dissolution. The Commissioners who visited St. Cross, however, (1535) allowed the continuation of daily dinners to the hundred poor, on condition that distribution was made

"to them who study and labour with all their strength at handywork to obtain food ; and in no case shall such alms be afforded to strong, robust and indolent mendicants, like so many that wander about such places, who ought rather to be driven away with staves, as drones and useless burdens upon the earth."

The "Wayfarer's Dole" still given at St. Cross is the only survival of the former indiscriminate entertainment of passers-by.

2. FIRING AND LIGHTS

The wood necessary for firing was collected from the vicinity by permission of the manorial lord. In Henry III's charter to St. John's, Oxford (1234), he granted wood from Shotover "to cook the portions of the poor and to warm the poor themselves." He also permitted the gathering of faggots for St. John's, Marlborough, one

[1] *Val. Ecc.*, i. 56.

man going daily for dry and dead wood "to collect as much as he can with his hands only without any iron tool or axe, and to carry the same to the hospital on his back for their hearth." Early rolls record constant grants of firewood. St. Leonard's, York, was supplied with turves from Helsington Moor.

The supply of fuel was regulated by the calendar. A benefactor (*circa* 1180) granted to the lepers of St. Sepulchre's near Gloucester, a load of firewood "such as a horse can carry" daily from November 1 to May 3, and thrice a week for the rest of the year. From Michaelmas to All Saints, the lepers of Sherburn—unconscious of the coalfield all around them—had for their eight fires two baskets of peat daily, after which until Easter four baskets were supplied; on festivals extra fuel was given, and at Christmas great logs were specially provided. Finally it was directed that :—"if any leprous brother or sister shall be ill so that his life is despaired of, he shall have fire and light and all things needful until he amend or pass away."

3. BEDDING

In early days, the sick and poor were laid on pallets of straw, but wooden bedsteads were probably introduced late in the twelfth century. A dying benefactor left to the brethren of St. Wulstan's, Worcester, the bed on which he lay and its covering of *bys*, or deer-skin (1291).[1] A Durham founder bequeathed money to "amend the beds what tyme they shall happyne to be olde or defective" (1491). A strange civic duty was performed at Sandwich. It was customary for the mayor and townsmen, as

[1] Giffard's Register, p. 388.

"visitors" of St. John's House, to examine the condition
and number of the feather-beds, and bedding, and to
ascertain if all was kept very clean. Where travellers
came and went, it was no light task to supply fresh linen.
At St. Thomas', Canterbury, an annual payment of
xlvj*s*. viij*d*. was made "to Rauf Cokker keper of the seid
hospitall and his wif for kepyng wasshyng of the bedds
for poure peple" (1535). The same year, the inquiry
made into the condition of the Savoy hospital included
these items :—

"Whether the hundred beddes appoynted by the founder be
well and clenely kept and repayred, and all necessaries to theym
belongyng.

"Whether any poore man do lie in any shetes unwasshed
that any other lay in bifore."

4. TOILET

Bathing and laundry arrangements are occasionally
mentioned. The regulations for the Sherburn lepers
direct a strict attention to cleanliness. Two bath-tubs
(*cunæ ad balneandum*) were supplied ; heads were
washed weekly ; and two laundresses washed the personal
clothing twice a week. In the fifteenth-century statutes
of Higham Ferrers matters of health and toilet are detailed.
None might be received "but such as were clean men of
their bodies" ; and if taken ill, a bedeman was removed
until his recovery. Every morning the woman must
"make the poor men a fire against they rise and a pan of
fair water and a dish by it to wash their hands." The
barber came weekly "to shave them and to dress their
heads and to make them clean." When the Savoy
was officially visited in 1535, the authorities were asked

"whether the bathes limitted by the founder be well obserued and applyed."

As to hair-dressing, "tonsure by the ears" was commonly used by the staff. After profession at Chichester it was directed :—"then let the males be cropped below the ear ; or the hair of the women be cut off back to the middle of the neck." Among the instructions in the register of St. Bartholomew's near Dover is one about the round tonsure, and there is a marginal note as to the mode of shaving the head. The visitation of St. Nicholas', York (*temp*. Edward I), showed that formerly brethren and sisters were tonsured, but that Simon, recently master, had allowed them to change both habit and tonsure.[1]

5. CLOTHING

(a) *The habit of the staff.*—The dress worn by the master and his fellow-workers was usually monastic or clerical, but it varied considerably, for the priests might be regulars or seculars, the brethren and sisters religious or lay persons. Occasionally the warden was not in orders ; it was directed at St. Leonard's, York, that " when the master is a layman, he shall wear the habit of the house." In an ecclesiastical type of foundation, the dress was commonly after the Augustinian fashion, consisting of black or brown robe, cloak and hood, with a cross on the outer garment ; white and grey were occasionally worn by officials of both sexes. The Benedictine brethren of St. Mark's, Bristol, were clothed in a black habit with a quaint device, namely, "a white cross and a red shield with three white geese in the

[1] P.R.O. Chanc. Misc. 20, No. 13.

same." Secular clerks had more latitude in costume ; the
sombre mantles were enlivened by a coloured badge, a
pastoral staff at Armiston, a cross at St. John's, Bedford,
etc.

(b) *The almsman's gown.*—The early type of pensioner's
habit is perpetuated at St. Cross. Ellis Davy, having
sober tastes, provided for his poor men at Croydon that
"the over-clothing be darke and browne of colour, and
not staring neither blasing, and of easy price cloth,
according to ther degree." This stipulation was probably
copied from the statutes of Whittington's almshouse, which
as a mercer he would know. The usual tendency of the
fifteenth century was to a cheerful garb. The bedeman of
Ewelme had "a tabarde of his owne with a rede crosse
on the breste, and a hode accordynge to the same." The
pensioners at Alkmonton received a suit every third year,
alternately white and russet ; the gown was marked with a
tau cross in red. At Heytesbury the men's outfit included
" 2 paire of hosyn, 2 paire of shone with lether and hempe
to clowte theme, and 2 shertys " ; the woman had the same
allowance, with five shillings to buy herself a kirtle. The
two servitors at St. Nicholas', Pontefract, wore a uniform
"called white livery."

(c) *The leper's dress.*—The theory of the leper's clothing
is described in the statutes of St. Julian's ; they ought "as
well in their conduct as in their garb, to bear themselves
as more despised and as more humble than the rest of their
fellow-men, according to the words of the Lord in
Leviticus : 'Whosoever is stained with the leprosy shall
rend his garments.'" They were forbidden to go out
without the distinctive habit, which covered them almost
entirely. The outfit named in the *Manual* consisted of

cloak, hood, coat and shoes of fur, plain shoes and girdle.

The hospital inmate in his coarse warm clothing was readily distinguished from the ragged mendicant. The brothers and sisters at Harbledown were supplied with a uniform dress of russet, that is to say, a closed tunic or super-tunic; the brethren wore scapulars (the short working dress of a monk), and the sisters, mantles. At St. Julian's hospital, the cut of the costume was planned; thus the sleeves were to be closed as far as the hand, but not laced with knots or thread after the secular fashion; the upper tunic was to be worn closed down to the ankles; the close black cape and hood must be of equal length. The amount of material is recorded in the case of Sherburn, *viz.* three ells of woollen cloth and six ells of linen. At Reading the leper's allowance was still more liberal, for the hood or cape contained three ells, the tunic three, the cloak two and a quarter; they also received from the abbey ten yards of linen, besides old leathern girdles and shoes.

Lepers were forbidden to walk unshod. At Sherburn, each person was allowed fourpence annually for shoes, grease being regularly supplied for them. Inmates of both sexes at Harbledown wore ox-hide boots, fastened with leather and extending beyond the middle of the shin. High boots were also worn by the brethren at St. Julian's "to suit their infirmity"; if one was found wearing low-cut shoes—"tied with only one knot"—he had to walk barefoot for a season.

For headgear at Harbledown, the men used hoods, and the women covered their heads with thick double veils, white within, and black without. Hats were sometimes

worn, both in England (Fig. 9) and in France. (Fig. 26.)
In the Scottish ballad (*circa* 1500), Cresseid is taken to
the lazar-house dressed in a mantle with a beaver hat.
This was probably a secular fashion.

26. A LEPER
(With clapper and dish)

CHAPTER XIII

HOSPITAL FUNDS

" To the which hospitals the founders have given largely of their moveable goods for the building of the same, and a great part of their lands and tenements therewith to sustain impotent men and women."

(Parliament of Leicester.)

ENDOWMENTS were to a certain extent supplied by the patron, but were supplemented by public charity. The emoluments included gifts of money, food and fuel, grants of property, admission fees, the profits of fairs, and collections. Receipts in kind are seldom recorded, and the changing scale of values would involve points beyond the scope of this volume. Particulars may be found in the extant manuscripts of certain hospitals and abbeys, in *Valor Ecclesiasticus*, etc. Extracts from the account-books of St. Leonard's, York, have been published in a lecture by Canon Raine. The finance of such an institution, with scattered and extensive property, necessitated a department which required a special clerk to superintend it, and the exchequer had its particular seal. Reports of the Historical MSS. Commission give details of the working expenses of hospitals at Southampton and Winchester.

I. ENDOWMENTS

(a) *Endowments in money.*—The earliest subscriptions are recorded in the Pipe Rolls, consisting of royal alms

PLATE XXI

ST. MARY MAGDALENE'S, WINCHESTER

(*a*) MASTER'S HOUSE AND CHAPEL.　(*b*) CHAPEL

(*Eleemosynæ Constitutæ*) paid by the Sheriff of the county from the profits of Crown lands. Three entries in the year 1158 will serve as specimens :—

Infirmis de Dudstan. xxs. Infirmis super Montem. lxs. Infirmis de Lundon. lxs.

At first sight this seems not to concern hospitals ; but a closer examination proves that sums are being paid to sick communities—in fact to lazar-houses. For the lepers of Gloucester dwelt in the suburb of Dudstan, and the infected inmates of St. Mary Magdalene's, Winchester, were known locally as "the infirm people upon the hill" —now Maun Hill. The grant was paid out of the farm of the city until, in 1442, the citizens were unable to contribute that and other sums on account of pestilence and depopulation. The infirm of London were the lepers of St. Giles' ; and the sixty shillings, originally granted by Henry I and Maud, was still paid in Henry VII's reign, for a writ of 1486 refers "to the hospitallers of St. Giles for their annuity of lxs." Between the years 1158 and 1178 subscriptions were paid to *infirmi* at the following places :—

Regular payments—"Dudstan," Hecham, Hereford, Lincoln, London, Maldon, Newport, Richmond, Rochester, St. Albans, St. Edmunds, Shrewsbury, "Super Montem." Occasional payments—Barnstaple, Barnwell or Stourbridge, Bradley, Burton Lazars, Chichester, Clattercot, Derby, Canterbury and Harbledown, Ely, Ilford, Leicester, Liteport, Newark, Northampton, Oxford, Saltwood, and Windsor.

Of the latter, some were grants on account of a vacant bishopric. In addition to the above, sums were given to *leprosi* of Southampton and Peterborough, and to hospitals of Gravesend, of Norwich, and "of the Queen." These contributions vary from 12*d*. paid to Hereford up to £6 given to Hecham (Higham Ferrers). In some cases corn and clothing were also contributed. There is a contemporary representation of one of these "infirm" persons on the seal of the lepers of Lincoln, dating from the days of Henry II and St. Hugh. The document to which it is attached contains a covenant between Bullington Priory and the hospital of the Holy Innocents, Lincoln, concerning a rent of three shillings from the hospital.

27. DOCUMENT AND SEAL OF THE LEPERS OF LINCOLN

Revenues also consisted largely in annual rents arising from land and house property, some being appropriated to specific works. An early grant to St. Bartholomew's, Gloucester (*circa* 1210), was to be expended upon the maintenance of a lamp in the chapel, and shoes for inmates, whilst the sum of 5*d*. was to go towards the provision of five beds.

(b) *Endowments in kind.*—The kings were generous in grants from royal forests. Henry III granted one old oak from Windsor to the sick of St. Bartholomew's, London (1224). He afterwards gave to St. Leonard's,

York, "licence to take what they need in the forest of Yorkshire for building and burning, and also of herbage and pasture for flocks and anything needful for their ease, as they had in the time of Henry II." Food was also supplied by patrons, especially in what might be termed manorial hospitals, consisting generally of a grant of tithes on produce. Another form of endowment was to impropriate livings. St. Giles', Norwich, owned six manors and the advowson of eleven churches. When funds were low at Harbledown, the archbishop impropriated Reculver church, thus augmenting the income by parochial tithes. This disgusted the parishioners who sought redress, thinking it "ill to be subject to lepers."

2. BEQUESTS

The money chest, larder and wardrobe were replenished largely by legacies. Amongst the earliest recorded are those of Henry II and his son, William Longespée. Henry left a large sum to religious houses in England and Normandy, and particularly to lepers. Longespée bequeathed cows to lepers in the hospitals of Salisbury, Maiden Bradley and Wilton, as well as to St. John's, Wilton, and St. Bartholomew's, Smithfield (1225). Men in humbler circumstances were likewise generous. A certain William de Paveli left 12d. each to eight hospitals in Northampton, Brackley, Towcester, Newport Pagnell, Hocclive and Stra[t]ford (*circa* 1240).[1] Wills abound in references of a similar character. Early legacies were made to the hospital as a body, but when the renunciation of individual property by the staff ceased, money was given to individuals; a benefactor of St.

---

[1] Madox, *Formulare Ang.*, p. 424.

Giles', Norwich, left 20 marks to the master and brethren, 40*d*. each to other officials, and 2*s*. to each bed (1357).[1] Gifts were frequently made to patients ; Stephen Forster desired that 100*s*. should be given away in five city hospitals, besides five marks in pence to inmates of St. Bartholomew's, Bristol (1458). An endowment of penny doles was provided by Lady Maud Courtenay in Exeter, namely thirteen pence annually for twenty years "to xiii pore men of Symon Grendon is hous" (1464). Testamentary gifts were also made in the form of clothes, bedding, utensils, etc. The founder of St. Giles', Norwich, left to it "the cup out of which the poor children drank," probably some vessel of his own hitherto lent for the scholars daily meal.

3. PROFITS BY TRADING

The fair was a great institution in mediæval England, and the funds of privileged charities were assisted in this way. At Maiden Bradley the leprous women and their prior held a weekly market and an annual fair. The Chesterfield fair was exchanged for a yearly payment of six pounds of silver from the royal Exchequer, which indicates the value set upon it. The most notable hospital-fairs were that of the leper-house near Cambridge (originally held in the close and still held on Stourbridge Common), and those connected with St. Bartholomew's and St. James' near London. The story of the former has been told by H. Morley ; and the "May-Fair" of St. James' leper-house was also famous. These galas were usually at the patronal festival and lasted two or three days, but occasionally these profitable festivities were carried on for a fortnight. Fairs were held at the following hospitals :—

[1] P.R.O. Ancient Deeds, A 11562.

Aynho, Bath (Holloway), Bury (St. Nicholas, St. Saviour), Baldock, Colchester (St. Mary Magdalene), Devizes (St. James & St. Denys), Dover (Buckland), Harting, Ipswich, Lingerscroft, Newbury, Newport, Newton Garth, Racheness, Royston (St. Nicholas), Swinestre near Sittingbourne, Thetford (St. John), Wycomb (2), etc.

This curious and interesting custom survives in connection with St. Bartholomew's, Newbury. The fair, originally granted by charter of King John (1215),[1] still takes place annually on the day and morrow of St. Bartholomew (*Old Style*), upon lands belonging to the hospital. A "Court of Pie Powder" is held on the morrow of St. Bartholomew's day; the proctor of this ancient charity with the steward and bailiff attend, and proclamation is made opening the Court. Tolls derived from stallages are collected, together with an impost of 2*d.* on every publican in Newbury (the latter due being resisted in a few cases). The following day the Court meets again, when the proceeds are divided amongst the almsmen.[2]

4. ADMISSION FEES

A considerable pecuniary benefit accrued to hospitals by the custom of receiving contributions from newly-admitted members of the household. In some cases a benefaction was made when persons were received into a community; thus Archbishop Wichwane as patron granted permission for a certain Gilbert and his wife to bestow their goods upon Bawtry hospital and dwell there (1281).[3]

[1] Charter Roll 17 John, m. 8.
[2] Communicated by the Town Clerk.
[3] Surtees Soc., 114, p. 278.

5. INVOLUNTARY CONTRIBUTIONS

Rates were levied for hospital maintenance on an organized system in some foreign countries. Sometimes a compulsory Hospital Sunday Fund was instituted, one penny being demanded from the richer, one half-penny from the middle-class, and a loaf from lesser folk. In England, however, the only obligatory support was an occasional toll on produce, perhaps first ordered by the feudal lord, but afterwards granted by custom. The Bishop of Exeter (1163) confirmed to lepers their ancient right to collect food twice a week in the market, and alms on two other days,—a custom resented by the citizens. (See p. 54.) King John conferred upon Shrewsbury lazars the privilege of taking handfuls of corn and flour from sacks exposed in the market (1204). By charter of the Earls, the Chester lepers were entitled to extensive tolls —upon salt, fish, grain, malt, fruit and vegetables, to a cheese or salmon from every load, and even one horse from the horse-fair. The lepers of St. Mary Magdalene's, Southampton, received "from time immemorial" a penny upon every tun of wine imported.

The mayor and commonalty of Carlisle granted every Sunday to the lepers a pottle of ale from each brew-house of the city, and a farthing loaf from every baker who displayed his bread for sale on Saturday. Their hospital was also endowed "time out of mind" with a corn-tax known as the "thraves of St. Nicholas" from every carucate of land in Cumberland. (The *thrave* is variously computed at twelve, twenty or twenty-four sheaves.) This county had a heavy poor-rate, for the great York hospital collected likewise from every plough working in the northern Archiepiscopate (Cumberland, Westmorland, Lancashire and Yorkshire). These "thraves of St. Leonard," or "Petercorn," belonged to the hospital by virtue of Athelstan's gift, which had been originally granted to him by his northern subjects in recognition of his destruction of wolves. The lands of the Durham Bishopric contributed "thraves of St. Giles" to Kepier hospital. The collection of such tolls was a constant difficulty, for it was resented by landowners, who had also the ordinary tithes to pay.

(6) VOLUNTARY CONTRIBUTIONS

(a) *Donations.*—At first, freewill-offerings were mainly in kind. The earliest collector whose name occurs is Alfune, Rahere's friend. While the founder was occupied at St. Bartholomew's, Alfune was wont "to cumpasse and go abowte the nye placys of the chirche besily to seke and prouyde necessaries to the nede of the poer men, that lay in the hospitall." It fell on a day that as Alfune visited the meat-market, he came to a butcher whose persistent refusal of help grieved him. After working what was regarded as a miracle, Alfune won him over, and departed with flesh in his vessel : henceforth butchers were more prompt to give their alms. Almsmen used sometimes to collect in person. It was customary for some of the brothers of St. John's House to "attend the churches in Sandwich every Sunday, with a pewter dish, soliciting money to buy meat for dinner on that day." Another brother was deputed to travel on an ass through Kent asking alms—"and he collects sometimes ten shillings a year, sometimes a mark, above his expenses."

All save richly-endowed houses were dependent upon

casual charity. In St. Mary's, Yarmouth, it is recorded "live a multitude of poor brethren and sisters, for whose sustenance a daily quest has to be made." One of the London statutes, enrolled in *Liber Albus*, directs that lepers shall have a common attorney to go every Sunday into the parish-churches to gather alms for their sustenance. Lest charitable offerings should diminish when lepers were removed from sight, a clause was added to the proclamation of 1348 :—"it is the king's intention that all who wish to give alms to lepers shall do so freely, and the sheriff shall incite the men of his bailiwick to give alms to those so expelled from the communion of men." It would appear from a London will of 1369, that special chests were afterwards provided; for bequests are then made to the alms-boxes (*pixidibus*) for lepers around London. Alms-boxes were carried about by collectors, and also hung at the gate or within the hospital. The proctor of the staff went on his mission with a portable money-box ; upon one occasion, a false proctor was convicted of pretending to collect for St. Mary of Bethlehem, for which fraud he was pilloried, the iron-bound box with which he had paraded the streets being tied round his neck. Boxes of this kind, sometimes having a chain attached, remain in almshouses at Canterbury, Leicester and Stamford. It was directed by the statutes of Higham Ferrers that a common box with a hole in the top should be set in the midst of the dormitory so that well-disposed people might put in their charity ; at certain times also two of the poor men were to "go abroad to gather up the devotions of the brotherhood," the contents being afterwards divided.

(b) *Small Subscriptions.*—Some fraternities formed

associations for the maintenance of charities. That of St. John Baptist, Winchester, helped to support St. John's hospital with the shillings contributed by its 107 members. The modern hospital of St. Leonard, Bedford, is kept up on this principle.

(c) *Appeals authorized by the King.*—The work of the proctor was not confined to the neighbourhood. Having first possessed himself of letters-testimonial, he journeyed in England, or even in Wales and Ireland. A "protection" or warrant was necessary, for unauthorized collectors were liable to arrest; it was in the form of a royal letter addressed to the archbishops, bishops, abbots, priors, bailiffs, lieges, etc. Henry III pleads with his subjects the cause of St. Giles', Shrewsbury:—"that when the brethren come to you to beg alms, you will favourably admit them, and mercifully impart to them your alms of the goods conferred by God upon you." Many letters-patent license the proctors, messengers or attorneys to collect in churches, or, as at St. Anthony's, Lenton (1332), in towns, fairs and markets. Sometimes the collector went forth supported by Church and State; as when the king issued mandates (1317, 1331) to welcome the proctor of the Romsey lepers "authorized by John, Bishop of Winchester and other prelates."

(d) *Appeals authorized by the Church, as Briefs, Indulgences, etc.*—Bishops likewise issued briefs, or letters of recommendation, on behalf of institutions in their own dioceses or beyond. The infirm of Holy Innocents', Lincoln, received from their diocesan a mandate (1294), ordering the parochial clergy to allow their agent to solicit alms after mass on three Sundays or festivals each year; later, the stipulation was added, that the Cathedral fabric fund should not suffer thereby. A typical document is found in the Winchester Register in favour of St. Leonard's, Bedford (1321). The mandate was addressed to the archdeacons, deans, rectors, vicars and chaplains, commanding them to receive accredited messengers of that needy hospital, to cause their business to be expounded by the priest during mass, after which the collection should be delivered without deduction. The brief was in force for two years and the clergy were bidden to help effectually by word and example at least once a year.

Episcopal Registers include many such documents, some being granted on special occasions, to make good losses by murrain, to enlarge premises, or to rebuild after fire, flood or invasion. Some briefs were not unlike modern appeals, with their lists of presidents and patrons ; for that on behalf of Romney hospital (1380) was signed by both archbishops and eleven bishops. It was a recognized source of raising funds. John de Plumptre in making arrangements for his almshouse at Nottingham (1414), provided that the widows, for the bettering of their sustenance, should "have and hold an episcopal bull and indulgence . . . procured from the archbishops and bishops of England, Wales and Ireland."[1]

It is curious to watch the increase of the privileges offered. The earlier bishops remitted penance for seven or thirteen days, those of a later period, for forty days. Roman indulgences knew no such limits. The form of a papal brief (1392) was as follows :—

"Relaxation of seven years and seven *quadragene* to penitents who on the principal feasts of the year and those of

[1] Records of Nottingham, ii. 99.

St. James in the month of July and the dedication, the usual octaves and six days; and of a hundred days to those who during the said octaves and days visit and give alms for the sustentation and recreation of the chapel of St. James' poor hospital without the walls, London."

William, Lord Berkeley directed the executors of his will (1492) :—

" to purchase a pardon from the court of Rome, as large as may be had, for this Chapple [Longbridge], from evensonge to evensonge, in the feast of Trinity for ever, for pleyne remission to them that will be confessed and contrite."

Offerings stimulated by such pardons were in money or in kind. A deed belonging to the Bridport Corporation sets forth that the writer has seen letters from famous ecclesiastics—including St. Thomas and St. Edmund of Canterbury—in favour of Allington leper-house, one being an indulgence of Alexander IV :—

" Item, to alle thos that gevyn broche, rynge, boke, belle, caudell, vestimente, bordclothe, towelle, pygge, lambe, wolle, peny, or penyworthe, be whiche the sayde hows and hospitale is amended and mentaynde, the sayd Pope grauntethe the remission of the vijth parte of penance injunct[ed]."

Thus the questionable trade of the pardoner[1] was often carried on by the hospital proctor; moreover, spurious bulls were circulated. The abuses to which the practice gave rise were recognized by Bishop Grandisson, who announced that questors collecting alms in the diocese of Exeter were forbidden to preach, or to sell fictitious privileges, or unauthorized pardons. A papal exhortation

---

[1] The word was retained after the Reformation, e.g. 1573, "paid to a pardoner that gathered for the hospital of Plympton" (T. N. Brushfield, *Devonshire Briefs*).

on behalf of St. Anne's, Colchester (1402), forbids these presents to be sent by pardoners (*questuarii*). Those who bought a pardon from the proctor of St. John's, Canterbury, were informed that the benefit of 30,000 *Paternosters* and *Ave Marias* was freely imparted to them. But although indulgences were liable to abuse, it must be remembered that authorized pardons extended to penitents only—to those who, being contrite, had already confessed and received absolution and penance. Upon the indulgenced feast of St. Michael, so many people flocked to St. Mary's, Leicester, that a special staff of confessors became necessary.

7. ALMS OF PILGRIMS

Such visits to hospitals lead to the further consideration of pilgrimage and devotion to relics, which directly affected charity. An indulgence was offered to penitents visiting Yarmouth hospital and the sacred relics therein and giving a helping hand to the poor inhabitants. The Maison Dieu at Dunwich possessed a holy cross of great reputation "whither many resorted to adore it, who bestowed much alms." When the precious relic was carried away and detained "by certain evil-wishers" connected with St. Osith's Abbey, the inmates were greatly impoverished.[1] The abbot having been prosecuted, came into chancery in person and rendered the cross to the king, who restored it to the master and brethren "to remain in the hospital for ever." Holy Cross, Colchester, claimed to keep a portion of the true Cross ; an indulgence was offered by various bishops to those paying pilgrimage visits and contributing to the hospital. (See pp. 248-9.)

[1] Prynne, *Usurpation of Popes*, p. 1137, and Close 34 Edw. I, m. 1.

PLATE XXII

LEPER HOSPITAL OF ST. BARTHOLOMEW, OXFORD

Other treasures visited by pilgrims were of a more personal character. Anthony à Wood found records of choice things formerly preserved in St. Bartholomew's, Oxford, whereby it was enriched :—"they were possest of St. Edmund the Confessor's combe, St. Barthelmew's skin, the bones of St. Stephen, and one of the ribbes of St. Andrew." The first and foremost of the sacred relics was evidently a personal possession of the local saint, Archbishop Edmund Rich, a native of Abingdon :— "Those that were troubled with continuall headaches," (University students, perhaps) "frenzies, or light-headed, were by kembing their heads with St. Edmund's combe restored to their former health." On high days and holy days these treasures were exposed to view in the chapel. (Pl. XXII.) They were of so great value that the authorities of Oriel College, having acquired the patronage, appropriated them, "which caused great complaints from these hospitalliers."

The alms of pilgrims and other travellers were a valuable asset in the funds, for it was customary for those so journeying to spend much in charity by the way. On the penitential pilgrimage of Henry II to Canterbury (1174) "as he passed on his way by chapels and hospitals he did his duty as a most devout Christian and son of Holy Church by confession of sin and distribution of offerings and gifts."[1] Halting at Harbledown he left the sum of forty marks, probably because the hospital belonged to the bereaved archbishopric. Long afterwards, another king—John of France—passed along the road, leaving at sundry hospitals a substantial proof of his gratitude for release from captivity. Among his

[1] Chron. and Mem., 67, i. 487.

expenses are included gifts to "les malades de 4 maladeries depuis Rocestre jusques à Cantobérie, pour aumosne"; also to the communities of St. James', St. John's at the Northgate, St. Mary's, and Harbledown, and to the brethren of Ospringe; whilst the king gave as much as twenty nobles to the Maison Dieu, Dover,

28. A HOSPITAL ALMS-BOX

where he was received as a guest.[1] Situated close to the highway, on the hill which eager travellers were about to climb to catch their first sight of the grand tower of Canterbury, the Harbledown lepers benefited by the gifts of pilgrims for three and a half centuries. Treasured in the hospital (Pl. V) was a relic of "the glorious martyr" to whose shrine they wended. "This fragment of his

[1] Soc. de l'Histoire de France, 1851, p. 194.

shoe supports this little community of poor men," says Ogygius in the *Colloquy on Pilgrimages*,[1] where Erasmus describes his visit to Canterbury with Dean Colet sometime before the year 1519. Shortly after leaving the city, where the road becomes steep and narrow, there is, he says, a hospital of a few old men. One of the brethren runs out, sprinkles the travellers with holy water, and presently offers them the upper part of a shoe, set with a piece of glass resembling a jewel. This the strangers are invited to kiss. (Bale satirizes this custom where he says, "here ys the lachett of swett seynt Thomas shewe.") Colet is indignant, but Erasmus, to appease the injured brother, drops a coin into his alms-box. The quaint old box is still kept at Harbledown, and is figured above.

[1] Pilgrimages of Walsingham and Canterbury—Ed. Nichols, 1849, p. 63.

CHAPTER XIV

RELATIONS WITH CHURCH AND STATE

" As to other hospitals, which be of another foundation and patronage than of the King, the Ordinaries shall enquire of the manner of the foundation, estate and governance of the same . . . and make thereof correction and reformation according to the laws of Holy Church, as to them belongeth."
(Parliament of Leicester.)

ATTENTION having been already called to the internal constitution of hospitals, we must now consider their relation to those in authority. The position of such a house was necessarily complicated; there arose a difficulty in reconciling its subordinate, yet partly independent character. We must see, first, how its welfare depended to a certain extent on king and bishop; secondly, its position with regard to the parochial system; and thirdly, how far it was affected by monasticism.

(i) RELATIONS WITH THE KING AND THE BISHOP

The hospitals of England have never been exclusively in the hands of Church or State. The relations which they bore to each may be subdivided under the headings of Constitution, Jurisdiction and Finance.

(a) *Constitution.*—As we have seen, the Church, usually represented by the diocesan bishop, was responsible for the rule and statutes by which a hospital was guided.

(b) *Jurisdiction.*—In the province of administration, visitation and reform, king and bishop played their respective parts. Speaking generally, the bishop was administrator, and the king protector ; to the former, matters of religious observance and conduct were referred, to the latter, questions of temporal privilege, immunity from taxation, etc. Both had rights as " visitors." Faithfully conducted, ecclesiastical visitation might be of great use, but owing to the huge extent of dioceses, it was infrequent and inadequate, and where the king was patron, the diocesan bishop's visitation was prohibited. Under Henry III, the royal almoner undertook the keeping of Crown hospitals, but afterwards this duty fell to the Chancellor, who alone had the right of visitation ; the diocesan bishop had no jurisdiction in such houses except by special arrangement, as in the Statute directing that ordinaries " by virtue of the king's commission to them directed " shall take inquisitions and return them into chancery. Royal interposition was not customary unless the king were patron ; thus an order to inquire into waste at certain hospitals was cancelled because the king had erred in believing that they were founded by his progenitors. When investigations were commanded, they were committed to a local jury, who were to find by inquisition on oath of the good men of the county how far rules had been observed, and they possessed full power "to deal with the hospital as well in the head as in the members." Detailed accounts of such special visitations may be found among Chancery Miscellanea in the Record Office.

(c) Finance.—The Lateran Council of 1179 decreed that leper-communities should not pay tithe from gardens and orchards, nor of the increase of cattle, and this was ratified in the Provincial Council of Westminster in 1200. The

Church wished to go a step further and ordain that neither lazar-house, Domus Dei nor poor hospital should pay taxes, which was set forth by Gregory X ; entries upon Papal Registers in 1278 declare that certain English houses, including Ospringe, should share this immunity. But the decree was not necessarily accepted in England, remission of taxation being a royal prerogative ; Ospringe was a Crown hospital to which exemption was renewed from time to time of the king's grace.   In the cases of lazar-houses, a curious distinction was made, witnessing incidentally to national independence—"And let not the goods of lepers be taxed where they are governed by a leper" (*par Sovereyn meseal*).   This rule occurs in the First Statute of Westminster (3 Edw. I),[1] and afterwards in rolls and writs dated 1297, 1307, etc.[2]   It was evidently in allusion to this custom that, in remitting a wool-tax, it is stated that St. Bartholomew's, Rochester, was governed by a leprous prior (1342), but a few years later the king granted it freedom from taxation for ever.   Many houses were freed by charter from local and general contributions and tolls.

Land-tenure may be included under finance.   Before the enactment of the Statute *De Religiosis*, benefactors met with no hindrance in promoting any plan for endowment, but after 1279 permission was sought "to alienate land in mortmain."   On payment of a small fine, communities were empowered to accept property to a certain value.   This developed into the "licence to found" named in fourteenth-century rolls, and subsequently into incorporation.

---

[1] Chron. & Mem., 72, *Reg. Malmes.* i. 232.
[2] Pat. 25 Edw. I, pt. ii. m. 11 ; Rolls of Parl. I, 239 *b*.

(ii) RELATIONS WITH THE PARISH PRIEST

Before the foundation of a hospital chapel, special permission was required from the bishop, with a guarantee that it should not interfere with the parochial system.   It was necessary clearly to define privileges, lest friction should arise.   Grants in civil and ecclesiastical registers include "a chapel, bell and chaplain," oblations, sepulture and "the cure of souls."

(a) *Oblations*.—One quarter of the offerings received at St. Katharine's, Ledbury, was reserved for parochial use. Unless some definite scheme was arranged, disputes quickly arose.   A serious collision of interests occurred at Brough.   The tiny hostel, founded with the sanction of bishop and archbishop (1506), developed into a pilgrimage-place.   The injured vicar, with solemn ritual, cursed with bell, book and candle all concerned with such oblations as were made in the chapel.   The founder, however, called forth upon his parson the archbishop's censure "as an abandoned wretch and inflated with diabolical venom for opposing so good a work."   The priest in turn appealed to the Pope.   At length it was agreed that 20*s.* yearly should be paid to the mother-church.[1]

(b) *Public and private Worship, Bells, etc.*—Agreements as to public worship on certain occasions were made between the parish and institutions within its boundary. The biographer of the Berkeley family, quoting from the episcopal register (1255), records :—

"That all the seculars in the hospitall of Longbridge, excepting a Cooke, and one person to kepe sick folkes, should in the spetiall solemne dayes, come to Berkeley Church and there

---

[1] Nicolson and Burn, *Antiq. of Westmorland*, ed. 1777, i. 574.

should receive all the ecclesiasticall Sacraments, (except holy bread and holy water) unles it bee by the dispensation and leave of the Vicar of Berkeley."[1]

To infringe such rules meant trouble. One Easter (1439), the chaplain of St. Leonard's, Leicester, permitted

two of the warden's servants to receive the Sacrament from him there, instead of repairing to the parish church ; but the following Sunday he was forced to do public penance.

The curious restriction of repeating divine service with closed doors and in an undertone was made at St. John's, Nottingham, when the patronal feasts were being celebrated in the parish. The rule for ordinary days was that of St. James' near Canterbury (1414), namely, that the canonical hours be said audibly after the sounding of the handbells or bells according to ancient custom.

The possession of a bell in a turret required a special licence, lest outside worshippers should attend. A chapel being added to St. Mary Magdalene's, Bristol (1226), the stipulation was made

29. GLASTONBURY

----

[1] J. Smyth, *Lives of Berkeleys,* i. 70.

" but the leprous women shall have no bells except hand-bells, and these shall not be hung up." It was agreed at Portsmouth (1229) that the two bells in God's House should not exceed the weight of those of the parish church, and should only ring at set hours. The *Annals of Dunstable Monastery* show how important the matter was considered :—

" In the same year (1293) the lepers of Dunstaple set up a mighty bell outside the precincts of their house on two timbers ; but the prior . . . brought that bell within our jurisdiction ; which afterwards he restored to them yet so that they should by no means use that or any other bell for calling together our parishioners or other people."

(c) *Burial Rights.*—The privilege of sepulture rendered the community more independent, and secured to it certain fees and legacies. A popular institution like St. Leonard's, York, or St. John's, Exeter, derived benefits from the burial of benefactors. There is a will entered on the Patent Roll of 1341 whereby a certain Vincent de Barnastapolia requested to be interred in the cemetery of St. Mark's, Bristol, to which house he left a consider-able legacy.[1] The conferring or denial of a place of sepulture seems to have been without rule, and was a matter of favour and circumstance. Thus St. Oswald's, Worcester, had a cemetery (probably because it was originally a leper-house), whilst St. Wulstan's had none.

(d) *Worship and Burial of Lepers.*—To lepers both chapel and graveyard were willingly granted. This was an early custom in England, as the Norman architecture of several chapels shows (e.g. Rochester, *circa* 1100). The

[1] Pat. 15 Edw. III, pt. i. m. 14.

Gloucester lazars were granted burial rights before 1160, when they already possessed a chapel, the chancel of which still stands ; the bishop's licence made the usual stipulation that none but lepers should be interred.[1] A fresh impetus was given to spiritual provision for outcasts by the Lateran Council of 1179. Pope Alexander III decreed as follows :—

"Seeing that it is very remote from Christian piety that those who seek their own and not the things of Jesus Christ do not permit lepers . . . to have churches or burial places of their own, nor to be assisted by the ministry of a priest of their own, we ordain that these lepers be permitted to have the same without any contradiction."

This privilege, it was declared, must not be prejudicial to the rights of ancient churches.

Digressing from the immediate subject of spiritual provision for the outcast, one point must be made clear. It is sometimes thought that the strict parochial discipline of mediæval England would insist upon the attendance of the leper at his parish church on certain occasions ; others on the contrary suppose that the leper was ex-communicate. The popular belief is that the Church provided for his worship the so-called "leper's window," frequently shown in old edifices. The existence of low-side-windows at such places as Bridgnorth and Spondon, where there were leper-colonies, is considered circum-stantial evidence of their origin and purpose. But name and idea alike are of entirely modern growth, arising from a misinterpretation of a wall-painting at Windsor, which Mr. Street took to represent the com-

[1] Chron. and Mem., 33, i. 147. ii. 7.

municating of a leper through an aperture. Administration would have been both difficult and irreverent; the opening, moreover, is often so situated that any such act would be physically impossible. A manuscript chronicle, indeed, records how Blase Tupton, who was dwelling near St. Chad's, Shrewsbury, about the year 1409, had a gallery made so that she might join in public worship :—

"Blase . . . cam by chance to be a leeper, and made the oryell which goythe allong the west side of the churche-yarde, throughe which she cam aloft to heare serveys throughe a doore made in the churche wale, and so passyd usually uppon the leades unto a glasse wyndowe, throughe which she dayly sawe and hard dayly serveys as longe as shee lyvyd."[1]

Now Blase was doubtless a privileged person, being the daughter of the well-known townsman who had founded the almshouse adjoining St. Chad's; and though now and again a lazar might make his way to a churchyard to gaze upon the holy mysteries, it is certain that only those living in a community with a chapel and priest could be confessed and receive the Blessed Sacrament. Most antiquaries are of opinion that the popular theory of the object of lowside-windows is untenable.

Careful provision was made for the religious observances of the untainted inmates of a hospital as well as for the leprous. They might use the chapel except on the greater festivals when they were required to attend the parish church and make oblations there. At St. Mary Magdalene's, Bristol, the infected confessed to their chaplain, but the rest to the parish priest. No parishioner of Bedminster might attend the chapel on Sundays or

[1] Owen and Blakeway, *Hist. of Shrewsbury*, 1825, ii. p. 257.

festivals to receive the blessed bread and holy water, the
distribution of which to other than inmates would infringe parochial rights.[1] It was provided by the founder's
statutes at Sherburn that on Sundays the lepers should
receive "the sprinkling of holy water, blessed bread, and
other things which are fitting."

(e) *Free Chapels.*—These were "places of worship
exempted from all relation to the mother church and also
from episcopal jurisdiction, an exemption which was an
equivocal privilege, obtained immediately from the
Crown, or appended to ancient manors originally belonging to the Crown."[2] St. John's, Oxford, was a privileged
proprietary chapel. The king withheld the right of
visitation from the bishop of the diocese, who, in turn,
seems to have refused to sanction and consecrate a graveyard. Henry III called in the Roman Pontiff to arbi-
trate ; whereupon "the pope at the instance of the king
commanded the Bishop of Lincoln to provide a burial
ground for the hospital of Oxford, for the brethren of the
hospital and for the poor dying therein, the indemnity of the
mother church and of the king as patron being provided
for."[3] The kings contrived to evade the Bishop of Lincoln's rightful authority. Edward I wrote to request
Bishop Giffard of Worcester to confer holy orders upon a
brother "because the same hospital is the king's free chapel
where the diocesan ought to exercise no jurisdiction."
The Close Roll of 1304 emphasizes the fact that the house
was wholly independent and therefore "quit of payments,
procurations and other exactions of the ordinary."[4]

[1] Chron. and Mem., 97, p. 173.
[2] Chetham Soc. F. R. Raines, *Lancashire Chantries.*
[3] Pat. 22 Edw. I, m. 3.
[4] Close 32 Edw. I, m. 2 *d.*

A few royal hospitals were subordinate to the Crown and the papal see. That of Basingstoke, with its "free chapel of the king", was granted immunity from episcopal control by Cardinal Ottobon (1268). The Maison Dieu, Dover, was taken under immediate papal protection by a bull of Nicholas III (1277). A unique case occurs where the lay founder of an almshouse at Nottingham gained for it freedom from the jurisdiction of the ordinary or judges, and subjection alone "to St. Peter and the Apostolic See" (1402).[1]

(f) "*The Cure of Souls*."—Whereas the "free chapel" had no parochial obligations, there were hospital churches to which full parochial rights were attached. How or why such houses as St. Paul's, Norwich, and Armiston came to possess "the cure of souls" is uncertain ; the little chapel of St. Mary Magdalene, Durham (now a ruin), was also a rectorial parish church. More curious is the fact that several *leper-hospitals* acquired this peculiar advantage. Thus in Northampton, although St. John's was "no parish church, but only for the company there inhabiting," St. Leonard's was a "liberty" having parochial rights, not only of burial, but of Baptism. St. Nicholas', York, required as master, "a fit clerk who shall be able to answer for the cure of souls belonging to the parish church of that hospital." The Lincoln leper-house had similar rights.

(g) *Almshouses and the Parish Church.*—Many of the later almshouses were closely connected with the parish. At Ewelme, for example, the almsmen resorted to the church constantly, and their presence was regarded as so important that even absence on pilgrimage was depre-

[1] Cal. Pap. Reg. vol. v. p. 489.

cated. Those institutions which had no chaplain of their own were brought into close touch with the parish priest, as at Croydon, where the poor men went every day to the church to "here all manner divine service there to be songe and saide."

(h) *Collegiate Foundations.*—Several large almshouses possessed collegiate rights or formed part of a college (e.g. St. Mary's, Leicester; Shrewsbury, Tong, Heringby). Sometimes, as at Higham Ferrers, there existed side by side a parish church, a bede-house for pensioners, and a college for the priests and clerks.

(iii) RELATIONS WITH MONK, KNIGHT AND FRIAR

Inquiry must now be made concerning the relation between hospitals and monastic life. Although the religious orders directly influenced certain houses, others were totally unconnected with them. Canon Raine says that St. Leonard's, York, was more of a secular than an ecclesiastical establishment; he regards it as principally a lay institution, although religion was, of course, a strong element in its working. In this hospital "which is of no order" (says a Papal Letter, 1429) the master might be a layman.

1. *The Monastic Orders*

Here it must be borne in mind that we have nothing to do with the infirmary and guest-house within conventual walls. Only such institutions are included as had an individual, though it may be subordinate, existence. Some hospitals were founded by an abbot or prior; these were chiefly dependent upon the mother-house for staff, income, food and clothing; they had an individual dedica-

PLATE XXIII

ST. JOHN'S HOSPITAL, WILTON

(*a*) SOUTH-EAST VIEW.   (*b*) NORTH VIEW

tion-name, but often no common seal (e.g. Bury, Peterborough). Others had a more independent existence, as
indicated by the possession of separate seals (e.g. Reading, Abingdon). A community which was under the
direct control of a religious house was of a more monastic
type than others. There was also the hospital established
by a private patron, and merely placed under the administration of some monastery ; here the endowment was distinct, and the staff might or might not be members of the
convent.

It is in truth often difficult to discriminate between
hospital and priory ; sometimes they are indistinguishable
in aim and scope. This was especially the case with the
English Order of St. Gilbert ; the two Gilbertine houses
at Lincoln and that of Clattercot were actual infirmaries.
Similarly, several foundations of the Order of the Holy
Sepulchre were pilgrims' hostels served by a few canons.
In certain cases hospitals developed into priories, some
losing their distinctively eleemosynary character (e.g.
Tandridge, Creak, Cockersand), while in others a mere
change of name took place, as at Maiden Bradley. In the
case of St. Bartholomew's, Smithfield, priory and hospital
existed side by side, with separate organization, revenue
and seals. Sometimes the titles were used interchange-
ably; and at Wilton the "priory" (Pl. XXIII) was merely
a hospital governed by a prior.

Many institutions observed the Augustinian rule.
Austin canons, according to Canon Venables, were
"regular clergy, holding a middle position between
monks and secular canons, almost resembling a community of parish priests living under rule." The five
largest London infirmaries were served by Augustinians.

Those of St. Thomas', Southwark, dressed after the manner of clergy of secular cathedrals and collegiate churches. The case of an Augustinian master of St. Thomas' shows that constitutions differed widely ; with the Bishop of Winchester's consent, he was transferred to Sandon hospital (Surrey) ; but being uneasy, he applied to the pope for absolution from his vow and sought permission to live "according to the custom of Sandon." St. Bartholomew's was likewise governed by Austin canons, although a papal document states that it "has not been approved by the apostolic see and is not subject to any regular order." Elsyngspital was founded for secular clergy, but, "taught by experience", regulars were substituted within twelve years. Among other Augustinian houses may be named Newcastle (St. Mary's), Brackley, Newstead, Bridgwater, Southampton, and Dover. The Benedictine rule was followed by the staff of St. Mark's, Bristol, Strood, and of course in all hospitals under Benedictine monasteries.

2. *The Military Orders*

Of the origin and introduction of these Orders more will be said under the heading of St. John Baptist and St. Lazarus in Part Two. Here we are rather concerned with the relations which existed between the knightly brethren and hospitals in general.

(a) *Knights Hospitallers and Templars.*—Both Orders were the recognized guardians of travellers, and much of their work was akin to that of the hospital for wayfarers. Thus King Stephen gave the Yorkshire manor of Steynton upon Blakhommer to the Master of the Temple :—" to find a chaplain to celebrate divine service daily and to receive and entertain poor guests and pilgrims there, and to ring and blow the horn every night at dusk lest pilgrims and strangers should lose their way." (Richard I afterwards re-granted the land to the Hospitallers.)[1] Similar hospitality was doubtless provided in all commanderies and preceptories. Although these were often called "hospitals" (e.g. at Greenham in Berks, Sutton-at-Hone, etc.) they are not included among the foundations enumerated in this volume.

Indeed, although these Orders exercised a certain influence upon hospitals, there was little actual intercourse. St. Cross, Winchester, was originally placed under the Knights of St. John of Jerusalem, but the connection was of short duration ; the habit and cross worn by the present pensioners serve as a reminder of this fact. The patronage of St. Saviour's, Stydd by Ribchester, and St. Leonard's, Skirbeck, afterwards came into the hands of the Order. St. Thomas' hospital in Cheapside was under the Templars, but since it was not suppressed with their preceptories (*circa* 1312), it may be classed among independent foundations. The full title remained (1340) "the master and brethren of the Knights Templars of the Hospital of St. Thomas the Martyr of Acon of Canterbury." It may be here observed that the misleading title "Commandery" often accorded to St. Wulstan's, Worcester, suggests a link with the Knights of St. John which did not exist ; although, curiously enough, the masters of both the Worcester hospitals were frequently named "preceptor."

(b) *Knights of St. Lazarus.*—Although, as has been said, commanderies and preceptories proper are not included, the leper-hospitals of the Order of St. Lazarus must of

---

[1] Close 14 Edw. III, m. 13.

necessity find a place. The principal one was at Burton Lazars, founded by a crusading Mowbray. Two important hospitals, those of London and Lincoln, were annexed to it by Edward I and Henry VI respectively. The staff of the former are referred to (1337) as the master and brethren of St. Giles of the Order of St. Lazarus of Jerusalem in England; soon after it appeared that the master of St. Giles' was not carrying out the traditions of the charitable Knights, having "ousted the lepers and put in brethren and sisters of his Order who were not diseased." It is said that all English leper-houses were in some way subject to Burton Lazars, but in truth this was not so. It was the parent-house of cells at Carlton in Moreland, Choseley and Tilton, the property at the former place being charged with the support of four lepers, but whether maintained there or at Burton Lazars is not stated. Spondon (or Locko) was originally subordinate to a French house. In time of war, Edward III ordered that the money hitherto paid over to the foreign superior, should henceforth be given to King's Hall, Cambridge (1347). That same year the master of Burton was also preceptor of "la Maudeleyne," Locko.

30. SEAL OF ST. ANTHONY'S, LONDON

(c) *Monks of St. Anthony.*— The Order of St. Anthony was likewise an offshoot of that of St. John. Two of the hospitals in honour of this saint were definitely under Antonine monks, *viz.* London and Hereford. St. Anthony's, London, was frequently called a preceptory. At first it was "alien," subject to the mother-house of Vienne, but it afterwards became naturalized. It was stated in 1424 that on account of international war and of the Schism (i.e. in the Papacy, 1378-1417) few or none of the French canons had come to England; in 1431 a canon of Vienne was appointed warden, but was subsequently replaced by one of the King's clerks. St. Anthony's, York, was independent of the Order.

(d) *"Alien" Hospitals.*—There were other hospitals sub-ordinate to foreign convents. The Great St. Bernard in Savoy established an offshoot at Hornchurch; Altopassu in Italy maintained St. James', Thurlow; the leper-house near Rye was affiliated to Fécamp. Farley, near Luton, was under Suntingfield by Boulogne; the staff were at one time brethren of the Order of St. William of the Desert.[1] The varying fortunes of the hospital near Charing Cross may be learnt from Dr. Jas. Galloway's *Story of St. Mary Roncevall.* Alien houses had a chequered history, being confiscated in time of war, and most were suppressed before the general Dissolution.

3. *The Friars*

By word and deed, St. Francis preached the duty of serving lepers. "He appointed that the friars of his Order, dispersed in various parts of the world, should for the love of Christ diligently attend the lepers wherever they could be found. They followed this injunction with the greatest promptitude."[2] In England, however, it would appear that there was not that close association between

---

[1] Pat. 37 Hen. III, m. 17.

[2] Chron. & Mem. 4. *Monumenta Franciscana*, vol. i. p. xxv., from " Mirror."

friars and hospitals which existed in Italy. Led by national reformers, the work of tending lazars had long been carried on. The great majority of refuges for them were founded between 1084 and 1224 before the brethren arrived in this country. Speaking of the friars' labours, Green says that "their first work lay in the noisome lazar-houses," and Brewer alludes to "their training for the leper-hospitals," but there seems to be little or no definite record of such service in this country. There were, however, many individual outcasts, who had not the comfort of the hospital, and to these the new-comers may have ministered.

A few hospitals—not for lepers—were indeed appropriated to the Mendicant Orders, or served by them. The association is of the slightest, and usually of short duration. Thus the Bamburgh spital had probably disappeared when Richard II gave its chapel to the Friars Preachers, "in part remuneration for a cross made from the wood of the Holy Cross presented by them to the king " (1382). The Crutched Friars once had some connection with Holy Cross, Colchester. The relation between hospitals and the Bethlehemite and Maturin Orders was closer, and dated from the friars' first century of work. St. Mary of Bethlehem in London was founded upon land belonging to that community, members of which were its original officials. Deeds of 1348 call them "the Order of the Knighthood of St. Mary of Bethlehem"; possibly the link with the Holy Land led them to adopt this military title. Maturin or Trinitarian houses were more akin to the infirmary and pilgrim-hostel than were any other friaries; one-third of their revenue was spent in relieving local poor. Their houses (often called "hospitals") are not included in the present volume, save when they were not merely friaries. For example, Stephen, Archdeacon of Wilts, who was rector and patron of Easton Royal, founded there a house for indigent travellers (1246).[1] The master was a Trinitarian brother, but he was presented by the patron, to whom he and the other priests owed obedience ; in 1287 the same man was minister of Easton and of the house of St. Mary Magdalene by Hertford. St. Laurence's, Crediton, was served by the Hounslow Maturin convent. The almsmen of God's House, Donnington, worshipped in the adjacent Trinitarian Chapel.

To recapitulate : the hospital was a semi-independent institution, subject to royal and episcopal control in matters of constitution, jurisdiction and finance, yet less trammelled in organization than most religious houses. It formed a part of the parochial system, and had also links of one kind and another with monastic life.

[1] Chron. and Mem., 97, pp. 301–6.

CHAPTER XV

DECLINE OF THE HOSPITALS.

" Many hospitals . . . be now for the most part decayed, and the goods and profits of the same, by divers persons, spiritual and temporal, withdrawn and spent to the use of others, whereby many men and women have died in great misery for default of aid, livelihood and succour."

SUCH is the preamble to the Statute for the reformation of hospitals (1414). Responsibility for use and abuse rested with the patron, but more immediately with the warden into whose hands he committed the administration. If this chapter is necessarily devoted to the seamy side of hospital life, let no one suppose that officials were all bad, or even all careless. There were men "in whose purity of conscience the king confides," chosen for "probity, character and knowledge." Yet upright, thrifty and faithful wardens were far from common, and it does not sound hopeful when one and another was appointed "during good behaviour."

Abuses by Patrons.—On the whole hospitals were well-treated by their patrons. Their first founders especially showed both generosity and care, but in many cases the descendants became indifferent and neglected that careful selection of wardens which would have done much to avert evils. But one of the outstanding grievances against patrons was their claim to " maintenance " free of charge whenever they desired it. They and the official "visitors" sometimes used these institutions as hostelries for themselves and their retinue. In the regulations of St. John's, Bridgwater (1219), which the bishop drew up for the manorial lord, it is said :—"We expressly forbid that either the rich or powerful, whether of diocesan rank or ordinary people, or the ministers and stewards of the patron, should lodge, sojourn or be entertained and be a burden." It was rather to be a *Domus libera Dei*, founded only for the poor of Christ. The kings exercised their right to lodge at the Maison Dieu, Dover (see Frontispiece), on their journeys to France. The hospital made a complaint, however, when Edward, eldest son of Edward I, was suddenly lodged there with the chancellor and their suite by the marshal of the household.

The "corrody" was an even greater, because a permanent, burden. The privilege of board and lodging was frequently given away by patrons as a reward for service, but sometimes it was created by grant of the community itself, or sold by greedy officials. This grievance marks a period of decline. Whereas Henry III pensioned his nurses from the Exchequer, Edward I imposed upon hospitals the maintenance of old servants of the Crown, sending a former damsel of the queen-mother and her man-servant to Ospringe to be maintained for life. He appointed only to houses of royal foundation, but his son went further, demanding admission, for example, to the episcopal hospital at Worcester. Caring little that Bishop Wulstan was the founder, Edward II declares that "the hospitals in the realm were founded by the king's progenitors for the admission of poor and weak persons, and especially of those in the king's service who were unable to work." An order is sent to Oxford to admit the king's chaplain to St. John's, finding him and his clerk food, drink, robes, shoe-leather, wood, litter, and a fitting dwelling-place. The Statute of 1314–15 condemned the tyrannous practice of burdening religious houses in this manner.

Edward III was checked in the first year of his reign by a more forcible enactment entitled, "There shall be no more grants of Corrodies at the King's Requests." It states that many have been hitherto grieved by such requests "which have desired them by great threats, for their clerks and other servants, for great pensions and corrodies." Edward declares that he "will no more such things desire, but where he ought"; and henceforth letters patent of this character are less numerous. Where the demand was considered unjust, resentment sometimes took the form of violence. Thus in 1341 the master of St. John's, Oxford, with eight men, assaulted and imprisoned a certain Alice Fitz-Rauf; they carried her off by night with veiled face, threw her into a filthy place, and so left her, having taken away the writ requesting her reception into the hospital. More often a mild protest was made by officials; they acquiesce "of mere courtesy," but beg to be excused in future. Forgetting that the courtesy of one generation may be the custom of the next, the much-abused York hospital submits (1331) provided the demand shall not form a precedent. Fifty years later, a strong-minded master of that house refuses to admit a man at King Richard's command, replying that it was "founded for the bed-ridden and not for the able-bodied."

Cases of oppression "by divers persons spiritual and temporal" are recorded. Even the mitred abbot of St.

Albans was more than once at fault.   In 1223 the pope
commanded him not to lay burdens on the leper women
of St. Mary's by virtue of patronage; and an early
Chancery Proceeding shows that another abbot had
oppressed the poor sick brethren and feeble folk of St.
Julian's. The Rolls of Parliament reveal that an abbot
of Colchester (*temp.* Edward I) withheld the accustomed
pension and tithe from "les povere freres malades" of
St. Mary Magdalene's; by cunning and force he abstracted
their common seal and muniments, and flung their
charters into the fire.   At Durham the inmates of St.
Mary Magdalene's begged redress of grievances (*temp.*
Edward II).   Some previous almoner of the priory, they
declared, had defrauded them of food and clothing; he
had even obtained their muniments by bribing the
guardian with the gift of a fur cloak.   The prior and
convent, however, endorse the petition : " but be it known
that this complaint does not contain truth for the most
part."[1]

Monastic houses were not as zealous as formerly in the
service of the needy.   The great abbey of St. Augustine,
Canterbury, had built and maintained the daughter
hospital of St. Laurence; but in 1341 this is declared to
be of a foundation so weak that it falls very far short of
what is sufficient for their sustenance.   The lay patron of
West Somerton leper-house entrusted its custody to
Butley Priory on condition that the usual number of inmates were maintained.   A later prior withdrew the
victuals and reduced the revenue from £60 to 10 marks,
until after twenty years of neglect, it was said (1399) "the
place where the hospital of old time was is now desolate."

[1] Surtees Soc., 95, p. 238.

Reading Abbey, which once cherished its charitable institutions, treated them ill in later days. When Edward IV travelled through the town (1479), wrongs were reported to him, including "howsys of almes not kept"; the abbot had appropriated the endowments and destroyed the buildings. The prior and convent of Worcester themselves suppressed St. Mary's, Droitwich, in 1536, and "expelled the poor people to their utter destruction."

Contention about patronage was another very serious evil, causing continual litigation. The representatives of the first founder, and those of subsequent benefactors, fell out as to their respective claims. The Crown was ever ready to usurp patronage, on plea of foundation, wardship, voidance of See, etc. Thus from generation to generation, St. Leonard's, York, was claimed by the Crown, whereas much of its property had been a gift to the clergy of the minster by Saxon and Norman sovereigns. A jury of 1246 decided in favour of the Dean and Chapter against royal patronage, but subsequently the Crown recovered it once more. [1] Such disputes were not limited to words. The See of Winchester being void, Edward II nominated a warden to St. Cross, afterwards declaring that he had recovered the presentation against the bishop. The writ was seized and the arm of the king's messenger was broken in the contest. The practice of keeping important posts unfilled was another abuse. A petition made in Parliament concerning this evil (1314-15)[2] maintained that hospitals were impoverished and destroyed during vacancy by temporary guardians, in reply to which, remedy was promised. The warden of St.

[1] Chron. and Mem., 71, iii. 162-5.
[2] Rot. Parl., i. 303.

Nicholas', Pontefract (in Queen Philippa's patronage), complained that during the last voidance, goods had been lost to the value of £200.

Patrons neglected personal supervision. The founders of Ewelme inserted in the statutes one clause concerning the imperative duty of visitation by their representatives ; for, in their experience :—

" Diuerse places of almesse had been yfounded of grete pite and deuocion to be rewled by many ryght resonable rewlis and statutis . . . yitte for defaute of dew execucion of the same and of dew uisitacion and correccion of the brekers of them such sede howses haue bene by myslyuyng and negligence ybought to grete heuynesse and at the last to grete desolacon."

Abuse by Wardens and Officials.—Doubtless wardens were responsible for the chief part of maladministration. Misrule by incapable and untrustworthy men was as frequent as it was fatal. The masters and their deputies had not the moral qualities of wisdom and honesty to fit them for so difficult a post. Master Hugh, warden of St. John and St. Thomas' at Stamford, reduced it to such a condition that he petitioned for liberty to resign (1299). The abbot of Peterborough committed it to a neighbouring rector until "through the blessing of God its most high guardian, it shall arrive at a more flourishing estate." After four months, however, Hugh was restored to office, and matters became worse. He defrauded the poor of their alms, locked up the rooms where strangers and sick should have been accommodated, and neglected the chapel. Meanwhile the mild abbot died ; a new superior interfered and Hugh was again deposed. But having enlisted the mediation of the bishop and archdeacon, he, after a solemn oath of " reformation of all my excesses," was actually entrusted for the third time with the warden-ship.[1]

A more interesting figure is the incorrigible Thomas de Goldyngton—warden of St. Nicholas', Carlisle, and St. Leonard's, Derby—who appears upon the roll as a flagrant offender, although a keen medical man. In 1341 he is perilously near forfeiting his Crown appointments for acting as leech to Scottish rebels; in 1348 he "exercises the office of the surgery of the common-alty [of Derby], neglects the duties of the warden-ship and has dissipated and consumed the goods and alienated the lands to the great decay of the hospital." Thomas had been previously warned after sundry visitations, for instance (1343): "the king com-mands the master at his peril to observe all the rules, constitutions and ordinances of the hospital [Carlisle] in their entirety."[2] It seems doubtful whether this energetic person ever became an exemplary house-surgeon and physician at that mediæval royal infirmary of Derby.

The staff like the warden defied authority, as is shown by visitation reports. The brethren and sisters of St. Nicholas', York, were cross-questioned by the jury. The general evidence was that they were living as they pleased, carrying on business, omitting services, and wandering. The sisters mostly confessed to knowing nothing, but one deposed that the brethren were dis-obedient; whilst the chaplain reported that "all are disobedient and do not observe humility."[3]

Community life was doubtless trying to the temper, and there were occasionally disturbances serious enough

[1] Peck, *Annals of Stanford*, ix. 32.   [2] Pat. 17 Edw. III, pt. i. m. 25 d.
[3] Yorks. Arch. Assn. Record Series, xxiii. Inq. ii. p. 123 et sq.

to reach the king's ears. Throughout the reign of
Edward II, the name of Nicholas de Staple occurs
periodically on Close Rolls. Brother Nicholas first
appears as an official of the Maison Dieu, Ospringe,
who had become intolerable to his fellows. The king,
in response to an appeal, orders him to transfer himself
promptly to St. John's, Oxford, to remain until further
notice : "the king wishing to avoid damages and dangers
and dilapidations of the goods of the hospital that, it is
feared, will arise if Nicholas remain there any longer, on
account of the dissensions between him and the other
brethren." The disturber of the peace retires from parch-
ment publicity for thirteen years, when an order is sent
to retain him for life as a chaplain-brother. Finally,
after a visit of twenty years to Oxford (whither he was
"lately sent to stay for some time"), the life-sentence is
remitted, and he is allowed to return to Ospringe. Two
years before Nicholas vanishes, Oxford becomes a re-
formatory for another Ospringe brother, Thomas Urre,
whom the king caused to be amoved on account of bad
conduct, and because he excited all manner of disputes.
Small wonder that a subsequent visitation of St. John's
should reveal misrule, dissolute living, disobedient and
quarrelsome brothers, sisters and ministers.

A few years later, the household at Newton in Holderness is in a like condition, witness the following entry :—

"Commission . . . to make inquisition and certify the king
whether, as he is informed, William Lulleman, chaplain, (who
pretends to be deaf and for that cause has at the king's request
been admitted to his hospital of Newton to have his sustenance
there,) is sometimes lunatic and mad, and daily stirs up
dissension between the brothers and sisters of the hospital, and

so threatens them and the poor residing there, and bears himself so importunately that he cannot have his conversation among the master and brethren, nor can the brethren and sisters live in peace while he is conversant among them."[1]

The offender was then removed, but imagine with what feelings the warden of Newton received the king's messenger four years later, and unfastening the roll read as follows :—

"To the master and brethren, etc. Request to admit William Lulleman of Bernleye, chaplain, who is detained by severe sickness, and to give him maintenance for life."[1]

Edward III, wishing to guard against the reception of unworthy men, forbade the master of Ospringe to admit any brother without special orders ; and he removed one for notorious excesses and disobediences.[2] St. Thomas', Birmingham, was found in a miserable plight, because "vile reprobates assumed the habit that they might continue their abominable lives *sub velamine Religiositatis*, and then forsake it, and cause themselves to be called hermits."[3] No clerk could be ordained without a "title," but hospitals were apt to offer this to unproved persons, which was fatal to the tone of the household. St. John's, Ely, was usually governed by clergy under rule, but in 1454 the Bishop of Dunkeld was collated to the mastership, because no regulars could be found capable of effecting its recovery from ruin and wretchedness.

The decline of hospitals was largely owing to the fact that many wardens were non-residents and pluralists. It was actually possible to represent one as having died ;

[1] Pat. 16 Edw. III, pt. ii. m. 22 *d*.   Close 20 Edw. III, pt. i. m. 4 *d*.
[2] Close 6 Edw. III, m. 29 *d*.
[3] Lichfield Reg , 1344, Wm. Salt, Soc. i.

several appointments are revoked because the master is discovered to be "alive and well," so that it was by "false suggestion that the office was reported as void." Meanwhile such men were being supported from the hospital funds; an absentee governor of God's House, Southampton, took his share of the best of its goods, living at its expense in a private mansion in the country. The king nominated to Crown foundations men constantly employed on service elsewhere, and a mastership was a mere stepping-stone to preferment.

Not only did clergy hold a benefice and hospital together, but sometimes one man held no less than three hospitals. About 1350, the "lack of clergy by reason of the pestilence" was a serious matter. On this plea the Bishop of Winchester appointed his nephew, a youth in his eighteenth year, as warden at Portsmouth; before long the latter held also the mastership of St. Cross, an archdeaconry, and two canonries. Such practices, begun of necessity, were continued in the century of lax Church life which followed. "One of the boys of the king's chapel" was given the wardenship of Ilford hospital in 1405. The mischief that happened through the plurality and non-residence of parochial and hospital clergy was at length insisted on in Parliament, when in response to the petition of the Commons, reformation was ordered (1425). St. Nicholas', Pontefract, had been "ruled by secular masters, some of whom hardly ever went there"; but in 1438 the management was undertaken by the prior of Nostell.

Dispensations from Rome were answerable for many bad appointments, as is shown by entries in the papal registers of 1427. The master of Newton Garth, for example, was Thomas Bourgchier—"who is in his sixteenth year only, is of a race of great nobles, and holds the said hospital, without cure, wont to be assigned to secular clerks"; moreover it was granted that after his twentieth year he might hold two houses, resigning or exchanging them at will. This youthful official seems to have been following in the footsteps of his ambitious namesake and contemporary, who secured constant promotion and finally "wore the mitre full fifty-one years," and died Primate and Cardinal. Well might the founders of Ewelme almshouse provide that, if possible, the master should be "a degreed man passed thirty winters of age."

Money was at the root of most ill-doing. Among the articles concerning ecclesiastical reform set forth by Henry V and published by the University of Oxford is one (No. 42) *De Reformatione hospitalium*, stating that the poor and needy of the hospitals have been cast out, whilst the officials convert the goods to their own purposes. The roll of "evil dispenders" is a long one.

St. Leonard's, York, is a notable example of the reduction of income by abuse and misfortune. In Canon Raine's lecture upon its history, he gives extracts from its account-books, which are here given in brief. The receipts for the year 1369–1370 amounted to over £1,369, the expenditure to £938. By 1409 the income had fallen to £546. The number of patients declined proportionably, falling from 224 in 1370 to 199 in 1377; and though it rose to 206 in 1423, it was reduced to 127 in 1462. From these facts several conclusions are drawn. The industrial and self-supporting character of the hospital was relaxed because war and pestilence left England shorthanded; land was uncultivated and the hospital lost its thraves of corn. All this is true, but much of the misery lay at the door of the wardens. One unscrupulous master made 500 marks yearly by the traffic in pensions; in 1391 the hospital was "charged with corrodies[1] sold and given, oppressed by the excessive expenditure of its heads, and laden with debt, so that its remaining revenues are insufficient to support master, brethren and sisters or the poor and needy inmates, whereby the hospital is threatened with extinction." On another occasion the poor "Cremettes" (as the inmates were called[2]) made a petition to the king because their master had put the chalices and ornaments of the hospital in pledge, etc. There are preserved in the Record Office a number of documents relating to visitations of this house; these confirm the evidence of contemporary Patent Rolls.

At Gloucester the sale of pensions, jewels, corn, and even of beds, is reported; bed-money was extracted from the poor (20s. from one, and 6s. 8d. from another, who had lost his legs). Part of St. Bartholomew's was unroofed, pigs had access to it, the inmates lacked food and clothing, whilst the utmost depravity prevailed in the household (1380). One extravagant warden of God's House, Portsmouth, spent eight or nine hundred marks yearly, yet kept no hospitality :—

" butt the master will not obey to that and so seruys the powr pepull at hys pleysure, that ys, with uere cowrse bred and smaller drynke, wiche ys contrary to all good consyens."

When a warden was to be elected to the Maison Dieu, Dover (1533), a certain John de Ponte announced to Cromwell :—"The master is dead, and a great benefice

[1] See p. 213.   [2] See p. 242.

is fallen unto the king, with which you may oblige your friends or take it yourself, and I will serve the same." If such was the prevalent tone of those in authority, it is small wonder that Brinklow wrote about the year 1536 :— "I heare that the masters of your hospitals be so fat that the pore be kept leane and bare inough." There is strong censure upon the administration of the London hospitals in the petition for their re-foundation (1538) ; they had been provided to relieve the poor, but "nowe a smalle nomber of chanons, preestes and monks be founden for theyr own synguler proffytt lucre and commodytye onely," and these do not regard "the myserable people lyeing in the streete offendyng every clene person passyng by the way." About the year 1536, Robert Copland, in *The hye way to the Spyttell hous*, says :—

> "For I haue sene at sondry hospytalles
> That many haue lyen dead without the walles
> And for lacke of socour haue dyed wretchedly
> Vnto your foundacyon I thynke contrary.
> Moche people resorte here and have lodgyng,
> But yet I maruell greatly of one thyng
> That in the nyght so many lodge without."

Many charitable institutions were in a languishing condition. Some, of course, had never been endowed, whilst others had only slender resources. Frequently the depreciation in money had caused a shrinkage in a once-adequate revenue ; sometimes the land had been filched away by neighbouring landowners. Writing of Sherborne, Leland observes that the almshouse "stondith yet, but men get most of the land by pece meales." He notes the dilapidated state of houses here and there ; at Beverley "ther was an Hospital of St. Nicholas, but it is dekayid," and at St. Michael's, Warwick, "the Buildings of the House are sore decayed." The condition of St. John's, Lutterworth, described in the Certificate of 1545, was such that no hospitality was kept;[1] there were "noe pore men within the same Hospytal remaynyng or inhabityng; and the house, with the chapel, gretly in decaye and ruyne." At Stoke-upon-Trent, it appeared that there was a priest called master of St. Loye's hospital, but he did not know to what intent or deed of charity it was founded.[2] Frequently the possessions had dwindled until they barely sufficed to support a chaplain, and no charity was distributed. The Certificate of St. John's, Calne, states that abuse is apparent, because there are no paupers, but all profits go to the master; these, however, only amounted to 66*s*. 5*d*. St. John's, Bedford, was worth 20*s*. a year, and "there is found neuer a poore person nor hath not ben by the space of many yercs." In some cases the foundation had entirely dropped out of existence, as at Winchcombe, where Leland notes that "now the Name onely of Spittle remaincth."

The Statute of 1545 stated that it was well known that the governors and wardens of hospitals, or the greatest number of them, did not exercise due authority nor expend the revenues in alms according to the foundation. The avowed object of the Act was " to reduce and bring them into a more decent and convenient order."

---

[1] It had been declining for above a century; a Papal Letter (1435-6) states that for fifty years, on account of the diminution of its fruits, etc., there were no brethren in the hospital.

[2] Aug. Off., Chantry Certificate 40 (36).

CHAPTER XVI

THE DISSOLUTION OF RELIGIOUS HOUSES AND ITS EFFECT UPON HOSPITALS

" The hospital . . . is like to go to utter decay. . . . For my own part I think
often, that those men which seek spoil of hospitals . . . did never read
the twenty-fifth chapter of Matthew ; for if they did, and believed the
same, how durst they give such adventure ?"

(Archbishop Grindal, letter to Burleigh, 1575.)

WHEN the Primate wrote thus to the Lord Treasurer, he added :—"that if any hospitals be abused (as I think some are) it were a more Christian suit to seek reformation than destruction." Although the decline of some hospitals led to the dissolution of many, it by no means follows that such a course was justifiable.

Speaking generally, charities which had outlived their usefulness had already been suppressed before the general Dissolution and their property transferred to other purposes. The leper-houses of Windsor and Huntingdon, for example, were evidently deserted and ruinous when they were annexed to Colleges at Cambridge (1462) ; and the hospitals of Romney, Aynho and Brackley had been appropriated to Magdalen College, Oxford (1481–5) because they were no longer carrying out the founder's intentions. St. John's, Reading, and St. Bartholomew's, Bristol, had already been converted into schools, the latter as recently.as 1532.

In most of the existing hospitals good work was being

PLATE XXIV

AMBULATORY OF ST. LEONARD'S, YORK

done ; the *Valor Ecclesiasticus* and Chantry Surveys show
that money was expended upon useful charities.   Layton's
report of St. Mary's, Leicester, that it was "well kept
and honest men therein" was true of many almshouses
throughout the land.   Where evils are complained of,
they were not so much breaches of morality on the part
of the household, as neglect and wastefulness in administration.   A carefully-regulated commission to inquire
into matters of finance could well have rectified abuses in
ill-managed institutions.   Had justice and magnanimity
held sway instead of rapacity and selfishness, the old
houses of mercy would have been refreshed and their
utility doubled just when a far wider charity was needful
on account of the annihilation of benevolent monasteries.
This was done in some foreign countries.   Through the
protection of Gustavus Vasa, Swedish lazar-houses survived the Reformation.   In Denmark, Dominican and
Franciscan friaries were transformed into hospitals, and
the leper-houses subsequently became places of isolation
for contagious diseases.   In France, where there was no
ecclesiastical upheaval, decayed hospitals were reformed
(1545) and put under the control of the bourgeois class
(1561).

The various Acts of Henry VIII's reign show that the
oppression of the poor was not at first intended.   The
Statute for the suppression of vagrancy (1530–1) approved
the charitable work of hospitals.   One clause in that of
1535–6 required that those who entered into possession of
the lands of religious houses should provide hospitality
and service for the poor as of old.   In the draft for the bill
of 1539 the Commons proposed that the greater monasteries not dissolved should build bede-houses in which

to maintain for life ten poor men over sixty years of age.

Here, indeed, was a golden opportunity to increase the benevolent institutions of the country. Much that was becoming useless might have been transformed into a great and permanent benefit. Charitable relief might have been placed under public control upon a sound religious and financial basis. But reformation too often proved to be mere destruction, as "Mors" shrewdly remarks :—

"Your pretence of putting downe abbeys, was, to amend that was amisse in them. . . . It is amended euen as the deuell amended his dames legge (as it is in the prouerbe) whan he shuld haue set it ryght, he bracke it quyte in peces." [1]

It is evident that the monastic system had been gradually losing its hold on the nation. The idea of partial disendowment had also been working in men's minds, no one foreseeing that the plunder of rich foundations would ultimately lead to the robbery of poor people. In 1410 the Commons petitioned in the Parliament of Westminster that the surplus wealth of ecclesiastics might be transferred to other uses, and that destitute persons might benefit by the provision of new hospitals. Henry IV replied that he would deliberate upon the matter, and although no revised appropriation of funds then took place, he did afterwards suppress certain alien priories, a policy which was followed by Henry V. In 1414 the above proposal was renewed in the Parliament of Leicester, but the astute Chichele undertook that the clergy should supply money for the wars :—"a thrust was made at all

[1] *Complaint of Roderyk Mors*, ch. xiiij.

Abbies," says Fuller, "which this Archbishop, as a skilful Fencer, fairly put by." In the following century Wolsey, not anticipating the wholesale destruction which was to follow, sought to dissolve certain small priories in order to assist educational institutions (1523). A contemporary writer observes that by this precedent "he did make loose in others the conscience towardes those houses."

The people desired the reformation of hospitals and an extension of the system. Sir John Oldcastle's bill in 1414 proposed the foundation of new institutions each to be endowed with one hundred marks yearly. The Commons suggested that money now wasted by churchmen might maintain a standing army and also suffice to provide :—

"an hundred houses of alms, to the relief of poor people . . . with oversight of two true seculars unto every house. And also with provision that every township should keep all poor people of their own dwellers, which could not labour for their living, with condition that if more fell in a town than the town could maintain, then the said almshouses to relieve such townships." [1]

A similar plan was proposed by Brinklow about the year 1542. He probably uttered what was in the minds of many when he suggested measures for the re-distribution of ecclesiastical wealth. One chapter of his *Complaint* contains "A Godly aduisement howe to bestowe the goodes and landes of the Bisshops &c. after the Gospell, with an admonytion to the Rulers, that they loke better upon the hospitals." A part might, he thought, be given in alms to the blind, sick and lame, to free schools, or to needy maidens for marriage portions, etc. Poor-

[1] Fabyan, *Chronicles*, ed. 1811, p. 578.

houses and parish doctors should be provided, and he adds :—

"Item, part of these forsayde goodes may be employed to this use, that in euery hundreth, good towne or citie, certein houses be mainteined, to lodge and kepe pore men in, such as be not able to labour, syck, sore, blind, and lame, and euery one of them to haue wherwith to liue, and to haue poore whole women to minister unto them. . . . Let Physycians and Chyrurgians be founde in euery suche town or cyte, where such houses be, to loke uppon the Poore in that Town, and in all other Joyninge unto it and they to lyue uppon their stipend onely, without taking any penny of their pore, uppon payne of lousing both his eares and his stipend also."

Henry VIII proposed to the Commons very much what their predecessors had suggested to Henry IV and Henry V, omitting, nevertheless, the clause relating to a hundred new almshouses. If they would grant him the religious houses, these should not be converted to private uses, and the army would be strengthened and taxes reduced. No provision, however, was made for these projects, but the king was put in possession of the monasteries, and then of the chantries, hospitals and free chapels. The Parliament, in granting the hospitals to the king and his heirs for ever, expressed its confidence in the royal benevolence towards them and desire for their improvement :—

"The Kinges Highnes of his most godlie and blessed disposicion entendeth to have the premisses used and exercised to more godlie and uertuouse purposes and to reduce and bringe them into a more decent and convenient order, for the commoditie and welthe of this his realme and for the suertie of the subjects."

When the king went to prorogue Parliament, he seems to

have alluded in his "Oration," as set forth by Foxe, to
the above expression of their hopes and wishes :—

"Surely if I, contrary to your expectation, should suffer the
ministers of the church to decay ; . . . or poor and miserable
people to be unrelieved ; you might say that I, being put in so
special a trust, as I am in this case, were no trusty friend to
you, nor charitable man to mine even-christened, [fellow Chris-
tians], neither a lover of the public wealth, nor yet one that
feared God, to whom account must be rendered of all our
doings. Doubt not, I pray you, but your expectation shall be
served more godly and goodly than you will wish or desire, as
hereafter you shall plainly perceive."

But although Henry VIII thus professed to remember the higher court of justice, his conduct gave no
evidence of it. Brinklow ventured upon a reminder in
A Supplication of the Poore Commons,[1] published shortly
after the king's speech :—

"We beseke you (most deare Soueraine) euen for the hope
you haue in the redemption of Christ, that you call to remem-
braunce that dreadfull daye, whan your Highnesse shall stande
before the judgement seat of God in no more reputation then
one of those miserable creatures which do nowe daylye dy in
the stretes for lack of theyr dwe porsion."

He continues to point out in forcible language that the
portion due by God's ordinance to poor impotent folk, the
lame, blind, lazar and sore members of Christ—who once
had been lodged in hospitals and almshouses—is now given
by the king and his nobles to "reward those gnatonical
elbowhangers, your chaplaines." In spite of the vehement
abuse of parasitical clergy in which the above writer in-
dulges, it was in the main lay-people rather than churchmen who divided the spoils. Fuller—who quaintly

[1] Early Eng. Text Soc., 77.

writes that "this king made three meals, or (if you will)
one meal of three courses, on Abbey-lands, besides what
Cardinal Wolsey (the king's taster herein) had eaten
beforehand "—goes on to say " yet surely more tender-
nesse was used to hospitalls," and finds " very few of
them finally suppressed." But hospital endowments did
certainly form a substantial dish at Henry's feast, to which
many royal favourites were bidden. Some fell with the
smaller priories (1536), a few with the greater houses
(1539), and others were extinguished under the Act for
dissolving chantries, free chapels, hospitals, and guilds
(1545); a further Act of confiscation marked the first year
of Edward VI's reign (1547). In some places charities
were indiscriminately swept away. A manuscript history
of Gorleston records, for example, that "Henry VIII
ordered that all the premises of . . . the Hospitals of St.
James, St. John, St. Bartholomew, St. Luke, and the
church and hospital of St. Nicholas . . . should be sold."
No consistent plan was followed, but—whether under
ecclesiastical or lay control—charities were destroyed or
spared at will. Speaking generally, institutions in private
hands were suppressed, those in the possession of cor-
porate bodies, retained.

Few houses of Crown patronage escaped. The Commissioners, announcing to Cromwell (1537) the dissolution
of certain northern monasteries, add :—" We have also
altered the howse of Sancte Leonerdes in Yourke, after
suche ordre and fassion as we trust shall appeir to your
lordship to be to the kinges honour and contentacion." [1]
In truth the alteration meant annihilation for St. Leonard's;
and St. Nicholas' hospital in the same city also disap-

[1] Camden Soc., 1843, p. 166.

PLATE XXV

ST. LEONARD'S, YORK

peared. In London, the Savoy, fresh from the hand of the builder, was dissolved. The sisters of St. James', Westminster, surrendered (receiving life-pensions), whereupon "the king builded there a goodly Mannor, annexing thereunto a Parke."[1] The Maison Dieu, Dover, a rich foundation with good buildings near the quay, was declared suitable for a victualling yard (1544) which it eventually became.

Hospitals attached to a cathedral or see were usually, but not always, spared. In the bishopric of Durham, for example, the houses of Sherburn and Greatham survived, but neither Kepier nor the bishop's hospital at Northallerton. God's House, Portsmouth, was surrendered and became an armoury; in the Library of the Society of Antiquaries is a document of 1547 concerning "Munycions within the Churche at Goddeshouse."[2] St. John's, Ely, was spared, yet only for a while. The episcopal hospitals at Bath and Norwich remained in use, but under the municipality.

If directly dependent upon a monastic house, the fate of a hospital was practically sealed. Take, for instance, the case of St. James', near the gate of Lewes Priory. From the monastery now demolished thirteen men and one woman had had all their living; wherefore Peter Thompson and the bedefolk begged relief (1538).[3] Hospitals of lay-foundation which had been subsequently placed under monastic supervision, but with distinct endowments, fell as forming part of the sequestrated property. In some cases the Crown kept up charities for a time. The

[1] Stow, *Survey of City of Westminster*, bk. vi. p. 4.
[2] MS. Soc. Antiq. cxxix. f. 274.
[3] Cal. of Letters and Papers, Hen. VIII, 13. i. 383.

return of pensions in 1552 shows that sums were paid out of the tenements of Nostell Priory to inmates of St. Nicholas', Pontefract. The poor dwelling in the so-called "Kings Majesty's almshouses" at Glastonbury (formerly abbey-pensioners) were also granted weekly allowances. This was generous, for although Henry VIII and Edward VI were fond of giving their names to charitable institutions, they too often gave little else.

The two Statutes authorizing the dissolution of Chantries, etc. (1545–1547) extinguished or reduced in means, some houses of charity. When an almshouse was spared, the Crown sometimes demanded an acknowledgment; at Beverley the rents in 1545 include a new item of £4 paid by the town to the king and queen for the Trinity Maison Dieu. "Hospitals" were not rightfully within the scope of the second Act. Thus Foster's almshouse in Bristol being, as the certificate states :—

"for the helpynge relief and comforte of a certeyn nomber of poore people there to contynue and haue their liuinge from tyme to tyme for euer, is without the compasse of the statute and the King's Majestie not entitled thereunto by force of the same."

In the preface to the *Yorkshire Chantry Surveys*, it is stated that most, if not all, of the hospitals which were returned on the certificates there printed were left undissolved, save that in a few cases funds were transferred to educational purposes. Testimony is borne in 1552 to the usefulness of one of the Pontefract almshouses, where fourteen bedemen were supported :—

"Thes persons be called cremettes and le pore and agyd people, and placyd in a howse, callyd Seynt Nycoles Hospytell,

PLATE XXVI

ABINGDON ALMSHOUSES

and when any of them dyeth another ys placyd in the dedes roome, and ys very convenyent to be contynuyd, as well for the helpe of the pore and agyd people of the towne as for others."

In many places, however, endowments were seized by virtue of this Act. A sixteenth-century MS. states :—

"Item, there ar within the towne and parishe of Taunton xliiij^{or} almshowses full of poore people whereunto there was certen Lande belonginge which by the Suppression of Chaunteries was taken awaie soe that now thinhabitaunts doe beare the whole burden them selues."[1]

The dissolution of fraternities also affected the maintenance of the poor. Of almshouses associated with gilds at Colchester, Stratford and Abingdon, none survived save the latter, which was incorporated by Edward VI. St. John's hospital in Winchester outlived the fraternity annexed to it. St. Thomas', York, which had been united to Corpus Christi Gild, weathered the storm, its officials afterwards diplomatically inviting the mayor and aldermen "to be brether with us in the same hospital."

Those houses were fairly secure which were already the property of municipal authorities, who indeed received fresh patronage at this time (e.g. at Canterbury, Norwich, Bath)—a policy which obtained the support of the great middle-class. At this crisis the public-spirited action of more than one corporation saved charities from extinction. In the Survey for Wiltshire (1548), quoted by Mr. Leach in *English Schools at the Reformation*, the following entry is made :—"There is an Hospitall within Marleborowe . . . wiche the sayd mayre and commons humbly desyre the Kingis Highnes and his mooste Honourable councell

---

[1] B.M. Add. 30277, f. 3.

to conuerte into a Free scole for the inducement of youth."
But before the townsmen obtained their school, it was
necessary to sell the stock of plate intended to pass from
mayor to mayor, "as hath byn credibly reported," says a
book formerly belonging to the Chamber. To cite
another example, the corporation of Bristol received
St. Mark's as a "gift," that is, the sum of £1000 was
paid into the treasury of the Court of Augmentations,
besides an annual rent of £20. The city obtained part of
the property in return on easy terms, for, as Fuller
would observe, there were "many good bargains, or
rather cheap pennyworths, bought of abbey lands." It is
said that more than half the purchase-money was raised
by the sale of church plate.

In London, the citizens, under the leadership of the
Lord Mayor, made an urgent petition to Henry VIII
(1538) for the re-foundation of certain hospitals :—

"for the ayde and comforte of the poore sykke, blynde,
aged and impotent persones, beyng not able to helpe theym-
selffs, nor hauyning any place certeyn whereyn they may be
lodged, cherysshed and refresshed tyll they be cured and holpen
of theyre dyseases and syknesse. For the helpe of the said
poore people, we enforme your grace that there be nere and
wᵗyn the cytye of London three hospytalls or spytells, comenly
called Saynt Mary Spytell, Saynt Bartylmews Spytell, and
Saynt Thomas Spytell, . . . fownded of good devočon by
auncyent fathers, and endowed wᵗ great possessions and rents."

The petitioners promise that if the king will grant the
governance of these hospitals to them with their possessions, they shall be reformed and their usefulness increased :—

"A greatter nombre of poore nedy sykke and indygent persones shalbe refresshed maynteyned comforted fownde heled

and cured of theyre infyrmytyes frankly and frely, by phisicions, surgeons, and appotycaryes, . . . so that all impotent per- sones not able to labor shall be releued . . . and all sturdy beggars not willing to labor shalbe punisshed, so that w^t Godd's grace fewe or no persones shalbe seene abrode to begge or aske almesse."

It appears that no response was made to this appeal until 1544. St. Mary's had been dissolved, never to be restored, St. Thomas' was deserted, and St. Bartholo- mew's, "vacant and altogether destitute òf a master and all fellows or brethren." After six years' delay, the king heeded the petition. He was exceedingly anxious to emphasize his compassionate character and eager desire for the improvement of hospitals. If the petitioners had invited him to win the name of conservator, defender and protector of the poor, he writes as though he were indeed all these :—

"We being of the same [hospital] so seised, and, divine mercy inspiring us, desiring nothing more than that the true works of piety and charity should not be abolished there but rather fully restored and renewed according to the primitive pattern . . . and the abuses, in long lapse of time lamentably occurring, being reformed, we have endeavoured . . . that henceforth there be comfort to the prisoners, shelter to the poor, visitation to the sick, food to the hungry, drink to the thirsty, clothes to the naked, and sepulture to the dead adminis- tered there . . . we determine to create, erect, found and establish a certain hospital."

By virtue of these letters-patent the name of the ancient institution was to be "The House of the Poor in West Smithfield of the foundation of King Henry VIII." The noble "founder" is commemorated by the gateway and by a portrait in the Common Room ; whilst a window in the hall depicts Sir R. Gresham receiving the "foundation-charter."

If the "creation" of St. Bartholomew's—after above four hundred years of usefulness—was due to Henry VIII, its preservation was due almost entirely to the good citizens of London. Its former possessions being now vested in the Crown, the king agreed by an Act of Common Council to endow it to the extent of 500 marks a year (about £333). The citizens—"thinkying it for their partes rather to litle then enough"—gladly met the offer with a similar sum annually; they also raised nearly £1000 for initial expenses and opened the repaired and refitted hospital for one hundred patients. They agreed henceforth to buy and provide all manner of apothecary's ware, and all that was necessary for making salves and all other things touching physic or surgery, for the healing of inmates. From this time onwards the citizens interested themselves in this great institution which they supported nobly. It did not become a municipal hospital, but was under the guidance of the Lord Mayor and Governors.

By the same covenant the king "gave" St. Mary's of Bethlehem to the city. Stow says:—"It was an Hospitall for distracted people. . . . the Mayor and Communalty purchased the patronage thereof with all the landes and tenementes thereunto belonging, in the yeare 1546, the same yeare King Henry the eight gave this Hospitall unto the Cittie." In other words, the citizens bought back that which had already been in the guardianship of the city for about two hundred years.

In "The Ordre of St. Bartholomewes"[1] drawn up in

---

[1] Early Eng. Text Soc. Extra liii. App. xvi.

1552, a report is given, so that all might know how things were administered and support the work. During the preceding five years, eight hundred persons had been discharged healed, and ninety-two had died. The charity had been carried on in spite of great difficulties, and now there was a design to increase it :—

"The Citie of their endlesse good wil toward this most necessarie succour of their pore brethren in Christ, . . . wyshe al men to be most assuredly perswaded, that if by any meanes possible thei might, they desire to enlarge the benefyght to a thousand."

A wish is expressed that all almoners and houses of alms might be stirred up to do likewise "at this tyme namely, when the mysery of the poore moste busily semeth to awake." This same year the manor of Southwark was purchased and St. Thomas' repaired, so that whereas it lately accommodated forty sick, it was reopened with 260 beds for the aged, sick and sore. This "Hospitall of great receite for the poore, was suppressed but againe newly founded and indowed by the benevolence and charitie of the citizens," says Stow. King Edward's letters-patent (1551) describe the miserable condition of the sick poor lying and begging in the streets, "to their no small grief and pain and to the great infection and molesting of his subjects. The king desiring the health of the citizens in general no less than the cure of the sick, therefore grants permission to the mayor and corporation to undertake the work."

The work of the re-founded houses of St. Bartholomew, St. Thomas, and Bethlehem was supplemented in 1553 by Christ's Hospital for fatherless children, and Bridewell for the correction of idle vagabonds. These institutions were provided partly from Edward VI's private purse and partly from the dissolved Savoy Hospital and Grey Friars. Their initiation was due to the influence of Ridley, Bishop of London, who took counsel with the Lord Mayor as to the condition of the poor, and reported it to the young king. With the charitable provision after 1547 we are not, however, concerned, and only the ultimate effect of the general Dissolution remains to be shown.

For, happily, this volume is no history of obsolete institutions. The heritage of the past is to a certain extent ours to-day, and we can rejoice in the uninterrupted beneficence of St. Bartholomew's which receives in the twentieth century as in the twelfth, "languishing men grieved with various sores." Words spoken by the Prince Consort in reference to another foundation at once ancient and modern, are equally true of St. Bartholomew's and of the sister-hospital of St. Thomas:—

"It holds to this day the same honourable position in the estimation of the country which it did in the time of its first formation, exemplifying the possibility, in this happy country, of combining the general progress of mankind with a due reverence for the institutions, and even forms, which have been bequeathed to us by the piety and wisdom of our forefathers."[1]

More has come down to us than perhaps we realize. Canterbury retains three venerable houses of alms. St. Mary's, Chichester; St. Nicholas', Salisbury; and St. Giles', Norwich, are still peaceful retreats in old age. In the city of Winchester—St. Cross is not merely a monument of unchangeable usefulness, but increased funds

[1] Speeches, p. 104.

enable it to give pensions in various parts of England to the value of £1200; the site of St. Mary Magdalene's is occupied by an isolation hospital, a portion of the original

St John's Hospital

31. GATEWAY OF ST. JOHN'S, CANTERBURY

endowment maintaining a small almshouse; while St. John's has been greatly enlarged.

Even where no ancient stones bear witness, modern bricks or coins may be eloquent, for a part of the original endowment may be applied to a renewed institution. For instance, the funds of the demolished leper-hospital at Chichester are applied to a modern infirmary. Sums arising from the "Lazarhouse Charity" (Launceston) or "Magdalene Lands" (in Devonshire) are now and again expended upon food and fuel for the poor. And although York shows in the fragment of St. Leonard's but a memorial of fallen greatness, what appears to be a remnant of its rich revenues is still paid to thirty-one poor people, for the curious name "Cremitt Money" is surely derived from the inmates of that hospital, commonly known as "cremettes" (a corruption of *eremites*). The connection is clear enough in the case of the "Almsmen of St. Bartholomew" at Oxford, and "St. Nicholas' Almsmen" at Carlisle, who represent former occupants of leper-houses. Again, the relation may be intimate even when a modern charity perpetuates the ancient only by force of association and memory. St. Leonard's, Bedford, was revived in 1889, the original charity for the sick, para-lysed, and lepers having lapsed at the Dissolution. No endowments survived, but it is supported locally. The present foundation is an association of religious and philanthropic persons who supply nourishing diet to invalids in their homes and assist them when convales-cent. Thus, although the sole trace of old buildings is onè pillar-shaft serving as a sun-dial, the charity itself is a living memorial of the ancient hospital.[1]

Finally, St. Leonard's, Sudbury, and Sherburn House, Durham, illustrate to what advantage the old order may yield place to new. The income of St. Leonard's, originally designed for three lepers, supplemented by

[1] Communicated by the Secretary.

voluntary contributions, is applied to the maintenance of fourteen beds for sick patients, the hospital being fully equipped with modern medical and surgical appliances whilst maintaining the former religious traditions. Sherburn, once a home for sixty-five outcasts, was transformed into an almshouse when the scourge was removed. In that "haunt of ancient peace" many are now sheltered in time of age or chronic sickness ; they worship daily in the old church ; they are visited and cheered by a master who has devoted his life to them, and whose work is a labour of love. The revenues and practical benefits of the hospital continue to increase ; a modern dispensary is fitted up there, by means of which hundreds of out-patients from the neighbouring city are relieved.

"It is this renewing of itself which brings to English institutions greatness, stability, and permanence. Thus the great traditions of the past can be happily, wisely, and usefully combined with the highest aspirations of the present and future."

PART TWO

NOTES ON
HOSPITAL PATRON SAINTS

"Hospitals . . . founded to the honour of God and of His glorious Mother." (Parliament of Leicester.)

THE words "**God's House**," and "**Maison Dieu**" were familiar enough in mediæval England. A hospital was the house of God, for therein Christ was received in the person of the needy :—"I was a stranger and ye took Me in, sick, and ye visited Me." It was also built in His Name and to His honour, for the principle underlying all dedications was, says Hooker, that they "were consecrated unto none but the Lord only." But with God's Name that of one of His saints was often associated, and by this the hospital was commonly called ; thus a charter of Basingstoke ran :—"I have given and granted to God and to the glorious Virgin His Mother, and to my venerable patron St. John the Baptist the house called St. John."

The Holy Trinity.—Hospitals bearing this title are not very numerous, though it often occurs as first of a group. There are a few single dedications early in the thirteenth century, which may be partly attributed to the institution of the Feast of Trinity by St. Thomas of Canterbury. Two hundred years later it was a fairly common dedication for almshouses. The seals depict various symbols. The "majesty" representing the Three Persons, occurs at Walsoken; the Almighty seated upon a rainbow (Salisbury); our Lord enthroned (Berkeley); whilst a triple cross ornaments the Dunwich seal. Bonde's almsmen at Coventry bore upon their gowns "the cognizance of the Trinity."

The Holy Saviour; Christ; Corpus Christi.—The Second Person of the Godhead is seldom commemorated, but the dedication to the Blessed Trinity was regarded as synonymous, for the almshouse at Arundel occurs indifferently as Christ's or Holy Trinity. The Maison Dieu at York, commonly called Trinity, was properly that of the Holy Jesus—or Christ—and the Blessed Virgin, and the chantry certificate is headed " The Hospital of the Name of Jhesus and Our Blessyd Ladye." St. Saviour was the invocation of houses at Norwich and Bury, and the fair in connection with the latter charity was held at the feast of the Transfiguration. " Y^e masendew of Chryste" at Kingston-upon-Hull was originally " Corpus Christi," but it is remarkable to find that rarely-preserved dedication-name upon an Elizabethan table of rules. The seal of the Holloway hospital, near London, shows Christ (with the orb) and St. Anthony.

The Holy Ghost.—This sacred title, closely associated with the mediæval charities of Germany and famous in Rome, was rarely used in England. At Sandon (Surrey) was a hospital " commonly called of the Holy Ghost,"[1] though an alternative name occurs. A hidden dedication is sometimes revealed, for the houses usually known as St. Thomas', Canterbury, St. Margaret's, Taunton,

[1] Pat. 14 Hen. VI, pt. i. m. 4.

St. John's, Warwick, and St. John's, Hereford, are mentioned once in documents as being built in honour of the Holy Ghost as well as of the saints named; all the above instances refer to the years 1334–1353. At Lyme there was the suggestive commemoration of the " Blessed Virgin and Holy Spirit."

The Annunciation; St. Gabriel; St. Michael; The Holy Angels.—Two fourteenth-century foundations at Leicester and Nottingham commemorate the Annunciation of the Blessed Virgin. The seal of the former house depicts St. Gabriel delivering his salutation. A kindred thought underlies the dedication " to our lady St. Mary the Mother of Christ and to St. Gabriel the Archangel " at Brough. (It is noteworthy that the parish church was St. Michael's.) Another institution, built by Bishop Bronescombe of Exeter, who had a special devotion to the Archangel, left its name to Clist Gabriel. The more ancient dedication to St. Michael occurs at Whitby and elsewhere in Yorkshire. Michael de la Pole founded an almshouse at Kingston-upon-Hull, partly in honour of " St. Michael the Archangel and all archangels, angels and holy spirits." A fraternity at Brentford commemorated " The Nine Orders of Holy Angels," and in the Valor it is termed *hospitalis Angelorum.*

The Blessed Virgin; The Three Kings of Cologne; The Holy Innocents.—The statement referring to hospitals in general as " founded to the honour of God and of His glorious Mother" explains more than one difficult point. First, numerous as are the dedications to St. Mary, they are fewer than those of some other saints, for instance, St. Mary Magdalene. Secondly, a certain number of houses are set down as having two patrons, yet the second

PLATE XXVII

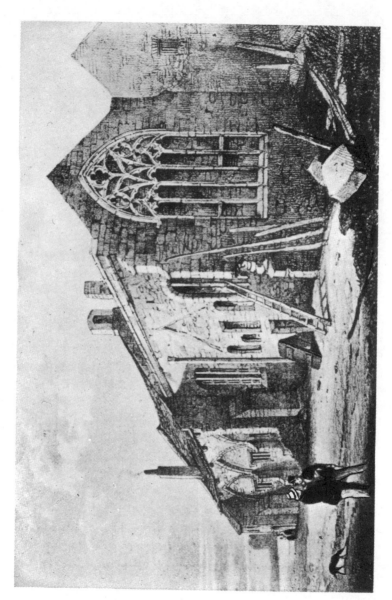

HOSPITAL OF ST. MARY THE VIRGIN, NEWCASTLE-UPON-TYNE

saint appears to eclipse the Blessed Virgin ; that of Newport in Essex (given as St. Mary and St. Leonard) usually
bore St. Leonard's name and kept its fair on his festival.
In many such cases there was in truth no double dedication ; and although gifts were made by charter to found a
hospital at Bristol "in honour of God, St. Mary and
St. Mark", later documents omit the formula and call
it "the house of St. Mark."

On the other hand many houses were dedicated
solely in honour of the Blessed Virgin, including five
important institutions in London alone. In addition
to St. Mary (without Bishopsgate), St. Mary of Ron-
cevalles (Charing Cross) and Our Lady of Elsyng
(Cripplegate), there was St. Mary's hospital or the House
of Converts,—a witness to the doctrine of the Incarnate
Christ,—and St. Mary of Bethlehem, a name chosen on
account of the founder's intense reverence for the holy
Nativity. Stow quotes the deed of gift made by Simon,
"son of Mary" :—

"having speciall and singulor deuotion to the Church of the
glorious Virgin at Bethlehem, where the same Virgin brought
forth our Saviour incarnate . . . and where [to] the same
Child to us there borne, the Chiualrie of the heavenly Company
sang the new Hymne *Gloria in excelsis Deo.*"

The Holy Innocents were commemorated in the ancient
leper-house outside Lincoln. The existing chapel of an
almshouse in Bristol built "in the honour of God and
the Three Kings of Cologne" (Leland's *fanum trium
regum*) is the sole witness in the way of dedication in
England to the veneration of the Magi. The title is said
to have been the choice of an Abbot of Tewkesbury
at the close of the fifteenth century.

Holy Cross and Holy Sepulchre.—Names commemorating the Death and Burial of the Saviour are not infrequent. The history of St. Cross, Winchester, touches that of the Knights of Jerusalem, with whom both name and badge are connected. (See p. 207.) On the common seal the master and priests are shown kneeling at the foot of the Cross ; the descent from the Cross is depicted upon the walls of the church. This dedication is also appropriately associated with the hospitals usually known as St. Mary Magdalene's at Stourbridge and near Bath, the fairs of which houses were held on the festivals of the Invention and Exaltation of the Holy Cross. The chapel of St. Thomas of Acon in Cheapside—under the Knights Templars—was dedicated to St. Cross. The church attached to St. Bartholomew's, Smithfield, was probably named out of veneration for the relics of "the tree of life" which the founder used in healing (see p. 95) ; and once exemptions were granted "out of the king's reverence for the Holy Cross, in honour of which the church of the hospital of St. Bartholomew is dedicated."[1]

The connection between St. Helen and the Holy Cross is best told in reference to the hospital at Colchester. Although authentic records only carry its history back to 1251, an illustrious antiquity is claimed in an episcopal indulgence purporting to be issued about 1406. The tradition is quoted (but with modernized spelling) from the *Antiquarian Repertory* :—

"Moreover, in the year of our Lord 670, Constantine, the son of the blessed and holy woman Saint Elyn, sent his mother unto Jerusalem to inquire of the Holy Cross that our Saviour Christ Jesu died upon, likewise as it was shewed to him by

[1] Pat. 16 Hen. VI, pt. ii. m. 17.

token in the air and also by revelation of the Holy Ghost. Then the holy woman, seeing the Will of Almighty God, departed out of the town of Colchester where she was born (there where the said hospital is founded in the honour of Almighty God, the holy Cross and St. Elyn) and took her journey unto Jerusalem and there . . . did win the same Cross. . . . Then the holy victorious woman gave laud and loving to God and took one part of the Holy Cross and closed it with gold and sent it to her hospital to Colchester evermore to be abiding, with her ring, her girdle, and her purse, with other 24 curious reliques."

Finally, after relating a visit of St. Thomas of Canterbury to that house, the story of the relic, inciting to devotion, pilgrimage visits and contributions, is brought up to date :—

" Also in the year of our Lord 1401, there came thieves unto the hospital by night and brake up the locks where the glorious relique was, and took it away . . . then they took the blessed Holy Cross (as it was, closed in gold the weight of 21 ounces) and cast it into the pond, but it would not sink . . . and so the folks that did pursue took it up and brought it home to the place again."

This Colchester foundation was associated with the gild of St. Cross (p. 18) and other gilds of that name maintained charities at Stratford-on-Avon, Abingdon and Hedon. In the latter place the hospital of St. Sepulchre gave its title to Newton St. Sepulchre. There were pilgrim-houses at Nottingham and Stamford with the same dedication.

St. John Baptist, St. Mary Magdalene and St. Lazarus.— The cult of these saints is intertwined with the history of the Religious Military Orders of Jerusalem. The work of the Knights Hospitallers was to care for sick and needy pilgrims. They maintained two important infirmaries at Jerusalem, St. John's for men, and St. Mary Magdalene's for women. Grateful guests returning from pilgrimage bore the report of these houses far and wide ; thus it came to pass that, throughout Europe, hospitals unconnected with the order were founded, and by force of association consecrated in honour of these saints. That of St. John Baptist, Lechlade, is referred to in one deed as "St. John of Jerusalem." Such "houses of St. John" were usually for travellers. One writer remarks that almost every town had a place to accommodate the sick and wayfarers, and that they "were invariably dedicated to St. John Baptist in connection with his wandering life." Although this saint did not monopolize the protection of strangers, he was certainly adopted as patron by some hundred hospitals (excluding commanderies of the Order of St. John).

Lanfranc's foundation in his cathedral city was placed by him under the patronage of St. John Baptist, on one of whose festivals (August 29) the archbishop had been consecrated. The hospital at Thetford kept a fair on that day called "The Decollation of St. John Baptist"; but the lepers of Harting celebrated their wake on June 24, "The Nativity of St. John Baptist." The strange customs connected with this latter festival were especially observed in houses of which he was patron ; in memory of St. John Baptist it was usual at Sherborne for a garland to be hung up on Midsummer Eve at the door of St. John's, which the almsmen watched till morning.

Seals usually depict the saint with his symbol of the Holy Lamb ; sometimes he points to a scroll (*Ecce Agnus Dei*). In two instances (Banbury and Bristol) a patriarchal cross, one of the symbols of the Knights Hospitallers, is shown ; this double-armed cross is likewise found on the gable of St. John's, Northampton, where it is considered a unique architectural feature.

St. Lazarus became the guardian of lepers partly through the influence of the Order whose aim was to relieve the sick, and especially the leprous, members of their brotherhood. They were introduced into England in Stephen's reign, when the hospital of the Blessed Virgin and St. Lazarus was founded at Burton, afterwards known as Burton St. Lazarus. The seal of this house depicts a bishop carrying in one hand a fork or trident,[1] in the other a book; Dugdale ascribes the figure to St. Augustine, but Mr. de Gray Birch attributes the mitred effigy to St. Lazarus, traditional Bishop of Marseilles. Of the other dedications to St. Lazarus little is known, some being of doubtful authenticity.

The question naturally arises—why were lepers called *lazars* in common parlance, and why was *Lazarus* chosen as their patron? A curious confusion of ideas is revealed. The original person intended was he who lay full of sores at the rich man's gate. The banner of a Flemish lazaretto displays scenes from the life of this Lazarus, who appears clad as a mediæval leper, and carries a clapper.[2] The same idea was familiar in England. David of Huntingdon having founded a leper-house, Aelred the chronicler prays at his death :—" Receive his soul into the bosom of Abraham with Lazarus whom he did not despise but cherished." A similar allusion occurs in Langland's

---

[1] Probably intended to represent the clappers; compare design on seal of St. Mary Magdalene's, Winchester.

[2] Lacroix, *Military and Religious Life*, 353.

Piers the Plowman : "And ich loked in hus lappe · a lazar lay ther-ynne." The *lazarus ulceribus plenus* of the allegory, however, soon became associated with the historical Lazarus of Bethany. Thus a colony of north-country lepers dwelt in Sherburn hospital founded "in

honour of the Saviour, the Blessed Virgin, St. Lazarus, and his sisters Mary and Martha." This dedication was abbreviated into St. Mary Magdalene, and the principal altar was in her honour. St. Mary Magdalene, universally identified with St. Mary of Bethany, was thus commonly involved in the curious double personality of St. Lazarus. In England, she was the most popular of leper-patrons, no one save St. Leonard attaining to half her number of dedications. We are told that St. Lazarus held this place in France, St. James in central Europe, St. George in the North ; but in England, the Magdalene was supreme. The "Maudlin-house" was almost synonymous with leper-hospital. Place-names testify to the devotion of our forefathers to St. Mary Magdalene, and in several places "Mawdlyn lands" mark the site of a leper-colony.

32. SEAL OF ST. MARY MAGDALENE'S, BRISTOL

St. Bartholomew had sixteen hospitals in England, chiefly in the South. An old hymn, quoted by Dr. Norman Moore, describes the Apostle's medical powers. "Lepers he cleanses"—and to him were dedicated ancient lazar-houses at Rochester, Oxford, Dover, etc. "The sick he restores "—the Apostle having appeared to Rahere, sick with fever in Rome (perhaps, it is suggested, upon the island of St. Bartholomew in the Tiber), he builds upon his recovery a house of healing near London, which for nearly eight hundred years has been a place of restoration. "The lunatic are made whole"—and the *Book of the Foundation* tells of such a cure at St. Bartholomew's:—

"ther yn a shorte space his witte was recoueryd, where a litill tyme he taried, blessyng God that to his apostles hath uouchsaf to commytte his excellent power, to hele syke, to clense lepers, and to caste owte feendys."

At St. Bartholomew's, Oxford, a relic was treasured, namely, a portion of the saint's skin. The legend of his martyrdom is depicted upon the seal of the Gloucester foundation, and he is shown knife in hand on the Rochester seal. (Tail-piece of this chapter.)

St. James.—Of all the Apostles, St. James has the largest number of hospitals, namely, twenty-six partly or wholly dedicated to him. This is doubtless due to the fact that his shrine at Compostella was the goal of Christendom, and the miracles of "Santiago" world-famous. St. James', Northallerton, was named as the direct result of a pilgrimage to Compostella in the year 1200 by Philip, Bishop of Durham. Several ports (Dunwich, Seaford, Shoreham) had houses in his honour. Hospital seals depict the saint as a pilgrim, with water-bottle and scrip, whilst one shows the token of escallop shells.

St. James & St. John.—Whereas there was apparently no parish in England commemorating the brother-apostles, three hospitals (Aynho, Royston, and Brackley) bore this double name. About Brackley, indeed, there is some

uncertainty. It occurs as "St. John and St. James"
(1226), "St. James and St. John Apostle" (1227); but
also as "St. John Baptist" (1301, 1471). The seal shows
two figures, of which one scantily clad and bearing a
palm suggests the Baptist.

St. John Evangelist & St. John Baptist appear in con-
junction at Exeter, Sherborne, Newport Pagnell, Northampton, and Leicester. The original and usual title at
Exeter was St. John Baptist; but in 1354 Bishop John de
Grandisson, a benefactor, mentions "St. John the Baptist
and Fore-runner of Christ and St. John His Evangelist
and Apostle." The seal of Northampton shows both
saints with their symbols, and the appellations BAPTI and
EWA are placed over the figures. On the Leicester seal
the eagle of the Apostle is shown, and the scroll in its
talons may represent the *Ecce Agnus Dei*. When

"St. John" occurs, the dedication
commonly proves to be to the Baptist;
and even where the Evangelist is expressly named, some later document
reverts to his namesake, e.g. Blyth,
Burford, Castle Donington, Ciren-
cester.

St. Matthew, St. Mark, and **St. Luke**
were not uncommemorated. "The
house of St. Matthew" at Maiden
Bradley, which occurs on one Patent
Roll (1242), was commonly called
St. Mary's; the double dedication is

33. SEAL OF ST. MARK'S,
BRISTOL

mentioned in the Obituary Roll of
Prior Elchester of Durham (1484),
viz. : *Eccles. B. Mar. et S. Math. Ap.* The fair, granted

in 1215, was upon the vigil and feast of St. Matthew the Apostle. The name of St. Mark's, Bristol, is preserved in the existing chapel of the hospital ; the seal (Fig. 33) shows the saint writing his gospel, the lion by his side. "The lepers of St. Luke the Evangelist at the bridge-end of Beghton" are mentioned in 1334, but the locality is not identified. There was also a hospital of St. Luke at Gorleston.

St. Andrew ; *St. Thomas ;* **St. Stephen.**—There were dedications to St. Andrew at Flixton, Denwall, Cokesford, and Hythe. It seems probable that the last named was a re-foundation of St. Bartholomew's, for "St. Andrew" only occurs during the few years following its restoration by Hamo, Bishop of Rochester, of which See that saint was patron. It is improbable that any of the hospitals of St. Thomas were under the patronage of that Apostle, although Tanner erroneously gives an instance at Birmingham. They sprang up when St. Thomas the Martyr of Canterbury was of paramount popularity. The ambiguous "St. Thomas-on-the-Green" at Sherborne, for example, is referred to by Leland as the "free chapel of Thomas Becket." St. Stephen, the almoner of the Early Church, was the appropriate patron of several houses of charity, including three in the eastern counties. One was at Bury St. Edmunds, where there were preserved in the abbey "certain drops of St. Stephen's blood which sprung from him at such time as he was stoned." The seals of Norwich and Hempton show their patron respectively as martyr and minister.

St. Paul the Apostle ; St. Paul the Hermit ; St. Peter ; St. Petronilla.—Although St. Peter and St. Paul are commemorated in hundreds of parish-churches, their hospitals number only nine, including those in York and London which were adjuncts of cathedrals and borrowed their dedication-names. At Norwich, St. Paul the Hermit was associated with his namesake. St. Peter and his daughter St. Petronilla were patrons of leper-houses for priests and maidens at Bury St. Edmunds. The virgin saint was famous locally and the skull of St. Petronilla or Pernell, which was preserved in the abbey, was considered efficacious in sickness. Indeed, the eastern counties were rich in her relics, for a casket from the treasury of a Norwich priory, lent to Henry III, contained, it was said, "of St. Petronella, one piece."

St. Clement; St. Lawrence.—There were dedications to the Bishop of Rome in Oxford, Norwich and Hoddesdon. On one seal, the last-named house is called "the hospital of St. Clement" (Fig. 34), upon another "of St. Anthony"; both depict not only the hermit but a mitred saint in vestments, with hammer and horse-shoe. The connection with the forge is not clear, but St. Clement is referred to as patron of ironworkers in Sussex, and of blacksmiths in Hampshire. He was popularly regarded rather as the seamen's saint, and was invoked by mariners of a fraternity of St. Clement connected with St. Bartholomew's hospital, Bristol. St. Lawrence the deacon, whose liberality to-

34. SEAL OF ST. CLEMENT'S, HODDESDON

PLATE XXVIII

HOSPITAL OF ST. PETRONILLA, BURY ST. EDMUNDS

HOSPITAL OF ST. JAMES, DUNWICH

wards the sick and poor was proverbial, was guardian of twelve hospitals, chiefly for lepers. This beloved martyr of Rome was venerated in Canterbury, and the lepers dependent upon St. Augustine's Abbey were under his protection on a site now marked by St. Lawrence's Cricket Ground. "Lawrence Hill," Bristol, also preserves the memory of a leper-house. The old seal of St. Lawrence's, Bodmin, shows the martyr with his gridiron.

St. Nicholas.—The dedications in this name amount to twenty-nine, eleven being in Yorkshire. St. Nicholas', leper-house, Harbledown, was founded by the Italian Lanfranc, whose native land had just acquired the bones of the benevolent bishop, translated to Bari in 1087. The hospitals of Royston and Bury St. Edmunds kept their fairs at the festival of his "Translation." So great was his popularity that Miss Arnold-Forster remarks that if any dedication to St. Nicholas could be traced in Derbyshire, he would have the distinction of being found in every county. This one lack among the parish churches to which she refers, is supplied by the existence of a hospital in his honour at Chesterfield, and of an almshouse chapel at Alkmonton.

St. Anthony. Whereas few churches were consecrated in memory of this hermit, twenty-one houses of charity were partly or wholly dedicated to him. His aid was invoked when pestilence (*feu sacré*) wasted France, and the initiation of the Order of St. Anthony spread his fame. The French priory at Lenton maintained a hospital for "such as were troubled with St. Anthony's fire," i.e. erysipelas. An indulgence offered to contributors towards St. Anthony's in London refers to inmates "of whom some are so tortured and scorched by burnings as of the pit, that being deprived of all use of their limbs, they seem to be rather horrible deformities than human beings." The saint was invoked against contagion and all diseases. In England most of his foundations were for lepers. One of the latest lazar-houses (Holloway, 1473) had a chapel of St. Anthony; but the full title on the seal is "Holy Jesus and St. Anthony."

The seals of the London, Hoddesdon, and Holloway hospitals (Figs. 30, 34) show St. Anthony with his tau cross, bell, and pig. When it was forbidden for swine to roam in the streets, the Antonine monks retained the right to turn out their pigs, which were distinguished by a bell. Although the York hospital was not under the Order, the master claimed one pig out of every litter. As late as 1538, when the London house of St. Anthony had been appropriated to Windsor, licence was given "to collect and receive the alms of the faithful, given in honour of God and St. Anthony, . . . together with swine and other beasts."

St. Augustine; St. Benedict; St. Bernard.—Whether the "hospital for lepers of St. Augustine" at Newport (Isle of Wight) should be considered a true dedication is hard to say; like the "Papey" in London it may merely have been a community under the Austin Rule. A leper-house in Norwich bore the name of St. Bennet's; although situated in St. Benedict's parish, this must be regarded as a genuine dedication, for the common seal depicts the patron. "St. Nicholas and St. Bernard's" at Hornchurch took its designation from the Great St. Bernard in Savoy. (See p. 209.)

PLATE XXIX

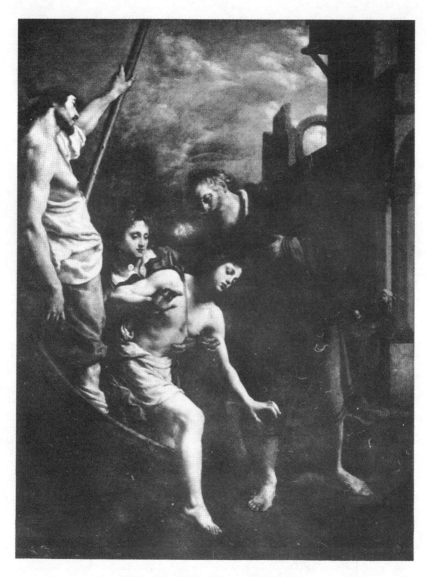

THE HOSPITALITY OF ST. JULIAN

FROM THE PAINTING BY C. ALLORI

St. Julian the Hospitaller was a singularly appropriate guardian. Gervase of Southampton was himself following the example of St. Julian when he turned his home into a resting-place for travellers. Leland refers to God's House, Southampton, as "dedicate to Saynct Juliane the Bisshop," but it was rather the "good harbourer" who was renowned in mediæval England. The saint has been depicted in art helping a leprous youth out of the ferry-boat and welcoming him to his house. (Pl. XXIX.) At the passage of the river at Thetford was a hospital, the chapel of which commemorated St. Julian; and the leper-house near St. Albans was in his honour.

St. Alexis.—The story of Alexis himself is some clue to the unique dedication found at Exeter. He forsook his home for many years, and when at last he returned he was recognized by no one, but his parents welcomed the ragged stranger for the sake of their wandering son. St. Alexis was therefore regarded as the patron of mendicants.

St. George and St. Christopher.—There were hospitals of St. George at Tavistock and Shrewsbury; the latter gave his name to one of the gates and contributed his cross to the arms of the town. That of Yeovil was dedicated to "St. George and St. Christopher the Martyrs"; each pensioner was to wear upon his breast a red cross "as a sign and in honour of St. George the Martyr, patron of the house of alms." The squire of Thame put his bedemen under the care of St. Christopher, as is set forth upon his tomb :—

" that founded in the church of Thame a chantrie, vi pore men and a fraternitye, In the worship of Seynt Cristofore to be relevid in perpetuyte."

St. Margaret; St. Katherine; St. Ursula.—There are eighteen houses in honour of St. Margaret, and they are chiefly for lepers. It is possible that in the case of Huntingdon the name may enshrine the memory of the saintly lady of Scotland, who died in 1093, although, it is true, she was not canonized until 1250; her son, David of Huntingdon, built St. John's in that town, and he may

35. SEAL OF ST. KATHERINE'S, BRISTOL

have founded St. Margaret's, of which his daughter and grandson were benefactors. The hospitals dedicated to St. Katherine also number about eighteen. That royal saint was chosen by Stephen's queen as the protector of her charitable foundation for women. Katharine of Aragon obtained for this house a gift of relics, including part of the tomb of the saint sent by the Pope, "out of respect for the Hospital of St. Katharine." The seal of this house and of that at Bristol (Fig. 35) show the saint crowned, with sword and wheel, and the latter device was also worn on the habit. Wigston's hospital, Leicester, was named "St. Ursula and St. Catherine." Bonville's almshouse at Exeter includes in its unique dedication St. Ursula's famed companions; it was in honour of "The Blessed Virgin, the Eleven Thousand Virgins and St. Roch."

St. Anne; St. Helen.—The mother of the Blessed Virgin was commemorated at Ripon, and together with other saints at Norwich, Oakham, Stoke-by-Newark, Brentford and Hereford. St. Helen, the mother of Constantine, had hospitals at Derby and Braceford, besides that alluded to under the title "Holy Cross."

SAINTS OF FRANCE

St. Leonard.—The attitude of France to this hermit-saint was one of deep devotion. Our Norman kings and nobles shared this veneration. Foundations bearing his name at Chesterfield, Derby, Lancaster and Nottingham, had privileges in the adjoining royal forests; and St. Leonard's, Launceston, was dependent on the Duchy. The hospital at Northampton showed a crown upon its seal, and that of York (re-dedicated to this saint by Stephen) bore the arms of England. St. Leonard's, Alnwick, was erected on the spot where the Scottish king Malcolm fell. This saint had a reputation as a healer: "il était le médecin des infirmes." Some fifty-five charitable foundations had St. Leonard for patron; they were mainly for lepers, and in certain counties (notably Derby and Northampton) even St. Mary Magdalene had to give place to him in this capacity.

The " Hospital of St. Leonard the Confessor " in Bedford was revived twenty years ago by a band of brothers who met on St. Leonard's Day and resolved to restore the lapsed memory of this patron saint.

St. Giles; St. Theobald.—The houses of St. Giles number about twenty-five. The chief one was that " in the fields " near London. He was the cripples' (and therefore the lepers') patron, partly because he himself suffered from lameness, and partly on account of the legend of the wounded hart which fled to him, an incident depicted upon seals at Norwich, Wilton and Kepier. Another French hermit, St. Theobald, shares the dedication of the leper-house at Tavistock with St. Mary Magdalene.

St. Denys; St. Martin; St. Leger; St. Laud; St. Eligius.—The hospital at Devizes built by the Bishop of Salisbury was in honour of St. James and St. Denys; the fair granted to the lepers was held on the vigil and day of St. Dionysius. The charitable St. Martin occurs, with or without St. John Baptist, at Piriho. St. Leger was commemorated at Grimsby. St. Laud (or Lo) is an alternative patron at Hoddesdon. St. Eligius (or Eloy) was venerated in houses at York, Stoke-upon-Trent, Cambridge and Hereford.

St. Louis; St. Roch.—These unique dedications are welcome among our patron saints. That to the saintly king occurs in the Ely Registers, contributions being invited in 1393 towards a chapel newly constructed at Brentford (*Braynford*) in honour of the Blessed Anne and St. Louis (*Ludovicus*) with houses for the reception of travellers. St. Roch, who ministered to the plague-stricken of Italian hospitals in the fourteenth century, was commemorated at Bonville's almshouse in Exeter, Rock Lane being a reminder of its chapel of St. Roch.

SAINTS OF ENGLAND

St. Oswald; St. Wulstan.—One hospital at Worcester "beareth the name of St. Oswald as a thinge dedicate of ould tyme to him." (See p. 2.) The foundation of the other is ascribed to St. Wulstan himself. The house grew in importance after the saint's canonization in the year 1203, which followed a fresh display of miracles at his shrine. The possession of the faithful bishop's famous staff was disputed between hospital and priory.[1]

The common seal shows the patron in the act of benediction, staff in hand.

St. Godwald; St. David.—The chapel of St. Wulstan's was dedicated to St. Godwald. "Some say he was a bishop" is Leland's commentary. Miss Arnold-Forster identifies him with Gulval, hermit-bishop in Wales. St. David, the Welsh Archbishop (canonized 1120), was commemorated at Kingsthorpe, by Northampton, the house being frequently called "St. Dewi's."

St. Brinstan; **St. Chad;** *St. Cuthbert, etc.*—Although Leland had read that "St. Brinstane foundid an hospitale at Winchester," nothing is known of it. "Here is a hospital of St. Chadde," he remarks at Shrewsbury, referring to the church and almshouse. Two dedications sometimes ascribed to St. Cuthbert, namely at Gateshead and Greatham, within "the patrimony of St. Cuthbert," hardly justify his inclusion among patrons, although he is named in the deed of gift. The same may be said

[1] F. T. Marsh, *Annals of St. Wulstan's*, p. 5.

of documentary allusions to St. Erkenwald, St. Hilda and St. Richard in connection with foundations at Ilford, Whitby and Chichester.

St. Ethelbert; St. Edmund, King & Martyr; St. Edmund, Archbishop & Confessor.—The royal Ethelbert and Edmund are included among our saints. St. Ethelbert's, Hereford, is attached to the cathedral and shares its patron. In the case of the ten houses of St. Edmund, it is not always possible to determine whether the Saxon king is intended or Edmund Rich, Archbishop of Canterbury. The "spital on the street" in Lincolnshire and the hospital by Doncaster Bridge were in honour of the royal martyr; whilst those of Leicester and Windeham commemorated the archbishop, the latter being founded by his devoted friend, St. Richard of Chichester, who had recently attended the solemn "Translation" at Pontigny.

St. Edmund's, Gateshead, has puzzled historians because the designations vary between King, Archbishop, Bishop and Confessor. Surtees and others concluded that all had reference to one foundation, but Mr. J. R. Boyle proves that there were two with distinct endowments, and that both chapels were standing a century ago. Now it is recorded that Nicholas of Farnham was the founder of that of "St. Edmund the Bishop." A sidelight is thrown upon the subject by Matthew Paris, whose narrative of the miraculous recovery of Nicholas in 1244 through the agency of St. Edmund has escaped the notice of local topographers. The emaciated sick man bade farewell and received the last rites when he was restored by the application of a relic of the archbishop. From this incident it seems likely that the hospital was a

PLATE XXX

CHAPEL OF ST. EDMUND THE KING, SPITAL-ON-THE-STREET

CHAPEL OF ST. EDMUND THE ARCHBISHOP, GATESHEAD

votive offering and that it was consecrated soon after Archbishop Edmund was enrolled among the saints. The
papal letter of canonization (1246) describes his beautiful
character and the miraculous events which followed his
death. When it declares that "he healed the swelling
dropsy by reducing the body to smaller dimensions,"
the allusion is surely to the recent recovery of Bishop
Nicholas, who had been suffering from that infirmity.

36. A PILGRIM'S SIGN

St. Thomas the Martyr of Canterbury was believed to
surpass all others in powers of healing. His miracles
were usually wrought by means of water mixed with a
drop of the martyr's blood; this was carried away in a
leaden *ampulla*, and its contents worked wonders. (See
Fig. 8.) Others would purchase a "sign," upon which
was announced in Latin :—" For good people that are sick
Thomas is the best of physicians." (Fig. 36.) Many of
these pilgrims to Canterbury lodged in the hospital of

St. Thomas (Pl. II), said to have been founded by the archbishop himself, whose martyrdom is depicted on the walls of the hall. The chapel was dedicated to his special patron, the Blessed Virgin. St. Thomas', Southwark, also claimed him as founder, and two other houses were intimately connected with him. One was Becket's early home in Cheapside, enlarged by his sister Agnes and her husband, whose charter grants land "formerly belonging to Gilbert Becket, father of the blessed Thomas the Martyr . . . being the birthplace of the blessed martyr." Privileges were accorded to it long afterwards "from devotion to the saint, who is said to have been born and educated in that hospital." (This foundation was usually called St. Thomas of Acon, but it is believed that the designation had at first no connection with Acres, but rather with the original owner of the property.) The second house with family associations was at Ilford, for while Becket's sister was abbess of Barking, the lepers' chapel was reconsecrated with the addition of the name of St. Thomas.

Nor were his friends less faithful, for when Becket's chancellor Benedict (afterwards his biographer) was transferred from Canterbury to Peterborough, he completed a foundation in his honour. Probably Benedict was also concerned in the choice of name at Stamford, especially as that dependent house adopted St. John Baptist and St. Thomas as joint patrons ; for the fact that the new martyr's body was laid near the altar of the Baptist called forth from several chroniclers (as Stanley points out) the remark that St. John Baptist was the bold opponent of a wicked king. In a document relating to the Stamford house, St. Thomas is referred to as "the proto-martyr," but the claim is hard to justify. He was commemorated with St. Stephen at Romney, a dedication which would have given him abundant satisfaction ; for previous to his flight in 1164 he celebrated, as having a special portent, the mass "in honour of the blessed proto-martyr Stephen."

It is a far cry from Kent to Northumberland, but there existed at Bolton a hospital of St. Thomas. Within a few miles had been fought the Battle of Alnwick, a victory won, it was believed, as the result of the king's public penance the same day (1174). The date of foundation is not recorded, but it was begun before 1225. About the same time a hospital of St. Thomas was being built at Hereford, by one of the Warennes, whose father had bitterly opposed the then unpopular Chancellor. The new devotion to St. Thomas was fanned into flame by the magnificent ceremony of 1220 on the removal of his body to its wonderful shrine. Soon after this, a hospital was founded at Bec, and the patronage annexed to the See of Norwich ; it was consecrated by Bishop Pandulph, who had taken a leading part in the "Translation," an event which was henceforth celebrated on July 7. For centuries the shrine was held in high honour. The Letter Books of Christ Church, Canterbury, record miracles in 1394 and 1445.[1] So notable was the first of these that Richard II wrote to congratulate the archbishop, acknow-ledging his thankfulness to "the High Sovereign Worker of miracles who has deigned to work this miracle in our days, and upon a foreigner, as though for the purpose of spreading . . . the glorious fame of His very martyr," adding a pious wish that it might result in the conversion of those in error at a time when " our faith and belief

[1] Chron. and Mem. 85, iii. 27-29.

have many more enemies than they ever had time out of mind." Such signs were, in fact, an antidote to Lollardy, as is implied by the public testimony of the Chapter to the cure of a cripple from Aberdeen in 1445.

The kings continued to pay pilgrimage visits, and even Henry VIII sent the accustomed offerings to Canterbury. His subsequent animosity towards St. Thomas was a political move, as is shown by the report of Robert Ward in 1535; having spied at the hospital of St. Thomas of Acon a window depicting the flagellation of Henry II by monks at the shrine, he pointed out to Thomas Cromwell that Becket was slain "in that he did resist the king." Bale afterwards alludes thus to this burning question :—

"A trayterouse knave ye can set upp for a saynte,
And a ryghteouse kynge lyke an odyouse tyrant paynte.

.   .   .   .

In your glasse wyndowes ye whyppe your naturall kynges."[1]

In 1538 Henry thought it expedient to inform his loving subjects that notwithstanding the canonization of St. Thomas "there appeareth nothing in his life and exteriour conversation whereby he should be called a saint, but rather . . . a rebel and traitor to his prince." Henceforth few windows remained depicting the acts of the martyr,—though one representation of the penance of Henry II is familiar to readers at the Bodleian. The name was to be no longer perpetuated ; "St. Thomas the Martyr, Southwark," becomes "Becket Spital" and then "St. Thomas the Apostle," whilst "Thomas House" is found at Northampton.

[1] Camden Society, *Kynge Johan*, p. 88.

All Saints.—In spite of many general references to All Saints, the invocation by itself was as rare for a hospital as it was common for a church. Leland and the *Valor Ecclesiasticus* give the dedication of the Stamford bedehouse as "All Saints." The founder had willed that "there be for ever a certain almshouse, commonly called William Browne's Almshouse, for the invocation of the most glorious Virgin Mary and of All Saints, to the praise and honour of the Name Crucified." The almsmen's special chapel in the parish church of All Saints was in honour of the Blessed Virgin. The existing silver seal shows the Father, seated, supporting between His knees the Saviour upon the Cross, whilst the Spirit appears as a Dove.

Alternative Dedications, etc.

There is frequently an uncertainty as to the invocation, even with documentary assistance. A Close Roll entry (1214) mentions a foundation at Portsmouth in honour of Holy Trinity, the Blessed Virgin, St. Cross, St. Michael and All Saints. Usually the name is simply "God's House," but often St. John Baptist or St. Nicholas. The seal seems to suggest the original designation, for it shows a Cross, with the Divine Hand, a scroll and angels. Again, God's House at Kingston-upon-Hull was called Holy Trinity or St. Michael's, or from its situation "the Charterhouse hospital"; but its full title was "in honour of God, and the most glorious Virgin Mary His Mother, and St. Michael the Archangel, and all archangels, angels and holy spirits, and of St. Thomas the Martyr, and all saints of God." It may be observed that inasmuch as the founder Michael Pole was Chancellor of England, he looked to his predecessor in office St. Thomas as patron, no less than to his name-saint. By the foundation-deed of Heytesbury almshouse, it was in honour of "the Holy Trinity, and especially of Christ our Redeemer, the Blessed Virgin Mary His Mother, St. Katherine and all saints." The almsmen wore the letters JHU. XRT. upon their gowns. The Chantry Certificate, nevertheless, gives St. John's. The original seal shows a Cross and the name *domus elimosinaria*, but the post-Reformation seal has St. Katherine. Varying dedications are some-times merely mistakes. It must, however, be remembered that occasionally hospital and chapel had different patrons, and that both were sometimes rebuilt and re-consecrated. As civil and ecclesiastical archives continue to reveal their long-hidden information, the dedication-names of many houses will doubtless come to light, together with notices of foundations at present unknown to us.

Some seventy titles of hospitals are here recorded, as compared with over six hundred different dedications of parish churches. In some instances the patron of a charitable institution bequeathed his name to a parish. At Tweedmouth, St. Bartholomew of the hospital was powerful enough to dispossess St. Boisil, the rightful patron of the place. The parishes of St. Mary Magdalene, Colchester, St. Giles-in-the-Fields, London, and St. Giles, Shrewsbury, have grown up round a former leper-house. Several modern churches, such as St. John's, Bridgwater, occupy the site and carry on the name of an old founda-tion.

In conclusion, it must be observed that since the subject of England's Patron Saints has been fully dealt with by

Miss Arnold-Forster, no attempt has here been made to make more than passing allusions to the lives of hospital saints. The foregoing notes on saints were suggested by her *Studies in Church Dedications*.

37. SEAL OF THE HOSPITAL OF
ST. BARTHOLOMEW, ROCHESTER

APPENDIX A

OFFICE AT THE SECLUSION OF A LEPER

[Translated from the *Manuale ad Usum Insignis Ecclesiæ Sarum*, printed in *York Manual, &c., Appendix*, Surtees Society, Vol. 63. p. 105*.]

The Manner of casting out or separating those who are sick with leprosy from the whole.[1]

FIRST of all the sick man or the leper clad in a cloak and in his usual dress, being in his house, ought to have notice of the coming of the priest who is on his way to the house to lead him to the Church, and must in that guise wait for him. For the priest vested in surplice and stole, with the Cross going before, makes his way to the sick man's house and addresses him with comforting words, pointing out and proving that if he blesses and praises God, and bears his sickness patiently, he may have a sure and certain hope that though he be sick in body he may be whole in soul, and may reach the home[2] of everlasting welfare. And then with other words suitable to the occasion let the priest lead the leper to the Church, when he has sprinkled him with holy water, the Cross going before, the priest following, and last of all the sick man. Within the Church let a black cloth, if it can be had, be set upon two trestles at some distance apart before the altar, and let the sick man take his place on bended knees beneath it between the trestles, after the manner of a dead man, although

---

[1] This is identical with the 3rd Ordo given in Martene, lib. iii. c.x., from the Ritual of Bourges and Sens issued by the command of Cardinal Borbonius (Henderson).

[2] *Domum* (Henderson); or, reading *Donum* (with Martene, etc.) we may translate this:—"may obtain the gift of everlasting salvation."

by the grace of God he yet lives in body and spirit, and in this posture let him devoutly hear Mass. When this is finished, and he has been sprinkled with holy water, he must be led with the Cross through the presbytery to a place where a pause must be made. When the spot is reached the priest shall counsel him out of Holy Scripture, saying : " Remember thine end and thou shalt never do amiss." [Ecclus. vii. 36.] Whence Augustine says : " He readily esteems all things lightly, who ever bears in mind that he will die." The priest then with the spade (*palla*) casts earth on each of his feet, saying : " Be thou dead to the world, but alive again unto God."

And he comforts him and strengthens him to endure with the words of Isaiah spoken concerning our Lord Jesus Christ :— " Truly He hath borne our griefs and carried our sorrows, yet did we esteem Him as a leper smitten of God and afflicted " [Isa. liii. 4, Vulgate]; let him say also : " If in weakness of body by means of suffering thou art made like unto Christ, thou mayest surely hope that thou wilt rejoice in spirit with God. May the Most High grant this to thee, numbering thee among His faithful ones in the book of life. Amen."

It is to be noted that the priest must lead him to the Church, from the Church to his house as a dead man, chanting the *Responsorium* Libera me, Domine, in such wise that the sick man is covered with a black cloth. And the Mass celebrated at his seclusion may be chosen either by the priest or by the sick man, but it is customary to say the following :—

Introitus. Circumdederunt me. *Quære in Septuagesima.*

Collecta. Omnipotens sempiterne Deus, salus æterna credentium.

Epistola. Carissimi, Tristatur quis vestrum.

Resp. Miserere mei.

Vers. Conturbata sunt. Alleluya. *V.* Qui sanat.

Si in Quadragesima, Tractus. Commovisti.

Evangelium. Intravit Jesus in Capharnaum.

Offertorium. Domine, exaudi.

Secreta èt Postcommunio in communibus orationibus.

Communio. Redime, Deus, Israel ex omnibus angustiis nostris.

When leaving the Church after Mass the priest ought to stand at the door to sprinkle him with holy water. And he ought to commend him to the care of the people. Before Mass the sick man ought to make his confession in the Church, and never again ; and in leading him forth the priest again begins the *Responsorium* Libera me, Domine, with the other versicles. Then when he has come into the open fields he does as is afore-said ; and he ends by imposing prohibitions upon him in the following manner :—

" I forbid you ever to enter Churches, or to go into a market, or a mill, or a bakehouse, or into any assemblies of people.

Also I forbid you ever to wash your hands or even any of your belongings in spring or stream of water of any kind ; and if you are thirsty you must drink water from your cup or some other vessel.

Also I forbid you ever henceforth to go out without your leper's dress, that you may be recognized by others ; and you must not go outside your house unshod.

Also I forbid you, wherever you may be, to touch anything which you wish to buy, otherwise than with a rod or staff to show what you want.

Also I forbid you ever henceforth to enter taverns or other houses if you wish to buy wine ; and take care even that what they give you they put into your cup.

Also I forbid you to have intercourse with any woman except your own wife.

Also I command you when you are on a journey not to return an answer to any one who questions you, till you have gone off the road to leeward, so that he may take no harm from you ; and that you never go through a narrow lane lest you should meet some one.

Also I charge you if need require you to pass over some toll-way (*pedagium*) through (?) rough ground (*super apra*), or elsewhere, that you touch no posts or things (*instrumenta*) whereby you cross, till you have first put on your gloves.

Also I forbid you to touch infants or young folk, whoso-ever they may be, or to give to them or to others any of your possessions.

Also I forbid you henceforth to eat or drink in any company except that of lepers. And know that when you die you will be buried in your own house, unless it be, by favour obtained beforehand, in the Church."

And note that before he enters his house, he ought to have a coat and shoes of fur, his own plain shoes, and his signal the clappers, a hood and a cloak, two pair of sheets, a cup, a funnel, a girdle, a small knife, and a plate. His house ought to be small, with a well, a couch furnished with coverlets, a pillow, a chest, a table, a seat, a candlestick, a shovel, a pot, and other needful articles.

When all is complete the priest must point out to him the ten rules which he has made for him ; and let him live on earth in peace with his neighbour. Next must be pointed out to him the ten commandments of God, that he may live in heaven with the saints, and the priest repeats them to him in the presence of the people. And let the priest also point out to him that every day each faithful Christian is bound to say devoutly *Pater noster*, *Ave Maria*, *Credo in Deum*, and *Credo in Spiritum*, and to protect himself with the sign of the Cross, saying often *Benedicite*. When the priest leaves him he says :— " Worship God, and give thanks to God. Have patience, and the Lord will be with thee. Amen."

APPENDIX B

TABULATED LIST OF
MEDIÆVAL HOSPITALS IN ENGLAND

i.e. Houses for Wayfarers, Sick, Aged and Infirm, Insane, and Lepers, founded before 1547.

EXPLANATION OF HEADINGS, REFERENCES, SIGNS, ETC.

Dedication. When names are stated thus : "St. John [& St. Anthony]," this signifies that the name in brackets is less frequently used.

Date. The date given is that of the first accredited reference. The foundation was frequently earlier. *c. = circa ; bef* = before.

Founder. This term includes benefactor and re-founder.

Patron. In the majority of cases entered as " Private," the advowson was vested in the Lord of the Manor. Where two names are inserted they represent a change of patronage.

L. i.e. Leper ; this denotes the nominal aim of the charity, which was not necessarily confined to lepers.

* An asterisk signifies that there are considerable architectural remains (chapel, hall, etc.).

| Indicates slight architectural remains (e g. masonry, windows)

‡ This sign before a dedication-name implies that some endowment exists under that name or the name of the founder.

Seal. Denotes that either a matrix or an impression is in existence. A specimen is usually to be found in the British Museum. *Soc. Antiq.* refers to the Society of Antiquaries, London.

Italics. The use of italics implies uncertainty.

Foot-notes. " Patent " and " Close " refer to the printed Calendars of the Public Record Office, space not permitting of fuller details.

I. BEDFORDSHIRE

Locality.	Dedication or Description.	Date.	Founder.	Patron.	
Bedford	‡St. John Baptist (Seal)	1216	R. de Parys	Town	
,,	‡St. Leonard	1207	—	Town, Private	L
Dunstable	St. Mary Magdalene	1209	Prior	Priory	L
Eaton,[1] nr. Dunstable	—	1291	—	—	
Farley,[2] by Leighton Buzzard	St. John Baptist	1198	—	Various[3]	
Hockcliffe (Occleve)	St. John Baptist	1227	—	Various[4]	
Luton	St. John Baptist	1287	—	—	L
,,	St. Mary Magd. (Seal)	bef 1377	—	—	
Stocwell, nr. Bedford	St. Mary[5]	1232	—	—	
Toddington	‡St. John Baptist	1443	J. Broughton	—	

[1] Lincoln Taxation.   [2] In parish of Luton, q.v.   [3] "Order of St. William in the Desert" (Patent 1253); Suntingfield-by-Boulogne (Charter Roll 1285, Pat. 1393); Crown; King's Coll. Camb. There was "a house of St. Cross belonging to them" (Pat. 1393); possibly Ludgershall, Bucks?   [4] Private; Bishop of Lincoln; Dunstable Priory.   [5] Pat. 1232.

II. BERKSHIRE

Locality.	Dedication or Description.	Date.	Founder.	Patron.	
Abingdon	††St. John B. (Seal)	1280	Abbot	Abbey	—
,, (without)	St. Mary Magdalene	1336	—	Gild.	—
,,	*‡Almshouse[1]	1441	G. Barbar & J. de St. Helena	—	—
Childrey	‡Holy Trinity & St. Katharine	1526	W. Fettiplace	—	—
Donnington, near Newbury	‡God's House	1393	R. Abberbury	Private	—
Fyfield	St. John Baptist	1442	J. Golafre	—	—
Hungerford	St. John Baptist	1232	King	Duchy of Lancaster	L
,,	St. Laurence	1228	—	—	—
Lambourn	‡Holy Trinity (Seal)	1501	J. Isbury	New Coll. Oxford	—
Newbury	‡St. Bartholomew	1215	King[2]	Town	L
,,	St. Mary Magdalene	1232	—	—	L
Reading	St. Mary Magdalene	bef 1175	Abbot Auchar	Abbey	—
,,	St. John B. (Seal)	c. 1190	Abbot Hugh	Abbey	—
,,	Almshouse	—	W. Barnes	—	—
,,	Almshouse	bef 1477	Leche or Larder	—	—
Thatcham	Almshouse	1433	T. Lowndyes	Parish	—
Wallingford	St. John B. (Seal)	1224	—	Town	—
,, or Newnham[3]	St. Mary Magdalene	1226	—	Town	L
Windsor	St. John	1316	—	—	—
,, (without)	St. Peter	1168	—	Crown, Eton College	L

[1] Re-founded as "Christ's."   [2] Called "King John's" locally.   [3] In Oxfordshire ; cf. Crowmarsh.

III.　BUCKINGHAMSHIRE

Locality.	Dedication or Description.	Date.	Founder.	Patron.	
Aylesbury	St. John Baptist[1]	xii cent.	Townsmen	—	L (?)
,,	St. Leonard[1]	,,	,,	—	L
Buckingham	St. John Baptist[2]	c. 1200	—	—	—
,,	St. Laurence	1252	—	—	L
,,	Almshouse	1431	J. Barton	—	—
Lathbury	St. Margaret[3]	1252	—	—	—
Ludgershall		1236	—	Alien[4]	—
Marlow, Great	St. Thomas[5]	1384	—	—	—
Newport Pagnell	St. Margaret	c. 1240	—	—	L
,, (Bridge[6])	‡St. John B. [& St. John Ev.][7] (Seal[8])	1220	J. de Somery	Private	L
,, ,,	St. Leonard[9]	1232	J. de Peynton	—	—
Stratford, Stony (without)	St. John Baptist	c. 1240	—	—	L
Wendover	St. John Baptist	1311	—	—	—
Wycombe, High	*St. John Baptist	c. 1180	—	Town 1344	—
,, ,, near	St. Margaret & St. Giles[10]	1229	—	Crown	L

[1] United 1384.　[2] Gervase of Canterbury.　[3] Pat. 1252.　[4] Under Suntingfield-by-Boulogne; cf. Farley, Beds.　[5] Pat. 1384.　[6] Cf. "House of lepers by bridge," Tickfort by Newport (Pat. 1275).　[7] Now "Queen Anne's."　[8] Soc. Antiq. E. II 4 B. 8.　[9] Probably Newport, Essex, but one called New Hospital existed c. 1240.　[10] St. Giles (Pat. 1228), St. Margaret (Close 1229). Cf. Pat. 1392. St. Gilbert & St. Margaret (Bp.'s Reg. 1368). Or the Loke.

IV. CAMBRIDGESHIRE

Locality.	Dedication or Description.	Date.	Founder.	Patron.	
Barnwell, v. Stourbridge					
Cambridge	†St. Anthony & St. Eligius	1392	H. Frost	—	L
,,	St. John Ev. (Seal[1])	xii cent.	H. Tangmer	Town, Bishop	L
,,	St. Anne	1397	—	—	
,,	†Almshouse	1469	T. Jakenett	—	
Ely	St. John Baptist[2]	1169	Bishop Nigel	Bishop, Priory	
,,	St. Mary Magdalene[2]	bef 1240	—	Bishop	
Fordham	—	1279	—	Priory	
Leverington	St. John Baptist[3]	1487	—	—	
Long Stow	St. Mary B.V.	1272	Walter, Vicar	—	
Newton-by-Sea	St. Mary B.V.[4]	1401	J. Colvill	Bishop	
Royston, v. Herts					
Stourbridge by Cambridge	*St. Mary Magd. or St. Cross[5]	bef 1172	King	Town, Bishop	L
Thorney		1166		Abbey	
Whittlesea	Poor's Hospital[6]	1391	Adam Ryppe	—	
Whittlesford (Duxford)	St. John Baptist	1307	W. Colvill	Bishop	
Wicken	St. John[7]	1321	Lady Basingburn	Spinney Priory	
Wisbech	St. John Baptist[8]	1343	—	Bishop	
,, (near Elm)	Spital	1378	—	—	L

[1] Soc. Antiq. E. II 4 B. 8.   [2] United c. 1240.   [3] Or Hermitage.
[4] Or Fraternity.   [5] Cf. Pat. 1256. Fair, Exaltation of Holy Cross.
[6] Bp. Fordham Reg. 1391, 1394.   [7] Or Knights Hospitallers.   [8] ? Now "King John's."

V. CHESHIRE

Locality.	Dedication or Description.	Date.	Founder.	Patron.	
Bebington	St. Thomas à Becket	1183	—	Private	L
Chester (without)	‡St. Giles[1] (*Seal*)	—	Earl	Earldom	L
,, (without North-gate)	‡St. John B.[2] (*Seal*)	1232	Earl Randle	Earldom and Birkenhead Priory	—
Chester	St. Ursula V.	1532	R. and T. Smith	—	—
Denwall in Nesse	St. Andrew	1238	—	Bishop of Lichfield	—
Nantwich	St. Nicholas	c. 1087	*W. Malbank*	Private	—
,,	St. Laurence	1354	—	Private	L

[1] Boughton Spital.   Seal(?) B.M. Cat. 2687.
[2] Or God, St. Mary and All Saints (Pat. 1283).

VI. CORNWALL[1]

Locality.	Dedication or Description.	Date.	Founder.	Patron.	
Bodmin	St. Anthony	1500	—	—	
,,	St. George	1405	—	—	
,,	St. Margaret[2]		—	—	L
,, (Pontaboye)	†St. Laurence (Seal[3])	1302	—	—	
Fowey, St. Blaise by Gild Martyn, v. Launceston	—				
Helston in Sithney	St. Mary M. or St. John Baptist	1411	Archdeacon or Killigrew	Knights Hosp.	
Launceston	‡St. Leonard (Seal[4])	1257	Richard, Earl	Earldom or Priory	L
,, Newport by	St. Thomas à Becket[5]	1400	—	—	L
Liskeard, Menheniot nr.	St. Mary Magdalene		—	—	L
Newport, v. Launceston					

[1] Lepers also at Redruth. Mousehole near Penzance, Dynmur near Bodmin, Truro, Glas, etc. (*Vide* will of Bishop Bitton, 1307; *Lancet*, 1890.) [2] Oliver. [3] *Archæologia* xxiv. 178. [4] Drawing in Pigott Collection, Taunton Castle. [5] Carew.

VII. CUMBERLAND

Locality.	Dedication or Description.	Date.	Founder.	Patron.	
Bewcastle	"Hospitale de Lennh"	1294	—	—	
Caldbeck	Hospital House	bef 1170	Gospatric	Carlisle Priory	
Carlisle (without)	St. Nicholas	bef 1201	King	Crown, Priory	L
,,	House of St. Sepulchre[1]	1251	—	—	
,, (Castlegate)	St. Catherine	xvi cent.	—	—	
Keswick, near[2]	House of St. John	xvi cent.	—	—	
Wigton, near	St. Leonard[3]	1383	—	Private	L

[1] See Pipe Rolls. Also Charter Roll 1290.
[2] In Vale of St. John.
[3] Cf. Pat. 1383.

VIII. DERBYSHIRE

Locality.	Dedication or Description.	Date.	Founder.	Patron.	
Alkmonton or Bentley .	St. Leonard [1]	c. 1100	R. de Bakepuze, Blount	Private .	L
Ashbourne [2]	*St. John Baptist*	1251	—	—	L
Castleton or High Peak[3]	St. Mary B.V.	*bef* 1330	Peverell .	Private, Crown	L
Chesterfield, near .	St. Leonard .	1195	—	Crown, etc.	L
,,	St. Nicholas	1276	—	—	
,,	St. John Baptist .	1334	—	Manor .	L
Derby	St. Leonard (Domus Dei)	1171	King	Crown .	L
,,	St. He.en	c. 1160	R. de Ferrers .	—	
,,	St.James [& St.Anthony[4]]	c. 1140	Waltheof Fitz-Sweyn	Darley Abbey .	
,,	St. John Baptist .	1251	—	—	
,,	St. Katherine .	1329	—	—	
Peak, *v.* Castleton					
Spondon or Locko .	‡St. Mary Magdalene [5] .	1306	—	Order of St. Lazarus	L

[1] St. Nicholas' chapel added 1406.
[2] Leper hospital, Pat. 1251, 1255, 1258. For St. John cf. *Rot. Hundredorum*, vol. ii. 298, 3 Edw. I.
[3] Or Spittel-on-Peak. [4] Pat. 1258. [5] Locko Charity exists.

IX. DEVONSHIRE [1]

Locality.	Dedication or Description.	Date.	Founder.	Patron.	
Barnstaple	St. Mary Magdalene	1158	—	—	L
,,	Holy Trinity	1410	—	—	
Clist Gabriel (Farringdon)	St. Gabriel the Archangel[2]	1276	Bishop Bronescombe	Bishop	
Collumpton	Almshouse	1522	J. Trott	—	
Crediton	†St. Laurence	1242	—	Manor (Bishop)	
Exeter (without Southgate)	St. Mary M. (Seal)	bef 1163	Bishop	Bishop, Town	L
,,	St. Alexis[3] (Seal)	1164	W. Prodom	—	
,,	St. John B.[4] [& St. John Ev.] (Seal)	1220	G. & J. Long	Town, Bishop	
,,	*†God's House[5]	1436	W. Wynard	—	
,,	*†St. Katharine	1457	J. Stevyns	—	
,,	†{St. Mary V., Eleven Thousand Virgins & St. Roch[6]}	1407	W. Bonvile	—	
,,	St. Anthony[7]	1429	—	—	
,,	"Ten Cells"	1399	S. Grendon	—	
,,	Almshouse	1479	J. Palmer	—	
,,	Almshouse	1514	Moore&Fortescue	—	
Heavitree (Wonford)	†St. Loye[8]	—	—	—	
Honiton	*†St. Margaret	1374	—	Ford Abbey	L
Moreton Hampstead	Almshouse	xv cent	—	—	

Newton Bushell . . .	—	1538	J. Gilberd .	Mayor of Exeter .	L
Pilton . .	†St. Margaret (Seal[9]) .	1197	—		L
Plymouth . .	[Holy Trinity &] St. Mary M.	1374	—		L
,, . .	St. Mary B. V. (Our Lady)	1501	—			
,, . .	Hospital House	—	—			
Plympton . .	‡[Holy Trinity &] St. Mary M.	1329	—	Priory	L
Tavistock, near .	St. Mary M. [& St. Theobald] (Seal)	1338	—		L
,, . .	St. George . .	—	Tremayne .		
Teignmouth, near .	‡St. Mary Magdalene .	1307	—		L
Teignton, Kings, v. Newton Bushell					
Tiverton . .	*‡Almshouse[10]	1520	J. Greneway	Wardens of Tiverton	L
Torrington . .	Holy Trinity, St. John Ev. & St. John B.	1400	re-f. R. Colyn .		
Torrington, Little (Tad-diport) .	*‡St. Mary Magdalene .	1344	Ann Boteler	Private .	L
Totnes . .	‡St. Mary M. (Seal[11]) .	1302	—		L
,, . .	Our Lady	xvi cent.	—			

[1] Lepers also at Okehampton, Sutton, Cleve, Modbury, Chadelynton, Dartmouth, Newton Ferrers, Topsham, Denbury, Tremeton, St. German's, etc. (Will 1307, cf. Cornwall.) [2] Or B.V.M., St. Gabriel & All Angels. [3] Or " Hospital behind St. Nicholas," afterwards united with St. John. [4] B.V.M., St. John B. & All Saints (Charter) [5] Chapel, Holy Trinity. [6] Or Combrew ; chapel, St. Roch. [7] Will (Somerset Rec. Soc. xvi. 129). [8] Present Almshouse St. Loye. [9] Archæologia, xii. 211. [10] Chapel, St. John Ev. [11] Seal B.M., lxii. 13. Cat. 4203 ascribes to Ben. Priory.

X. DORSET

Locality.	Dedication or Description.	Date.	Founder.	Patron.	
Allington, v. Bridport					
Blandford, by	St. Leonard	1282	—	Private	L
,,	God's House[1]	xvi cent.	—	Town	⫶
Bridport	St. John Baptist	1240	—		
,, or Allington	St. Mary M. [& St. Anthony]	1232	re-f. W. de Legh	Private	L
Dorchester	St. John Baptist	1324	—	Crown, Eton, etc.	L
,,	Hospital	xvi cent.	—	—	L
Lyme	†St. Mary B.V. & the Holy Spirit	1336	—	—	
Rushton, v. Tarrant					
Shaftesbury	†St. John B. (Seal[2])	1223	—	Abbey, Crown	
,,	St. Mary Magdalene	1386	—	Abbey	
Sherborne	*†SS. John B. & John Ev.	1437	Bishop, &c.	Governors	
,,	†St. Thomas à Becket	1228	—	Abbey, Crown.	
Tarrant Rushton	St. Leonard	1298	—	Private, Twynham Priory	
Wareham	Hospital[1]	xvi cent.	—	—	
Wimborne	*†St. Margaret V. [& St. Anthony]	1241	—	Manor (Duchy of Lancaster)	L

[1] Chantry Cert.   [2] Seal B.M. Mediæval Room, Case D, matrix.

XI. DURHAM

Locality.	Dedication or Description.	Date.	Founder.	Patron.	
Barnard Castle	†St. John Baptist	c. 1230	J. Balliol	Private	—
Darlington, near	"Bathele Spital"	c. 1195	—	—	L
Durham	St. Leonard[1]	c. 1200	—	—	L
,, (Silver Street)	†St. Mary Magdalene	1326	J. Fitz Alexander	Priory	—
,, v. Kepier, Sherburn	Pilgrim House[2]	1493	—	—	—
Friarside, nr. Derwent	†Hospital or Hermitage	1312	—	Private	—
Gainford	—	1317	—	—	—
Gateshead	Holy Trinity[3]	c. 1200	H. de Ferlinton	—	—
,,	*St. Edmund, Abp. & Conf.[3]	c. 1247	Bp. N. Farnham	Bishop, Newcastle Priory	—
,,	†St. Edmund, K. & M.[4]	1315	—	Bishop	—
Greatham	†St. Mary B.V.[4] (Seal[5])	1272	Bp. R. de Stichill	Bishop	—
Kepier, by Durham	*St. Giles (Seal)	1112	Bp. R. Flambard	Bishop	—
Pelawe, by	St. Stephen	1260	—	—	—
Sedgefield[6]	—	c. 1195	—	—	—
Sherburn	* {Christ, B.V. Mary, SS. Lazarus, Mary [Magd.] & Martha[7]} ++	c. 1181	Bp. H. Puiset	Bishop	L
Staindrop	St. Mary B.V.	1378	Earl Nevill	—	—
Werhale[8]	—	1265	—	Bishop	—
Witton Gilbert	†St. Mary Magdalene	bef 1180	Gilbert de la Ley	Durham Priory	L

[1] Durham Convent's Almoner's Book, p. 139. In St. Oswald's parish (Pat. 1292).   [2] Will, Mickleton MSS., vol. 47.   [3] United.
[4] St. Cuthbert added in charter.   [5] Seal, Soc. Antiq. E. II 4 B. 7.   [6] *Vita S. Godrici.*   [7] Now "Christ's."   [8] Between Wear and Tyne.

XII. ESSEX

Locality.	Dedication or Description.	Date.	Founder.	Patron.	
Bocking	Maison Dieu	1440	J. Doreward	—	—
Braintree	St. James	1229	—	—	—
Colchester (suburbs)	†St. Mary Magdalene	bef 1135	Henry I & Eudo	Abbey	L
,,	Holy Cross [& St. Helen][1] (Seal[2])	1235	W. de Lanvalle	ref St. Helen's Gild	—
,, by	St. Katharine	1352	—	—	—
,, ,,	St. Anne[3]	1402	—	—	—
Hedingham, Castle	—	c. 1250	De Vere	—	—
Hornchurch (Havering)	SS. Nicholas & Bernard	1159	Henry II	Alien,[4] New Coll. Ox.	L
Ilford, Great	*†St. Mary B.V. [and St. Thomas M.]	c. 1150	Adelicia, Abbess	Barking Abbey	L
Layer Marney	St. Mary B.V.	1523	Lord Marney	—	L
Maldon, Little	†St. Giles[5]	c. 1164	—	Various[6]	L
Newport (Birchanger)	St. Leonard	1157	—	Dean of St. Martin's	L
South Weald,[7] Brook Street	St. John Baptist	1233	Bruin	Private	L
Tilbury, East	St. Mary[8]	bef 1213	Earl Geoffrey	Earldom	—
Walthamstow	‡Almshouse	xvi cent.	G. Monnox	—	—

[1] Holy Cross (Pat. 1283). Afterwards "Almighty God, Mary the Mother of Jesus Christ, St. Helen, St. Katherine and All Saints." [2] Seal of Gild. [3] Pap. Letter 1402. Ely Reg. 1404. "Hermitage," Pat. 1402. [4] Under Mont Joux, Savoy. [5] Cf. St. Mary (Pat. 1349). [6] Private, Crown, Bykenacre Priory, Beeleigh Abbey. [7] Or Sydeburnebrok (Pat. 1341), near Brentwood. [8] Chapel, St. Margaret.

XIII. GLOUCESTERSHIRE

Locality.	*Dedication or Description.*	*Date.*	*Founder.*	*Patron.*	
Berkeley, Longbridge, near	Holy Trinity (Seal)	1189	Maurice de Berkeley	Private	—
Bristol, without Lawfords Gate	St. Laurence	*bef* 1208	Prince John	Various[1]	L
,, Frome Bridge	†St. Bartholomew[2]	*bef* 1207	—	Private	L (?)
,, Billeswick	*St. Mark (Seal)	1229	Maurice de Gaunt	Private	—
,, Bedminster[3]	St. Katherine (Seal)	1219	Robert de Berkeley	Private	—
,, Brightbow[3]	St. Mary M. (Seal)	1219	Thomas de ,,	Private	L
,, Redcliffe[3]	St. John B. (Seal)	1242	King or John Farcey	Crown, Town	—
,, Lawfords Gate	‡Holy Trinity	{1396 1408	J. Barstaple	Town	—
,, Steep Street	*‡Three Kings of Cologne (chapel)	1492	J. Foster	—	—
,, Long Row	‡Almshouse	*c.* 1292	S. Burton	—	—
,, Redcliffe	,,	1422	W. Canynge	—	—
,, without Temple Gate	,,	—	R. Magdalen	—	—
,, Lewin's Mead	*Trinity*	1460	W. Spencer	—	—
,, Redcliffe Gate	—	1471	R. Forster	—	—

[1] Manor of Bristol, Crown, Westbury College, etc. [2] Domus Dei by Frome Bridge (Pat. 1387). [3] In Somerset.

XIII. GLOUCESTERSHIRE—continued

Locality.	Dedication or Description.	Date.	Founder.	Patron.	
Cirencester	*‡St. John Ev.[1]	bef 1135	Henry I	Crown, Abbey	—
,,	‡St. Laurence	xiii cent.	Edith Bisset	Abbey	L
,,	‡St. Thomas M.	1427	W. Nottingham.	Weavers	—
Gloucester	*‡S. Mary Magdalene	bef 1160	—	Lanthony Priory	L
,, or Dudstan.	*‡St. Margaret or St. Sepulchre	bef 1163	—	Abbey, Town	L
,,	‡St. Bartholomew[2] (Seal)	1200	Townsmen, Henry III	Crown	—
Lechlade	St. John Baptist[3]	1228	Peter Fitz Herbert[4]	Private	—
Longbridge, v. Berkeley					
Lorwing[5]	—	1189	Maurice de Berkeley	—	—
Redcliffe, v. Bristol					
St. Briavels	St. Margaret[6]	1256	—	—	—
Stow-in-Wold	Holy Trinity	—	Aylmer, Earl of Cornwall	—	—
Tewkesbury[7]	Almshouse	1476	W. Chestre	—	—
,,	—	1199	—	—	L
Winchcombe	Almshouse	—	—	Abbey	—
,,	Spital	—	—	—	—

[1] Or Baptist (Pat. 1306). [2] Chapel, St. Ursula. [3] "St. John of Jerusalem" (Papal Letters 1291). [4] Or Isabel Ferrers. [5] Lorrenge, near Dursley. [6] Pat. 1256. [7] Charter, 1 John.

XIV. HAMPSHIRE

Locality.	Dedication or Description.	Date.	Founder.	Patron.	
Alton	St. Mary Magdalene	1235	—	—	L
Andover	St. John B.[1] (Seal)	1247	—	Town	|
,,	St. Mary Magdalene[1]	1248	—	—	L
Basingstoke	St. John Baptist	bef 1240	W. de Merton	Merton College	L
Christchurch[2]	—	1318	—	—	L
Fareham[3]	—	1199	—	—	|
Fordingbridge	St. John Baptist	1283	—	Bishop, St. Cross, etc.	|
Portsmouth	*God's House or St. John B. and St. Nicholas[4] (Seal)	1224	Peter des Roches	Bishop	|
,, by	St. Mary M. [and St. Anthony[5]]	1253	—	—	|
Romsey	St. Mary M. and St. Anthony[6]	1317	—	—	L
Southampton (without)	St. Mary Magdalene	1173	Townsmen	Town, Priory	L
,,	‡St. Julian or God's House (Seal)	c. 1197	Gervase	Crown, Queen's College, Oxford	|
,,	St. John[7]	1315	—	—	|

[1] United (Pat. 1340).   [2] Close 1318.   [3] Charter to lazars of Ferham (Pemb. Coll. Camb.).
[4] Or Holy Trinity, B.V.M., St. Cross, St. Michael & All SS. (Close 1215); cf. Seal.   [5] Pat. 1340.   [6] Pat. 1317.
[7] Pat. 1315.

XIV. HAMPSHIRE—continued

Locality.	Dedication or Description.	Date.	Founder.	Patron.	
Winchester (near)	*‡St. Cross (Seal)	c. 1136	Henry de Blois	Knights, Bishop	—
,, (without)	‡St. Mary Magd. (Seal¹)	1158	Bishop	Bishop	L
,,	*‡St. John B. (Seal²)	c. 1275	John Devenish	Town	—
,,	"Sisters' Hospital"	1393	—	St. Swithin's	—
Newport (Isle of Wight)	St. Augustine³	1352	—	Town	L

¹ Soc. Antiq., and *Vet. Mon.* III 12.   ² Seal, Soc. Antiq. E. II 4 B. 8., *v.* also Cal. Anc. Deeds II.
³ "Hospital for lepers of St. Augustine" (Pat. 1352).

XV. HEREFORDSHIRE

Locality.	Dedication or Description.	Date.	Founder.	Patron.	
Blechelowe, *v.* Richards Castle					
Hereford (Wye Bridge)	St. Thomas	1226	W. de Warenne	—	—
,,	‡St. Ethelbert	1231	—	Dean and Chapter	—
,,	St. Giles	1250	—	—	—
,,	‡St. Giles	—	—	Town	L
,,	[Holy Ghost¹ &] St. John	1340	—	Town	—
,,	St. Anthony	1294	—	Knights Hosp.	—
,,	St. Anne and St. Loye²	xvi cent.	—	Order (Vienne)	—
Ledbury	‡St. Katharine	1232	H. Foliot, Bishop	—	L
Richards Castle (Blechelowe)	St. John & St. Mary M.³	1397	—	Dean and Chapter	—

¹ Pat. 1340.   ² Hist. MSS. 13th R. (4) 314.   ³ Pat. 1397.

XVI. HERTFORDSHIRE

Locality.	Dedication or Description.	Date.	Founder.	Patron.	
Anstey (Biggin)	St. Mary	1325	—	—	—
Baldock (Clothall, by)	St. Mary Magdalene	1226	—	—	L
Berkhampstead	St. John Baptist	1216	Fitz Piers, Earl of Essex	Private; St. Thomas of Acon, London	—
,,	St. John Ev.	1216	—	,, ,,	L
,,	St. James	—	—	,,	—
,,	St. Leonard	—	—	—	—
,,	St. Thomas M.[1]	1317	—	—	—
Broxbourne, v. Hoddesdon					
Hertford (without)	St. Mary Magdalene[2]	1287	—	—	—
Hoddesdon	SS. Anthony & Clement or St. Laud & St. Anthony (Seals)	1391	—	—	L
,,	Almshouse	xv cent.	R. Rich	—	—
Royston	[St. Mary B.V. & St. James or] St. John & St. James	1227	—	Private	—
,,	St. Nicholas[3]	1213	Ralph	Private	L

[1] Pat. 1317 may refer to one of above hospitals.
[2] Cf. Cal. of Inquisitions I 538 ; cf. also Trinitarian Friary (Pat. 1287).
[3] In Cambridgeshire.

XVI. HERTFORDSHIRE—continued

Locality.	Dedication or Description.	Date.	Founder.	Patron.	
St. Albans (Eywood)	St. Julian the Confessor	1146	Abbot Geoffrey	Abbey	L
,, (without)	St. Mary de la Pré[1] (Seal)	1202	—	Abbey	L
,,	St. Giles[2]	1327	—	Abbey	—
Stevenage	All Christian Soul House	1501	Hellard, Rector	Parish	—
Wymondley, Little	St. Mary[3]	1232	—	—	—

[1] Afterwards Priory.
[2] Close 1327.
[3] Charter 1232 and *Liber Antiq. Hugonis Wells* (1209–35); or Priory.

XVII. HUNTINGDONSHIRE

Locality.	Dedication or Description.	Date.	Founder.	Patron.	
Huntingdon	St. John Baptist	1153	Earl David	Earldom, Town	—
,, (without[1])	St. Margaret	1165	King Malcolm (*ben*)	Crown (Scotland, England, etc.)	L
,,	St. Giles[2]	1328	—	—	L

[1] In Great Stukeley (Pat. 1391).
[2] Pat. 1328.

XVIII. KENT

Locality.	Dedication or Description.	Date.	Founder.	Patron.	L etc.
Bapchild[1]	—	c. 1200	—	—	—
Blean[1]	St. John	c. 1200	—	—	L
Bobbing	Spital	—	George Clifford	Private	L
Boughton-under-Blean	Holy Trinity[2]	1384	Thomas atte Herst		L etc.
Buckland, v. Dover					
Canterbury (Northgate)	*‡St. John B. (Seal)	bef. 1089	Lanfranc	Archbishop	—
,, (Eastbridge)	*‡St. Thomas M.[3] [and the Holy Ghost] (Seal)	c. 1170	Becket, Langton	Archbishop	—
,,	St. Nicholas and St. Katharine[4]	1293	W. Cokyn	—	—
,,	*‡[St. Mary B.V. or] Poor Priests' (Seal)	1225	ref. S. de Langton	Archdeacon	—
,,	‡St. Mary B.V.	1317	J. Maynard	Town	L
,, near	St. Laurence	1137	Hugh, Abbot	St. Augustine's	L
,, Harbledown	*‡St. Nicholas (Seal)	bef. 1089	Lanfranc	Archbishop	L
,, Thanington or Wynchepe	St. James (Seal)	bef. 1164	—	Christchurch	—
Chatham, v. Rochester					
Dartford	St. Mary Magdalene	1256	—		L
,,	Holy Trinity	1453	Townsmen	Parochial Governors	—

[1] Gervase of Canterbury mentions hospitals of Bakechild and St. John in Blen; cf. Blien, Pipe Rolls and Rot. Cancell.
[2] Or St. Nicholas (Harris).   [3] Chapel St. Mary V. (Pat. 326).   Double Dedication Pat. 1353.   [4] United with St. Thomas M.

XVIII.   KENT—*continued*

Locality.	Dedication or Description.	Date.	Founder.	Patron.	
Dover, Buckland in	St. Bartholomew	1141	Monks	Priory	
Dover	*St. Mary B.V. (Seal)	1221	Hubert de Burgh	Crown	L
Gravesend, *v.* Milton					
Harbledown, *v.* Canterbury					
Hythe	†St. John Baptist	1426	Townsmen	Town	
" Saltwood[1] nr.	{†St. Bartholomew (Seal) [or St. Andrew]	{1276, 1336	—	—	
Ivychurch,[2] near New Romney	—	1229	Bishop Haymo	Private	
Lullingstone[3]	*Almshouse*	—	Sir J. Peche	—	
Maidstone	*St. Peter & St. Paul [& St. Thomas M.][4] (Seal)	—	Abp. Boniface	Archbishop	
" (bridge)	Almshouse[5]	1422	Hessynden	—	
Milton nr. Gravesend	—	1189	—	Private	
Mepham	†St. Mary B.V. (Seal)	1396	Archbishop	—	
Ospringe	St. Nicholas[6]	1234	Henry III	Crown	
" (without)	St. John[7]	1241	—	—	
Otford	—	1343	—	—	L
Puckeshall or Tong	St. James	*1228*	—	—	L
Rochester (Langeport)	*†St. Bartholomew (Seal)	*bef*1108	Bishop Gundulf	Priory	L

				Governors	L etc.
Romney (Eastgate)	St. Katharine	1316	S. Potyn	Private	L
Romney	St. Stephen and St. Thomas M. (Seal[10])	c. 1180	Adam de Cherring[9]	Private	L
Sandwich	St. John Baptist	1396	—	Town	—
Sandwich	†St. Bartholomew (Seal)	bef 1227	Crawthorne, etc.	Town	—
Sandwich	‡St. Johr. B. (Seal[11])	bef 1287	—	Town	—
Sandwich	‡St. Thomas M.	1392	Thos. Ellys	Town	L
Sandwich (Each End)	St. Anthony[12]	1472	—	—	—
Sevenoaks	St. John Baptist	1338	re-f. Cherwode & Multon	Archbishop	—
Sittingbourne[13]	‡Almshouse	1418	Sir W. Sevenoke	Parochial Governors	—
Sittingbourne, Swinestre nr.	—	1216	Samuel		—
	St. Leonard[14]	1232			L
Strood	Holy Cross[14]	1225	—	Bishop or Priory	—
Strood	St. Mary B.V.[15] (Seal)	1193	Bp. G. Glanvill		—
Sutton-at-Hone	Holy Trinity, St. Mary, and All SS.	1216	FitzPiers & W. de Wrotham		—
Thanington, v. Canterbury					
Tong, v. Puckeshall					
Wynchepe, v. Canterbury					

[1] Cf. "Infirmis de Salt Wuda" (Pipe Rolls, 1168-9).   [2] Close 1299.   [3] Harris.   [4] Thus *Gent. Mag.*, 1842; also called Newark.   [5] Papal Lett. 1422.   [6] Pat. 1241.   [7] Close 1343.   [8] Lepers "de Albo Fossato" (Pat. 1253) or "Wyddych" (Pat. 1443) or "next Strood" (Wills).   [9] *Re-f.* 1363 by J. Franceys (*Lit. Cant.* ii. 436).   [10] Canterbury Chapter Library.   [11] Soc. Antiq. E. II 4 B. 8.   [12] Or "Maldry."   [13] Chapel, St. Thomas, M. (V.C.H.)   [14] Possibly identical.   [15] Or "Newark."

XIX. LANCASHIRE

Locality.	Dedication or Description.	Date.	Founder.	Patron.	
Burscough . . .	—	bef 1311	—	Priory . .	L
Clitheroe[1] . .	St. Nicholas	1211	Townsmen	Town . .	L
Cockersand . .	Hospital[2]	1184	Hugh Garth .	—	L etc.
Conishead . .	Hospital[2]	1181	Penington or W. de Lancaster	Priory .	L
Lancaster . .	St. Leonard .	1189	Prince John .	Various[3] .	L
,, . .	Almshouse, St. Mary B.V.	1483	J. Gardyner .	Town .	—
Lathom (Ormskirk)	—	1500	Sir T. Stanley .	—	L
Preston in Amounderness	St. Mary Magd. (Seal[4]).	c. 1177	—	Honor, Crown	—
Stydd nr. Ribchester .	St. Saviour[5] .	bef 1216	—	Knights	—

[1] In Yorkshire; called "Edisford."   [2] Afterwards Priory.   [3] Honor of Lancaster, Crown, Seton Nunnery.
[4] Fitzwilliam Museum, Cambridge.
[5] Or St. Mary and Holy Saviour, or "under Longridge"; afterwards under Templars or Hospitallers.

XX. LEICESTERSHIRE

Locality.	Dedication or Description.	Date.	Founder.	Patron.	
Burton Lazars	[St. Mary B.V. and] St. Lazarus (Seal)	1146	R. de Mowbray	Order of St. Lazarus	L
Castle-Donington	St. John Ev.[1]	xii cent.	John Lacy	Earldom, Crown	L
Leicester	St. Leonard (Seal)	1199	William of Leicester	Earldom, Crown, etc.	L
,,	+St. John Ev. and St. John B. (Seal)	1200	—	—	—
,,	St. Edmund Abp. and Conf.	1250	—	—	—
,,	St. Mary M. and St. Margaret	1329	—	—	L
,,	*+Annunciation of B.V. Mary[2] (Seal)	1330	Henry of Lancaster	Duchy (Collegiate Foundation)	—
,,	+St. Ursula [and St. Catherine]	1513	W. Wigston	—	—
Lutterworth	St. John B. [& St. Anthony[3]]	1218	Roise de Verdon	Private	—
Stockerston	St. Leonard	1307	—	Earldom	—
Tilton	St. Mary [and All Saints]	1465	J. Boyvile	—	—
Tilton	—	*1189*	*W. Burdett*	*Burton Lasars*	L

[1] St. John B. in Valor Ecc.   [2] Or Newark; now Trinity.   [3] Pap. Lett. 1435-6.

XXI. LINCOLNSHIRE

Locality.	Dedication or Description.	Date.	Founder.	Patron.	
Boothby Pagnell	St. John Baptist	xii cent.	Hugh of Boothby	—	L
Boston[1] (without)	St. John Baptist	1282	—	Private (Multon[1])	—
Carleton in Moreland	St. Lazarus	1301	De Amundeville	Order of St Lazarus.	—
Dunston, v. Mere					
Edenham[2]	—	1319	—	—	—
Elsham by Thornton	St. Mary & St. Edmund[3]	1166	B. de Amundeville	—	—
Glanford Bridge (Wrauby)		xii cent.	Paynell	Selby Abbey	—
Grantham	[Our Lord &] St. John B.	1441	W. Tirwhit	—	—
Grantham by ,,	St. Margaret	1328	—	—	—
Grimsby (without)	St. Leonard	1428	—	—	L
,,	St. Mary M. & St. Leger	1291	—	—	—
,,	St. John[4]	1389	—	—	—
Holbeach	All Saints	1351	J. de Kirketon	—	—
Langworth	St. Margaret	1313	—	—	L
Lincoln without	Holy Innocents [& St. Mary M.] (Seal)[5]	bef 1135	Henry I	Crown, Burton Lazars	L
,, without	†† St. Giles	c. 1275	—	Dean & Chapter	L etc.
,,	St. Leonard	1300	—	—	L etc.
,, without	St. Bartholomew	1314	—	—	—
,,	St. Mary B.V. or St. Mary M.	1311	—	—	—

		Date	Bp. Robert Bloet	Gilbertine Order	
Lincoln without	Holy Sepulchre[6]	1123	,,	,,	
,, without	St. Katherine[6] (Seal)	1123	,,	,,	L
Louth	Spital	1314	—	Gild.	
,,	Trinity Bedehouse	xvi cent	—	,,	L
,,	St. Mary B.V.	,,	,,	,,	
Mere or Dunston	St. John Baptist	1243	S. de Roppele	Bishop	
Newstead by Stamford[7]	St. Mary B.V.[6]	xii cent.	W. d'Albini		L
Partney	St. Mary Magdalene	bef 1138	—	Bardney Abbey	
Skirbeck	{† St. Leonard, afterwards / St. John Baptist	1230	T. de Multon	Knights Hosp.	
Spalding	St. Nicholas	1313	—	—	L
Spittal-on-Street, Hemswell	St. Edmund K.M.	1322	*ref.* T. Aston	Dean & Chapter	
Stamford, *v.* Northants					
Tattershall[8]	Holy Trinity (Seal)[8]	1438	R. Cromwell	Collegiate Foundation	
Thornton	St. James (chapel)	1322	—	Abbey (probably)	
Threckingham	*St. Lazarus*[9]	1319	—		
Uffington, *v.* Newstead					
Walcot	St. Leonard	1312	—	—	L

[1] Close 1294, 1335. Cf. Skirbeck. [2] Pat. 1319. [3] Afterwards Priory. [4] Hist. MSS., 14th R. (8), 258.
[5] Double dedication Pat. 1346; chapel, St. Mary Magd. (Pat. 1339). Called Mallardly.
[6] Or Priory. [7] Or Uffington.
[8] Collegiate Church of Holy Trinity, SS. Mary, Peter, John Ev. & John B. [9] Pat. 1319.

XXII. MIDDLESEX AND LONDON

Locality.	Dedication or Description.	Date.	Founder.	Patron.	
Brentford[1]	St. Anne & St. Louis[1]	1393	—	—	—
,, Syon by	Nine Orders of Holy Angels (Seal)	c. 1447	J. Somerset	Fraternity	—
Hackney or Kingsland	St. Katherine[2]	1334	—	—	L
Holborn, v. London					
Holloway or Highgate	[Holy Jesus &] St. Anthony (Seal[3])	1473	W. Pole	Crown	L
Hounslow[4]	—	1200	—	—	—
Kingsland, v. Hackney					
Knightsbridge	St. Leonard[5] (Seal)	1485	—	Westminster Abbey	L
London,[6] Holborn	St. Giles[7] (Seal)	bef 1118	Queen Maud	Crown, Burton Lazars	L
,, West Smithfield	*†St. Bartholomew[8] (Seal)	c. 1123	Rahere	—	—
,, by Tower	†St. Katharine (Seal)	1148	Queen Matilda	Crown	—
,, Cheapside	[St. Mary &] St. Thomas M. "of Acon"[9] (Seal)	c. 1190	Fitz Theobald	Knights Templars	!
,,	St. John B.[10] (Seal) or "Savoy"	1505	Henry VII.	Crown	—
,, Threadneedle St.	St. Anthony (Seal)	1254	—	Order of Vienne, Crown, etc.	—
,, Churchyard	St. Paul	1190	Henry, Canon	Dean & Chapter	—
,, Paternoster	Holy Ghost, B.V.M., St. Michael & All SS.	1424	R. Whittington	Collegiate Foundation	—

		3 Priests	Fraternity	
London, nr. Aldgate	"St. Charity & St. John Ev."[11]	1442		
„ without Bishopsgate	St. Mary B.V. (Seal)	1197 W. Brune	—	
„ without Temple Bar	St. Mary or "Domus Conversorum"[12]	1231 Henry III.	Crown	
„ nr. Cripplegate	St. Mary, "Elsyng Spital" (Seal)	1329 W. Elsyng	Dean, etc., of St. Paul's	
„ without Bishopsgate	=St. Mary of Bethlehem (Seal[13])	1247 S. FitzMary	Order of Bethlehem, City Alien	
„ Charing Cross	St. Mary "of Rouncevall" (Seal)	bef. 1231	—	
„ Crutched Friars	Almshouse, St. Mary	c. 1524 J. Millborn	Drapers	
	St. James, v. Westminster			
	St. Thomas, v. Southwark, Surrey			
Mile End[14] or Stepney	St. Mary Magd. (Seal)	1274		L
Shoreditch[15]	Spital House	xvi cent.	—	
Westminster	St. James (Seal)	xii cent. ref. Henry III.	Abbey, Crown	L
„	Almshouse	xvi cent. Lady Margaret	—	

[1] Braynford, "S. Ludowicus," Ely Reg. Fordham f. 180.   [2] Cf. St. Bartholomew's Chapel, Hackney, called Loke.
[3] Soc. Antiq. E. II 4 B. 9.   [4] "Hundeslawe," Rot. Chart., 2 John, m. 32 d.
[5] Cf. Seal, B.V.M. & St. Leonard. Chapel, Holy Trinity.
[6] Stow mentions Alien Hospitals at Holborn, Aldersgate, Cripplegate.
[7] Parish church, St. Giles; chapel, St. Michael.   [8] Chapels, SS. Catherine, Nicholas & Andrew.
[9] Or "of Acres." Chapel, St. Cross (Pap. Let. 1365).   [10] Or Blessed Jesus, B.V.M. & St. John B.
[11] "The Papey," or St. Augustine's, for Priests.   [12] Chapel, Holy Trinity.   [13] Dugdale.
[14] Between Mile End and Stratford.   [15] Between Shoreditch and Stoke Newington.

XXIII. NORFOLK

Locality.	Dedication or Description.	Date.	Founder.	Patron.	
Bec (Billingford) Boycodeswade, v. Cokesford	St. Thomas M.[1] (Seal)	1224	William de Bec	Bishop	—
Burnham Overy or Peterstone	St. Peter[2] or St. Nicholas	1200	Cheney	—	—
Choseley	St. Lazarus	1291	—	Burton Lazars	L
Cokesford[3]	St. Andrew	c. 1181	Hervey Beleth	Cokesford Priory	—
Creak, North (Lingerscroft)	St. Mary[4]	1221	Robert de Nerford	—	—
Croxton	Domus Dei	1250	—	Hospital, Thetford	—
Gaywood, v. Lynn					
Hardwick (S. Lynn)[5]	St. Laurence	1327	—	Private	L
Hautbois, Great	St. Mary (God's House)	1235	Peter de Hautbois	Horning Hospital	—
Hempton (Fakenham)	St. Stephen[6] (Seal)	1135	De S. Martin	Private	—
Heringby	God's House (Seal)	1447	H. Attefenne	Collegiate Foundation	—
Hingham	Almshouse	1483	S. Lyster	—	—
Horning	St. James	1153	Abbot Daniel	Hulme Abbey, Bishop	—
Ickburgh or Newbridge	SS. Mary & Laurence	1323	W. Barentun	Private	L
Langwade (Oxburgh)	—	1380	—	—	L

					L etc.
Lingerscroft, v. Creak					
Lynn or Gaywood	=St. Mary Magd. (Seal[10])	1145	Peter, Chaplain	Town, Bishop	—
Lynn, Bishops	St. John Baptist	c. 1135	Ulfketel	—	L
,, West Lynn	—	—	—	—	L
,, Cowgate	—	1352	—	—	—
,, v. Hardwick					
Massingham	Domus Dei[7]	1260	—	Crown	—
Newbridge, v. Ickburgh					
Norwich	St. Paul Ap.[8] [& St. Paul, Hermit] (Seal)	bef 1119	Bishop Herbert	Bishops and Priory	—
,,	*+St. Giles, etc.[9] (Seal)	1246	W. de Suffield	,, ,,	—
,, Conisford	St. Mary B.V. (Seal[10])	1200	Hildebrond	Bishop	—
,, in Coselany	St. Saviour	1297	R. de Brekles		—
,,	God's House	xiii cent.	John le Grant	Bishop	—
,,	God's House	1292	Robert de Aswardby		—
,,	Almshouse	—	Croom		—
,,	,,	1418	Danyel		—
,,	,,	—	Hugh Garzon		—
,, (Sprowston)	St. Mary Magd. (Seal[10])	bef 1119	Bishop Herbert	Bishop	L
,, St. Austin's Gate	[St. Mary &] St. Clement	1312	Bishop	—	L
,, Fybridge Gate	St. Mary Magdalene	1448	—	—	L
,, Westwick Gate	St. Bennet (Seal[10])	—	—	—	L

[1] Chapel, St. Paul. [2] Afterwards Priory. [3] Or Boycodeswade in E. Rudham.
[4] Chapel, St. Bartholomew; afterwards Abbey. [5] Or Setche Parva. [6] Or St. Mary & St. Stephen; sometimes Priory.
[7] Or Priory. [8] Norman's Spital.
[9] Holy Trinity, B.V.M., St. Anne, St. Giles and All Saints, or St. Mary and St. Giles (Pap. Lett. 1255).
[10] *Index Monasticus.*

XXIII. NORFOLK—continued

Locality.	Dedication or Description.	Date.	Founder.	Patron.	
Norwich (cont.) Newport	St. Giles	1308	Balderic	—	L
,, Nedham	St. Stephen (Seal¹)	—	—	Horsham Priory	L
,, without	St. Leonard²	1335	—	—	
Racheness (Southacre)	St. Bartholomew	xii cent.	—	Castleacre Priory	L
Somerton, West	St. Leonard	1189	R. de Glanvill	Crown, Butley Priory	L
Snoring Parva	—	1380			L
Sprowston, v. Norwich					
Thetford	St. John Baptist²	xii cent.	Roger Bigod	Earldom, Town	L
,,	St. Mary Magdalene²	xiii cent.	J. de Warenne	Private	L
,,	St. Mary B.V.³	1325	—	—	
,,	St. Margaret	1304	—	Private	L
,,	St. John⁴	—	—	Private, Priory, etc.	L
,,	God's House⁴	1319	Earl of Surrey	Private	L
Walsingham	—	1486	—	—	
Walsoken	Holy Trinity (Seal)	bef 1200	—	Burton Lazars	L
Wymondham (Westwade)	—	—	—	—	
Yarmouth	St. Mary B.V. (Seal⁵)	1278	T. Fastolf	Private, Town	L
,, (Northgate)	—	1386	Townsmen	Town	L
,,	—	1349	—	—	
Yarmouth, Little, v. Gorleston, Suffolk	—	1349	—	—	L

¹ Close 1335, but probably Benedictine Cell.   ² United.   ³ Chapel, St. Julian.   ⁴ In Suffolk.
⁵ B.M. lxvi. 10, Cat. 3974, unidentified, but cf. *Sigilla Antiq. Norfolk.* (Ives); also Palmer I, 368.

XXIV. NORTHAMPTONSHIRE

Locality.	Dedication or Description.	Date.	Founder.	Patron.	
Armston (in Polebrook)	St. John Baptist	1231	R. de Trubleville	Private	—
Aynho	{St. James & St. John [or St. Mary & St. James]	1208	Roger Fitz Richard	Private, Magd. Coll. Oxford	—
Brackley	*St. James & St. John Ap. & Ev.[1] (Seal)	c. 1150	Robert Earl of Leicester	Private, Magd. Coll. Oxford	—
„ (without)	St. Leonard (Seal[2])	1280	—	Private	L
Byfield	St. John[3]	1313	—	—	L
Cotes by Rockingham	St. Leonard	1229	—	Peterborough Abbey	—
Fotheringhay	—		—		
Grimsbury, v. Banbury, Oxon					
Higham Ferrers[4]	St. James[5]	1163	Ferrers	Private	—
„ „	*‡Bede House	1423	Abp. Chichele	Collegiate Foundation	—
Kingsthorpe by Northampton	†St. David (Dewy) or Holy Trinity	1200	Peter Fitz Adam or King John	St. Andrew's Priory	—
Northampton (Cotton)	St. Leonard (Seal)	c. 1150	King	Town	L

[1] Originally St. John Ap.; St. John B. occurs 1301. [2] B.M. Mediæval Room, Case D, matrix.
[3] Cal. of Inq. V, p. 256. [4] Cf. "Infirmis de Hecham" (Pipe Rolls).
[5] Probably identical with St. James', Rushden, 1230, Reg. of Hugh of Wells (Cant. and Yk. Soc., p. 153).

XXIV. NORTHAMPTONSHIRE—continued

Locality.	Dedication or Description.	Date.	Founder.	Patron.	
Northampton (cont.)	*‡St. John B. [& St. John Ev.] (Seal)	c. 1140	William, Archdeacon	Bishop of Lincoln	—
„ (Northgate)	‡St. Thomas-à-Becket Hospital of Walbek	c. 1450 1301	Townsmen —	Town —	L
„ v. Kingsthorpe					
Peryho (in Southwick)	[St. John B. &] St. Martin, Bp.[1]	1258	Knyvet	Private, Cotherstoke Coll.	—
Peterborough	St. Thomas M.	bef 1194	Abbot Benedict	Abbey	L
„ near Higham Ferrers	St. Leonard	1125	Abbot	Abbey	
Rushden, v. Higham Ferrers					
Southwick, v. Peryho					
Stamford (Baron)	St. Giles	bef 1189	—	Peterborough Abbey	L
„ (without)	‡St. John B. & St. Thomas M.	c. 1174	Siward, Brand de Fossato, etc.	Abbey	—
„	Holy Sepulchre	bef 1189	—	„	
„ (without)	"St. Logar"[2]	bef 1199	W. de Warenne	—	
„	*‡Bedehouse or All Saints (Seal)[3]	bef 1485	W. Browne	—	
Thrapston	St. Leonard	1246	—	—	L
Towcester	St. Leonard	1200	—	Earl of Pembroke	L

[1] Pat. 1258, Bridges II, 473.   [2] Peck, Antiq. Annals, vii. pp. 7, 12; Survey, p. 5.   [3] In Lincolnshire.

Locality.	Dedication or Description.	Date.	Founder.	Patron.	
Alnwick, near	St. Leonard	xii cent.	Eustace de Vesci	Private, Abbey	—
Alribourn	St. Leonard	1331	—	Private	—
Alwynton	—	*1272*	*Bishop Philip*	—	L
Bamborough	St. Mary Magdalene	1256	—	Crown	—
Berwick-on-Tweed [1]	St. Mary Magdalene [2]	1301	—	—	—
,, ,,	God's House [3]	1286	Philip de Rydale	—	—
,, ,,	*St. Edward* [4]	1246	—	—	—
Bolam [5]	*St. Mary*	1285	—	—	L
Bolton (in Allendale)	Holy Trinity or St. Thomas M. (Seal)	1225	Robert de Ros	Rievaulx, Kirkham	—
Capelford by Norham	St. Mary Magdalene	1333	—	—	—
Catchburn nr. Morpeth	St. Mary Magdalene	1282	Roger de Merlay	Private	—
Corbridge	—	1378	—	—	L
Eglingham, Harehope by [6]	—	1331	—	—	—
Elleshaugh by Otterburn [7]	—	1240	Umfreville	Bishop	—
Embleton [8] near	—	1314	—	Private	—
Hertford Bridge [9]	St. Giles	1256	Merlay	—	—
Hexham	—	1200	Archbishop	Archbishop, Priory	L
,,	Pilgrims' Hospital	xiv cent.	—	—	—
Mitford nr. Morpeth	St. Leonard	xii cent.	William Bertram	Barony	—

[1] In Scotland.   [2] Segden by Berwick.   [3] Cf. Papal Letters, 1290, Pat. 1348.
[4] Pat. 1246. Cf. Trinitarian House on Bridge, but J. Scott mentions three hospitals besides Friary.
[5] Cal. Inquisitions II.   [6] Pat. 1331.   [7] In Redesdale.   [8] Spiteldene.   [9] Upon Blyth.

XXV. NORTHUMBERLAND—*continued*

Locality.	Dedication or Description.	Date.	Founder.	Patron.	
Morpeth, *v.* Catchburn					
Newbiggin-by-Sea[10]	—	1391	—	Private	
Newcastle-upon-Tyne (without)	‡St. Mary Magdalene (Seal)	*bef* 1135	*Henry I*	Town	L
,, (Westgate)	‡St. Mary B.V. (Seal) [& St. John Ev.]	*bef* 1189	Aselack	St. Bartholomew's Priory, Town	
,, (Sandhills)	St. Katherine (Maison Dieu)	{ 1403 / 1412	R. Thornton	Private, Town	
,, ,,	Trinity Almshouse	1492	—	Seamen's Gild	
,, ,,	Maison Dieu	1475	J. Ward	—	
,, ,,	,, ,,	1504	C. Brigham	—	
,, ,,	,, ,,	1360	W. Acton	—	
Rothbury	—	xvi cent.	—	Hulparke Priory	
Shipwash	—	1379	—	—	L
Tweedmouth (Spittal)	St. Bartholomew	1234	—	Bishop	
Tynemouth, near	St. Leonard	1293	—	Priory	L
Warenford	*St. John Baptist*	1253	—	Private	
Warkworth	St. John Baptist (Seal[11])	1292	—	Private, Hulparke Priory	
Wooler	St. Mary Magdalene	1302	—	Private	

10 Pat. 1391.　　11 *History of Northumberland*, V, 237.

XXVI. NOTTINGHAMSHIRE

Locality.	Dedication or Description.	Date.	Founder.	Patron.	
Bawtry (without)	*‡St. Mary Magdalene	1280	ref. Robert de Morton	Archbishop	—
Blyth (without)	‡St. John. Ev.[1]	1226	W. de Cressy	Private	L
„ (without)	St. Edmund	1228	—	—	L
Bradebusk, v. Gonalston					
Gonalston	St. Mary Magdalene	1252	W. Heriz	Private	L
Harworth, v. Bawtry					
Hodsock, v. Blyth					
Lenton	St. Anthony[2]	1330	—	Alien Priory	—
Newark (without N. gate)	‡St. Leonard	1125	Bishop Alexander	Bishop of Lincoln	—
„ v. Stoke by N.					
Newark (Milnegate)	Almshouse	1466	—	—	—
„ (Churchyard)	„	„	—	—	—
„ (Appiltongate)	„	„	—	—	—
Nottingham	St. John Baptist	1202	—	Town	L
„	St. Leonard	1189	—	Town	—
„	St. Sepulchre	1267	—	Palmers	—
„	St. Michael[3]	1335	—	—	—
„	St. Mary	1330	—	—	L
„ (Westbarre)	‡Annunciation of B.V.M.[4]	1390	J. Plumptre	—	L
„ (Leen Bridge)	St. Mary Magdalene		—	—	—
Southwell, near	St. Mary Magdalene	1255	—	Archbishop	L
Stoke-by-Newark, within	St. Leonard & St. Anne[5]	bef 1135	—	Private, Crown	—

[1] Occasionally "Baptist." [2] Pat. 1330, 1332. [3] Records, i, 126. [4] Chapels, St. Mary, St. Thomas M.
[5] Chapel St. Mary B.V. (1311).

XXVII. OXFORDSHIRE

Locality.	Dedication or Description.	Date.	Founder.	Patron.	
Banbury	St. John B. (Seal)	1241	R. Whiting	Bishop of Lincoln	
„	New Almshouse	1501	—	—	L
„ or Grimsbury[1]	St. Leonard	bef 1307	—	—	
Bicester	St. Mary B.V. & St. John B.[2]	1355	N. Jurdan	—	
Burford	S. John Ev.[3] (Seal)	1226	—	Private	
„	Great Almshouse	1457	—	—	
Clattercote in Claydon[4]	St. Leonard (Seal)	1166	—	Bishop, Priory	L
Cold Norton	St. Giles	c. 1158	—	Priory	L
Crowmarsh[5] in Bensington	St. Mary Magdalene	1142	—	Osney Abbey	
Ewelme	*†God's House (Seal)	1437	De la Pole	Private	
Eynsham	—	1228	—	Abbey	
Newnham Murren, v. Wallingford, Berks					
Oxford (without E. gate)	*St. John B. (Seal)	c. 1180	ref. Henry III	Crown	L
„ (without)	*St. Bartholomew	1126	Henry I	Crown, Oriel Coll.	
„ (suburbs)	St. Giles[6]	1330	—	—	
„	St. Peter	1338	—	—	

Locality.	Dedication or Description.	Date.	Founder.	Patron.	L
Oxford . . .	St. Clement[7] .	1345	Henry III	—	—
,, . . .	Domus Conversorum .	1234	—	—	—
,, . . .	"Bethlem"[8] .	1219	—	—	—
Thame . .	St. Christopher[9] .	1460	R. Quartermayne	·	—
Woodstock[10] .	St. Mary V. & St. Mary M.[11] .	1339	—	—	—
,, (without) .	St. Cross[11] .	1231	—	—	L

[1] In Northants.   [2] Possibly never completed.   [3] Occasionally "Baptist."   [4] Near Cropredy; Gilbertine Priory.   [5] Cf. Wallingford and Newnham.   [6] Pat. 1330, 1346, at Rotherweye.   [7] Pat. 1345.   [8] See Wood.   [9] Fraternity.   [10] Also House of SS. Nonne and Sonndaye, c. 1560 (W. A. Bewes, Briefs).   [11] One almshouse built 1220 (Close Rolls). Cf. Leper women of Woodstock (Close, 234).

XXVIII. RUTLAND

Locality.	Dedication or Description.	Date.	Founder.	Patron.	L
Casterton, Great .	St. Margaret.	1311	—	—	
Oakham .	*†St. John Ev. & St. Anne	1398	W. Dalby .	Private .	L
Tolethorpe[1] .	—	1301	John de Tole-thorpe	—	

[1] Afterwards College.

XXIX. SHROPSHIRE

Locality.	Dedication or Description.	Date.	Founder.	Patron.	
Bridgnorth (without[1])	"Vetus Maladeria"	—	—	—	L
,, (without)	S. James (Seal[2])	1224	—	—	L
,,	(St. John Ev. or Holy Trinity, B.V.M. and St. John B. (Seal[3])	c. 1199	R. le Strange	Crown, Lilleshall Abbey	—
Ludlow	Holy Trinity, St. Mary & St. John B.	1253	P. Undergod	—	—
,,	St. Giles[4]	—	—	—	
,,	†Almshouse	1486	J. Hosyer	Palmers' Gild	
Nesscliff, Great Ness	"St. Mary de Rocherio"	c. 1250	Le Strange	Private	
Newport[5]	S. Giles	1337	—	—	
,,	†St. Nicholas[6]	1446	W. Glover, etc.	Town	
Oswestry	St. John Baptist	1210	Bishop Reyner	Haughmond Abbey	L
Richards Castle, v. Herefordshire					
Shrewsbury (without)	St. Giles (Seal[7])	1136	King	Crown, Abbey	L
,, (Frankvill)	S. John B. (Seal[8])	1221	—	Crown, St. Chad's	
,,	St. George M.[9]	1162	—	—	
,,	St. Chad's Almshouse	1409	B. Tuptun	Mercers' Fraternity	—

					Drapers' Fraternity.
Shrewsbury	†St. Mary's Almshouse	c. 1444	Degory Watur	Private,	—
Tong	St. Bartholomew	c. 1410	De Bohun, Pen-bridge	Private, Collegiate Foundation	—
Wenlock, Much	St. John	1267	—	—	—
Whitchurch	—	xiii cent.	Le Strange (ben.)	Private, Haughmond	—

[1] Towards Oldbury. Cf. "St. Lazarus," Close 1231.
[2] Eyton's *Salop*, I 16, 349.
[3] Soc. Antiq. E, II 4 B. 7.
[4] Existing 1554, Hist. MSS. 13th R. (4) 281.
[5] "Del Path by Newport."
[6] St. Nicholas, Christ, B.V.M. and All SS.
[7] Owen and Blakeway's *Hist.* ii. 173.
[8] id. ii, 470. c² B.M. lxxi 34
[9] Annexed to St. John's.

XXX. SOMERSET

Locality.	Dedication or Description.	Date.	Founder.	Patron.	
Bath	†‡ St. John Baptist[1]	c. 1180	Bishop John or Reginald	Bishop, Prior	
„ Holloway or Lyncomb	*‡ [St. Cross &] St. Mary Magdalene	bef 1100	Walter Hosate	Priory	L
Beckington	Almshouse	1502	—	—	
Bedminster, v. Glos					
Bridgwater	St. John B. (Seal)	1214	W. Briwere	Private	L
„	St. Giles	xiv cent.	—	—	
Bristol v. Glos.					
Bruton[2]	Almshouse[3]	1291	—	—	
Croscombe	*Almshouse (Women's)	xvi cent.	—	—	
Glastonbury	*‡St. Mary Magdalene[4]	bef 1246	re-f. Abbot Beere	Abbey	
„		xiii cent.	—	„	
Holloway, v. Bath					
Ilchester[5]	St. Margaret[5]	1212	—	—	L
„	Holy Trinity	1217	W. Dacres	Private	
„	Almshouse	1426	R. Veal	—	

Keynsham . .	St. John B. (Seal[6]) .	xv cent.	—	—	L
Langport,[7] near .	St. Mary Magdalene .	1280	—	Private, Glastonbury Abbey	L
Selwood[8] .	—				L
Taunton (W. Monkton) .	*‡[Holy Ghost &[9] St. Margaret	1212	—	—	L
		1185	Abbot Beere (ben)	Priory . .	L
Wells . .	‖St. John B. (Seal). .	1206	Hugh & Jocelyn	Bishop . .	—
,, . .	*‡St. Saviour [B.V.M. & All Saints]	1436	Bishop Bubwith	Dean, Mayor, etc. .	—
Yeovil . .	‡St. George & St. Christopher	1477	J. Wobourne	—	—

[1] Chapel of St. Michael attached.
[2] Cf. Lincoln Taxation.
[3] Chant. Cert.
[4] W. Phelps gives St. Margaret's; cf. Warner.
[5] Will of Bishop Hugh, 1212, Pat. 1235.
[6] B.M. civ. 13. Cf. Soc. Antiq. *Minutes* iv. 189.
[7] In Curry Rivell.
[8] Will, *supra*.
[9] Pat. 1334.

XXXI. STAFFORDSHIRE

Locality.	Dedication or Description.	Date.	Founder.	Patron.	
Cannock	St. Mary[1]	1220	—	—	
Freeford, *v.* Lichfield					
Lichfield	*‡St. John B. (Seal)	—	Bishop Roger	Bishop	L
,, (Freeford)	St. Leonard	1257	—	—	
,, (Bacon Street)	‡Almshouse	1504	Milley	—	
Radford, *v. infra*					
Stafford (Forebridge)	†St. John B. (Seal[2])	1208	Earl Ralph	Private	L
,,	St. Leonard	—	,,	,,	
,, (Retford)	Holy Sepulchre [or St. Lazarus]	1254	—	,,	L
Stoke-upon-Trent	St. Loye[3]	xvi cent.	—	—	
Tamworth or Wigginton	†St. James	1285	P. de Marmyon	Private	
Wigginton, *v. supra*					
Wolverhampton	St. Mary B.V.	1392	Luson, Waterfall, etc.	—	

[1] Rot. Claus. 1220. [2] Soc. Antiq. E. II 4 B. 9. [3] Chant. Cert.

XXXII. SUFFOLK

Locality.	Dedication or Description.	Date.	Founder.	Patron.	
Beccles	St. Mary M. [& St. Anthony]	1327	—	—	L
Bury St. Edmunds	St. John Ev. (God's House)	1256	Abbot Edmund	Abbey	—
,, without Eastgate	†St. Nicholas	c. 1215	—	,,	—
,, without Northgate	†St. Saviour[1]	c. 1184	Abbot Sampson	,,	L etc.
,, without Risbygate	†St. Peter	xiicent.	Abbot Anselm	,,	L
,, at Southgate	†St. Petronilla	xvi cent.	—	,,	—
,,	St. Stephen[2]	—	—	,,	L
Clare	Almshouse	1462	J. Bingley	—	—
Dunwich	‡†St. James (Seal)	1199	Prince John or W. de Riboff	—	—
,,	‡Holy Trinity or Maison Dieu (Seal[2])	1251	—	Crown	—
Eye (without)	†St. Mary Magdalene	1329	—	Town	L
Gorleston[3]	St. Mary & St. Nicholas (Seal[4])	1331	—	—	L
,,	St. James	—	—	—	—
,,	St. John Baptist	xiii cent.	Queen Eleanor	—	L
,,	St. Mary Magdalene	xvi cent.	—	—	—
,,	St. Luke	,,	—	—	—

[1] Chapel, St. Thomas M.   [2] Index Mon.
[3] Southtown or Little Yarmouth. See B. M. Egerton, 2130.   [4] B. M. lxxi, 103. Cat. 3216.

XXXII. SUFFOLK—*continued*

Locality.	Dedication or Description.	Date	Founder.	Patron.	
Gorleston	St. Bartholomew	xvi cent.	—	—	
Hadleigh	Almshouse	1497	W. Pykenham, Rector	—	
Ipswich	St. James[1]	1199	—	Bishop	L
,,	St. Mary Magdalene[1]	1199	—	Bishop	L
,, near	St. Leonard[2]	xvi cent.	—	—	L
	St. Thomas[2]	—	—	—	
,,	Almshouse	1515	E. Dandy	—	L
Orford	St. Leonard	1320	—	—	
,,	St. John Baptist	1389	—	—	
Sibton	†Hospital	1264	—	Abbey	L
Stratton-in-Leverington	—	—	—	—	
Sudbury	Holy Sepulchre	1206	Wm. Earl of Gloucester	Earldom of St. Clare, etc.	
,,	Jesus Christ & St. Mary B.V.	—	Countess Amicia	—	
Thetford, v. Norfolk	†St. Leonard	1372	John Colneys	Governors	L
Thurlow, Great	St. James	1291	—	Alien, etc.	

[1] United.   [2] N. Bacon's *Annalls*.

XXXIII. SURREY

Locality.	Dedication or Description.	Date.	Founder.	Patron.	
Bermondsey	—	*1399*	*Richard II*	—	L
Croydon	‡St. John Baptist	1443	Ellis Davy	Governors	—
Guildford	St. Thomas M.[1] (Spital)	1231	—	—	L
Kingston-on-Thames	St. Leonard, Domus Dei	1227	King	Crown	—
Newington Butts	Our Lady & St. Katherine	xvi cent.			—
Reigate	St. Mary V. & Holy Cross[2] (Seal)	*bef* 1240	W. de Warenne	—	—
Sandon by Cobham	The Holy Ghost[3] [or St. Mary M.] (Seal[4])	xii cent.	R. de Wateville	Bishop; St. Thomas', Southwark	—
Southwark	‡St. Thomas M.[5] (Seal)	*bef* 1215	Becket, Peter des Roches	—	—
„ (Kent Street)	[St. Mary &] St. Leonard[6]	1315	—	—	L
Tandridge	St James[2]	xii cent.	Odo de Dammartin	—	—

[1] Pat. 1231, 1331. [2] Afterwards Priory. [3] "Commonly called of the Holy Ghost" (Pat. 1436); St. Mary & All SS. (Stow).
[4] Seal shows St. Michael. Soc. Antiq. E. II 4 B. 8. [5] Originally Holy Trinity & St. Thomas; now in Lambeth.
[6] "Le Loke"; "atte Stonok"; without St. George's Bar; or the lepers of St. Thomas Wateryng.

XXXIV. SUSSEX

Locality.	Dedication or Description.	Date.	Founder.	Patron.	
Arundel	St. James	1189	Fitzalan	Earldom	L
,,	Holy Trinity or Christ (Seal)	1380	,,	,,	
Battle	Pilgrim House, afterwards St. Thomas M.[1]	1076	—	Abbey	
Bramber (Bidlington)	St. Mary Magdalene	1216	—	Private	L
Buxsted	—	*1404*	*W. Heron*	—	
Chichester	*†St. Mary B.V. (Seal)	1172	William, Dean	Dean & Chapter	L
,, without Eastgate	††St. James & St. Mary Magdalene (Seal[2])	1202	Bp. Seffrid II	Crown	L
,, *Loddesdown*	St. Mary Magdalene	—	—	—	L
,, *Rumboldswyke*	—	—	—	—	L
,, *Stockbridge*	—	—	—	—	L
Cookham in Sompting	[St. Mary V. &] St. Anthony	1272	W. Bernchius	Various[3]	L
Harting (Dureford)	St. John Baptist	1162	H. Hoese	Private, *Dureford Abbey*	
Hastings	†St. Mary Magdalene	1293	Petronilla de Cham (*ben*)	Town	

Place	Dedication	Date	Founder	Patron					
Hemsworth (in Burn)	St. Mary Magdalene[4]	1251	—	Priory	—	•	•	•	—
Lewes	St. James	—	W. de Warenne	,,	•	•	•	•	—
,, (Westout)	St. Nicholas	c. 1085	,,	,,	•	•	•	•	—
Pevensey	Holy Cross	1292	—	Town	—	•	•	•	—
,, or Westham[5]	†St. John Baptist	1302	—		—	•	•	•	—
Playden, v. Rye									
Rye or Playden	St. Bartholomew	1219	—	Alien, Crown, Town	—	•	•	•	L
Seaford, near	St. James	1171	Roger de Fraxeto	Chichester Cathedral	—	•	•	•	L
,, without	St. Leonard	bef 1256	,,	,,	—	•	•	•	—
Shoreham	St. James	1249	—		—	•	•	•	—
,,	St. Katherine[6]	1366	—		—	•	•	•	—
Sompting, v. Cookham									
Westham, v. Pevensey									
West Tarring	St. Mary	1277	—		—	•	•	•	—
Winchelsea[7]	†St. Bartholomew	1292	—	Town	—	•	•	•	—
,,	†St. John	1292	—	,,	—	•	•	•	—
,,	Holy Cross[8] (Seal)	1253	—		—	•	•	•	—
Windeham	St. Edmund, Conf.[9]	1253	Bishop Richard	Bishop	—	•	•	•	—

[1] Occurs 1345. [2] Lewes Museum (64). [3] Private, Heringham Priory, Knights Hosp. [4] Pat. 1251.
[5] Called Gorogltown. [6] Afterwards St. Saviour (Seal). Cf. Leper-house, 1287. [7] Leper-house mentioned 1287.
[8] Pat. 1253; or Holy Rood, Pat. 1426. [9] Or with St. Mary.

XXXV. WARWICKSHIRE

Locality.	Dedication or Description.	Date.	Founder.	Patron.	
Birmingham	[St. Mary V.[1] &] St. Thomas M.	1286	—	—	
Bretford (Wolstan)	St. Edmund[2]	1180	Turville	Private	L
Coventry	St. John B. (Seal)	1175	Archdn. & Prior	Priory	
,, Spon near	St. Mary Magd. (Seal[3])	1181	Hugh Keveliog	Various[4]	L
,,	St. Leonard[5]	1252	—	—	L
,,	Hospital[6]	1370	William Walssh	—	
,, Bablake	*‡Holy Trinity	1507	T. Bonde	Gild, etc.	
,,	*‡Almshouse[7]	1529	W. Ford	Gild	
Henley in Arden	—	re-f1449	—	Fraternity	
Stratford-on-Avon	Holy Cross (Seal)[8]	1269	—	Priory	
Studley	[Holy Ghost[9] &] St. John B.	c. 1183	W. de Cantilupe	—	
Warwick	—	c. 1135	Earl Wm. or Henry	Earldom	
,,	St. Michael	—	Earl Roger	Knights Templars	L
,, (without)	St. Thomas of Canterbury	1255	Earl	—	
,,	St. Laurence		—		L

[1] Pap. Lett., 1437.   [2] There was Leper-house, c. 1180; cf. Pat. 1274. St. Edmund occurs Pat. 1257.
[3] Soc. Antiq. E. II, 4 B. 8.   [4] Priories of Basingwerk, Coventry, and Studley.   [5] Pat. 1252, 1256.
[6] W. Salt Arch. Trans. 8, New Series.   [7] Called Greyfriars.   [8] Cf. Papal Petition, 1364; Pap. Lett., 1427, 1432.
[9] Double dedication, Pat. 1337.

XXXVI. WESTMORLAND

Locality.	Dedication or Description.	Date.	Founder.	Patron.	
Appleby .	St. Nicholas . .	*bef* 1240	—	Private, Shap Abbey	L
Brough under Stanemoor	St. Mary V. & St. Gabriel	1506	J. Brunskill .	Shap Abbey . .	—
Kendal (Kirkby-in-) [1] .	St. Leonard . .	1189	De Ros .	Private, Conishead Priory	L
Kirkby, *v.* Kendal					

[1] Cf. " Haye " (Pat. 1297).

XXXVII. WILTSHIRE

Locality.	Dedication or Description.	Date.	Founder.	Patron.	
Bedwin	St. John Baptist[1]	—	—	—	
Bradford-on-Avon	St. Margaret[2]	1235	King	Shaftesbury Abbey	L
,, ,,	St. Katherine[3]	—	—		L
Bradley, Maiden	St. Mary V. [and St. Matthew[4] or [St. Lazarus] (Seal)	c. 1190	Manser and Margery Bisset		
Calne, near	St. John B. [& St. Anthony[5]	1202	Lord Zouche		
Chippenham	St. Laurence[6]	1338	—		
Cricklade	St. John Baptist	1231	Guarin	Bishop of Sarum	
Devizes	St. John Baptist	1207	—	Town	L
,, (Southbroom)	St. James & St. Denys	1207	—		
Easton Royal[7]	—	1246	Stephen, Archdeacon	Private	
Fugglestone, v. Wilton					
Heytesbury	†St. John or St. Katherine (Seal)	c. 1449	Walter, Lord Hungerford	Various	
Malmesbury	†St. John Baptist[8]	—	—		
,,	St. Anthony[9]	1245	—		
,, (Burton by)	St. Mary Magdalene[10]	bef 1222	—		L

Marlborough[11] . .	St. John Baptist .	1215	Levenoth .	Town	—
,, . .	St. Thomas M. .	bef 1246	—	Manor (Crown), Gilbertine Priory	—
Salisbury (Harnham Bridge)	*†St. Nicholas[12] (Seal)	1214	Bishop .	Bishop, Dean & Chapter	—
,, . .	†Holy Trinity [& St. Thomas M.] (Seals)	bef 1379	Agnes Bottenham[13]	Town .	—
,, (East Harnham)[14]	—	1361	—	—	L
Sarum, Old[15]	—	1195	—	—	L
,, or Stratford[16]	St. John Baptist .	1231	—	—	—
Southbroom, v. Devizes					
Stratford, v. Sarum					
Trowbridge .	Almshouse	1483	J. Terumber	—	L
Wilton or Fugglestone .	††St. Giles [& St. Anthony[17]] (Seal)	c. 1135	Queen Adela	Crown, Town	—
,, (Ditchampton) .	*†St. John Baptist .	1190	Bishop Hubert .	—	—
,, .	†St. Mary Magdalene	1307	—	Abbey	—
Wootton Bassett .	St. John Baptist .	1256	P. Basset & Rector	Various[18]	—

[1] P.R.O. Ancient Deeds, C. 3000. [2] Pat. 1235, *Wilts Mag.*, v. 36. [3] *Wilts Mag.*, xx. 316. [4] Pat. 1242. Fair on Feast of St. Matthew (Charter 1215); cf. Surtees Soc. xxxi. 83, 91. [5] Pat. 1248. [6] Pat. 1338. [7] Served by Maturin Friars. [8] *Reg. Malmes.* ii. 75; cf. Pat. 1344-5 and *Wilts Mag.*, xxix. 122. [9] Pat. 1245; cf. leper-house, near South Bridge (Leland). [10] *temp.* Abbot Walter, *Reg. Malmes.* ii. 80; cf. Pat. 1235. [11] Leper-house, 1221. [12] Chapels, St. Nicholas, St. Mary V. [13] Re-f. J. Chaundeler (Pat. 1394). [14] Wills, Hoare vi. 92. [15] Feet of Fines, 7 Ric. I. [16] By the Castle. [17] Pat. 1465. [18] Despenser, Crown, etc., Bradenstoke Priory.

XXXVIII. WORCESTERSHIRE

Locality.	Dedication or Description.	Date.	Founder.	Patron.	
Droitwich or Dodderhill .	St. Mary B.V. [1] (Seal) .	bef 1285	Wm. de Dover, Rector	Worcester Priory .	—
Worcester, near . .	‡St. Oswald [2] . .	bef 1205	Bishop Oswald .	,, ,,	L
,, . . .	St. Mary [2] .	1257	—	,,	L
,, (without) .	*St. Wulstan [3] (Seal) .	c. 1085	Bishop Wulstan	Bishop . .	—
,, . . .	Trinity Hall Almshouses	xvi cent.	—	Gild . .	—

[1] "Wichio," Pat. 1285.
[2] Probably identical.
[3] Chapel, St. Godwald.

XXXIX. YORKSHIRE

Locality.	Dedication or Description.	Date.	Founder.	Patron.	
Aberford[1]	—		—	—	—
Allerton, v. Northallerton					
Bagby[2]	—	c. 1200	Mowbray	St. Leonard's, York	—
Bawtry, v. Notts					
Beverley	St. Giles	bef 1223	Wulse	Abp., Wartre Priory	—
,, in Friary by	St. Nicholas	bef 1286	—	Town	L
,, without Kell-gate Bar		1392	—	Town	—
,, Crossbridge	Holy Trinity	1398	John Ake	Town	—
,, Laithgate	St. John *Baptist*	1454	—	—	—
,, without N. Bar	St. Mary B.V.	1442	—	Gild, Town	—
Blyth, v. Notts					
Braceford[3], nr. Harpham	St. Helen	bef 1389	—	Private	—
Bridlington[4]	—	1342	—	Priory	—
Brompton, Brough, v. Catterick					
Broughton nr. Malton	St. Mary Magdalene	1154	Eustace FitzJohn		—
Catterick nr. Brompton-on-Swale	St. Giles	1231	*H. FitzRandolph*	Private	—

[1] Yks. Arch. Soc. Record Ser. 39, p. 108.
[2] In Kirkby Knowle.
[3] Cf. Breydeford (Linc. Tax., 1291).
[4] Pap. Letters, 1342.

XXXIX. YORKSHIRE—continued

Locality.	Dedication or Description.	Date.	Founder.	Patron.	
Clitheroe, v. Lancs					
Doncaster	St. Nicholas	1213	—	Beigham Abbey	—
,,	St. James (Seal)	1227	—	Private, St. Thos. of Acon	L
,, (by bridge)	St. Edmund K.[1]	1318	—	—	—
,,	*St. Leonard*	—	—	—	—
Edisford, v. Lancs					
Flixton[2]	St. Mary V. & St. Andrew	x cent.	Acehorne	·	—
Foulsnape, v. Pontefract					
Fountains	Almshouse	1247	Abbot John (*ben.*)	Abbey	—
Gainsborough	—	1495	·	—	L
Hedon, Newton by	St. Sepulchre	1205	Alan FitzHubert	Private	L
Hedon or Newton Garth[3]	St. Mary Magd. (Seal)	1162	Wm. le Gros	Earls of Albemarle, Crown	—
Hedon	St. Leonard	1413	—	—	—
Hessle	St. James[4]	—	—	—	—
Hoperton	*Bedehouse*	1500	—	—	—
Hutton Locras, v. Low-cross					
Killingwoldgrove[5]	St. Mary Magdalene	c. 1169	—	·	—
Kingston-upon-Hull	God's House	1344	J. de Kingston	Archbishop	—

Place	House		Date	Founder / Patron			
Kingston-upon-Hull (Myton)	‡ { Maison Dieu, or St. Michael, St. Thomas M., etc., or Holy Trinity (Seal)[6] }	·	1365	W. and Michael Pole	Private	·	—
,,	Mariners or Trinity and Blessed Virgin	·	1369	—	Fraternity	·	|
,,	Corpus Christi[7]	·	1416	John Gregg	—		|
,,	Holy Trinity or New Maison Dieu	·	1482	—	—		|
,,	Maison Dieu or Alms-house	·	1380	Ravenser & Selby	—		|
,,	,,	·	1400	Simon de Grimsby			
,,	,,	·	1412	Bedforth ·	—		|
,,	,,	·	1439	Aldwick ·	—		|
,,	,,	·	1503	Adrianson ·	—		|
,,	,,	·	1509	Riplingham ·	—		|
,,	,,	·	1513	—			|
,,	St. James ·	·	1294	J. Lythegrayns ·		·	|
Laysingby nr. Northallerton	St. Mary B.V. ·	·	—	—	Bishop of Durham ·	·	
Lowcross[8]	St. Leonard ·	·	—	—	Private, Guisborough Priory	·	L
Malton, v. Norton							
Myton, v. Kingston							
Newton, v. Hedon							

[1] Pat., 1318.   [2] Or Carman's Spital.
[3] Neuton by Overpaghe.e in Holderness (Charter, 1301).   [4] Guisboro' Chartulary.
[5] In Bishop Burton.   [5] Seal, Soc. Antiq. E. II, 4 B. 8.   Now Charterhouse Charity.
[7] Or Maison Dieu of Christ.   [8] Or Giseburn.

XXXIX. YORKSHIRE—*continued*

Locality.	Dedication or Description.	Date.	Founder.	Patron.	
Northallerton (Romanby)	St. James (Seal)	*bef* 1208	Bishop Philip	Bishop of Durham	
,,	‡Maison Dieu	1476	Moore & Strangways	—	
Norton nr. Malton	St. Nicholas	1189	R. de Flamvill	—	
Otley	—	1311	Abp. *Thurstan*	Archbishop	L
Pickering	St. Nicholas	1325	—	Duchy of Lancaster, Crown	
Pontefract	‡St. Nicholas	*bef* 1135	*re-f.* R. de Lacy	Duchy, Nostell Priory	L
,, by	St. Mary Magdalene	1286	Henry de Lacy	—	L
,,	St. Mary B.V.	1335	Tabourere	—	
,,	‡Holy Trinity & B.V.M.[1] (Seal)	1385	R. Knolles	Duchy, Nostell Priory	
,, or Foulsnape	St. Michael the Archangel	1220	—	St. John's Priory or Burton Lazars	L
Rerecross, *v.* Stanemoor					
Richmond, near	St. Nicholas (Seal[2])	1172	Henry II. or Glanvill[3]	Various[4]	
,, by	St. Giles	1402	—	—	
Ripon	*‡St. John Baptist	1114	Abp. Thomas II	Archbishop	L
,, (Stammergate)	*‡St. Mary M. (Seal[5])	*bef* 1139	Abp. Thurstan	,,	
,, (Bondgate)	St. Nicholas[6]	1350	—	—	L
,,	††St. Anne (Maison Dieu)	1438	Neville	—	

Place	Dedication	Date	Founder	Owner	
Scarborough, by	St. Nicholas	bef 1298	—	Town	
,,	†St. Thomas M.	1189	H. de Bulemore	,,	
Sheffield	St. Leonard	1189	W. de Lovetot	—	
Sherburn-in-Elmet	St. Mary Magdalene	1311	—	Archbishop	
Skipton	St. Mary Magdalene	1306	—	—	
Sprotburgh, near	St. Edmund	1363	Fitzwilliam	Private	
Stanemoor or Rerecross	"Spital upon Stanemoor"	1171	—	Private, Marrick Nunnery	
Terrington[7]	—	1288	—	—	
Tickhill (without)	St. Leonard	1225	—	—	L
,, (Blyth Road)	Maison Dieu	1326	—	Humberston Priory	
,, Well, nr. Bedale	†St. Michael the Archangel	1342	John of Gaunt, re-f. R. de Neville	—	
Wentbridge	*St. Mary*[8]	1348	—	—	
Whitby	St. Michael[9]	1109	Abbot William	Abbey	L
,,	St. John Baptist	1320	—	—	
Yarm, near	St. Nicholas	1185	Brus	Private, Helaugh Park	
York	(St. Feter (Seal)	x cent.	Athelstan	Minster	L
,, without Walmgate	(*St. Leonard[10] (Seal)	re-f 1135	Stephen	Crown	
,,	St. Nicholas	1142	King & Abbot	Crown	
,, without Micklegate	St. Giles	1274	—	—	
	†St. Thomas M. (Seal)	1390	—	—	

[1] Or Hardwick Spital. [2] Yks. Arch. Journ. XIII 45. [3] Re-f. W. Ascogh 1448. [4] Earls of Richmond, Crown, Private.
[5] C. Hallett, Bell's Cath. Series, p. 138. [6] Pat. 1350. [7] Cal. of Inq. p.m. II, 666.
[8] Pat. 1348. [9] Whitby Chartulary. [10] Or Cremet-house Chapels. St. Katherine, St. Michael.

XXXIX. YORKSHIRE—*continued*

Locality.	Dedication or Description.	Date.	Founder.	Patron.	
York, Boothum	St. Mary B. V. (Seal[1])	1318	R. de Pickering, Dean	—	—
,, ,,	St.Mary B.V. "the Less"	1481	J. Gysburgh, Precentor	—	L
,, Dringhouses	‡St. Katherine[2]	1333	—	—	—
,, Fossgate	‡[Holy Jesus & B. V. M. or] Trinity[3] (Seal)	1365	John de Roucliff	Merchant Adventurers	—
,, Monkbridge	St. Loy[4]	—	—	—	—
,, ,,	St. Leonard[5]	1350	—	—	L
,, Gillygate, Peasholm	‡St. Anthony[6]	bef 1429	J. Langton & Gild	—	—
,, Fishergate	Spital	1399	Bygod	—	—
,, Laithorpegate	Maison Dieu	—	—	—	—
,, Ousebridge	,,	1319	—	—	—
,, Markyate	,,	1406	R. Howme	—	—
,, Hestergate	,,	1390	T. Howme	—	—
,, Mickelgate	,,	—	Sir R. de York	—	—
,, Whitefriars	,,	1481	—	—	—
,, Peterlane	,,	1390	J. de Derthyngton	—	—
,, Northstreet	,,	1397	J. Acastre	—	—
,, S. Andrew's Lane	,,	1397	R. Duffield	—	—

[1] B.M. lx. 69. Cat. of Seals 2685, ascribed to Boughton, Chester. [2] Pat. 1333. [3] St. John & Our Lady (Drake).
[4] Drake. [5] Pat. 1350. Probably for lepers, cf. *Test. Ebor.* I. 414. [6] Pap. Lett. 1429. Cf. Pat. 1446.

N.B.—The County of Monmouth is not included as it formed part of Wales until the sixteenth century.

UNIDENTIFIED

Locality.	Dedication.		Date.	County.
Beghton[1] . .	St. Luke Ev.	(L)	Pat. 1335	—
Chestnuts, Wood of[2] .		(L)	Pat. 1256	? Kent
Cheston . .	St. Erasmus & St. Mary M.[3]		—	—
Clayhanger . .	.		Pat. 1253	? Middlesex
Clelecombe[4] . .	St. John Baptist .		Pat. 1332	—
Hareford[5] . .	St. Mary . .		Close 1309	—
Lanford[6] . .		(L)	Will 1307	Exeter Diocese
Langeford . .		(L)	Pat. 1275	—
Merston, nr. Chelworth .	St. John Baptist[7] .		temp. Henry III.	Wilts
Newenham . .	St. Mary Magdalene	(L)	Pat. 1256	Newnham Regis, Warwick, or
Newenham . .	St. Mary Magdalene .		Pat. 1226	Newnham-on-Severn, Glos.
Newenham . .	St. Margaret .		Pat. 1332–3–4	Cf. Newnham Murren, Oxon.
"Novus Locus" .	—		Close 1235	Cf. New Place by Guildford
Scevenloke, de la[8] .	St. Leonard .		Pat. 1232	—
Teneleshend[9] .	St. Leonard .		c. 1270	Yorks

[1] "atte briggesende." Cf. Beighton, Derbs.   [2] "Chastynners." Cf. note 3.

[3] Seal, ? Bodleian; cf. Soc. Antiq. E. II, 4 B. 9. "Sig hospitalis Scōrum Erasemi et marie magdalene de Chestoñ." Cf. note 2.

[4] Cf. Chilcombe, Dorset.   [5] Cf. Hertford, Hereford.

[6] Cf. Lamford, Cornwall; drawing of seal in Taunton Castle, Pigott Coll.

[7] Walcott, Eng. Minsters II 275.   [8] Cf. St. Leonard "atte Loke" in Southwark.   [9] Bodleian Charter, No. 160.

BIBLIOGRAPHY

Monasticon Anglicanum.	Dugdale.
Notitia Monastica.	Tanner.
Monasticon Diœcesis Exon.	G. Oliver, 1846.
Index Monasticus.	R. C. Taylor, 1821.
English Minsters, etc., Vol. II.	M. E. C. Walcott, 1879.
Dictionary of National Biography.	
Itinerary.	Leland, ed. Hearne.

Calendars of Patent and Close Rolls, Papal Registers, Chronicles and Memorials and others of Rolls Series.

Rolls of Parliament, Statutes, *Valor Ecclesiasticus.*

Calendar of Letter-books, London.	R. R. Sharpe.
,, Wills ,,	,, ,,

Royal Wills (Nichols). *Testamenta Vetusta* (Nicolas).

Hospitals and Asylums of the World [Early Systems, etc.].	H. Burdett.
Hospitals of Middle Ages, etc. [Architecture].	F. T. Dollman, 1858.
The Builder. Oct. 1908 to July 1909 ,,	Sidney Heath.
Catalogue of Seals in British Museum. I.	W. de Gray Birch.
Studies in Church Dedications.	F. E. Arnold-Forster, 1899.

County Histories of Durham (Surtees), Leicester (Nichols), Wilts (Hoare), etc.

History of Northumberland, 1893.

Victoria County History.

Hedon (J. R. Boyle, 1895), Higham Ferrers (J. Cole, 1838), Kingston-upon-Hull (G. Hadley, 1788), Newark (C. Brown, 1904), Sandwich (W. Boys, 1792), Survey of London (Stow), etc.

MONOGRAPHS ON HOSPITALS

Canterbury.	*Bibliotheca Topographica Brit.*, Vol. I, No. xxx.	J. Duncombe and N. Battely.
„ See also	Ancient Cities.	J. C. Cox.
Chichester.	Domus Dei.	H. P. Wright, 1885.
Croydon.	*Bib. Top. Brit.*, II.	Ducarel.
Durham.	Kepier, etc.	Surtees Society, Vol. 95.
Gretham.	Collections, 1770.	
Kingsthorpe.		C. A. Markham.
London.	Book of the Foundation of St. Bartholomew.	Norman Moore.
„	Domus Conversorum.	Michael Adler, 1900.
„	„ „ Rolls House, etc.	W. J. Hardy, 1896.
„	Royal Hospital of St. Katharine.	F. S. Lea, 1878.
„	St. Mary Roncevall.	James Galloway, 1907.
„	Memorials of the Savoy.	W. J. Loftie, 1878.
„	St. Thomas M. of Acon.	J. Watney, 1892.
Portsmouth.	Domus Dei.	H. P. Wright, 1873.
Salisbury.	Cartulary of St. Nicholas' Hospital (*Wilts Record Soc.*)	C. Wordsworth, 1902.
Sherburn.	Collections, 1773.	G. Allan.
Southampton.	God's House.	J. A. Whitlock, 1894.
Stamford.	Domus Dei.	H. P. Wright, 1890.
Wells.	Archit. History of.	J. H. Parker and T. Serel.
Winchester.	Memorials of St. Cross.	L. M. Humbert, 1868.
„	Hospital „ „	W. T. Warren.
Worcester.	Annals of St. Wulstan's.	F. T. Marsh, 1890.
York.	Account of . . . St. Leonard's Hospital.	Raine, 1898.

RECORDS, REGISTERS, ETC.

Camden Soc., 1876, XI, Historical Collections [W. Gregory].
of Citizen.

Canterbury and York Society.

Exeter, Episcopal Registers of.   Ed. F. C. Hingeston-
                                               Randolph.

Pipe Roll Society.

Record Soc. of Hampshire (Winchester   Ed. F. J. Baigent.
                       Registers).

   ,,   ,,   Lincoln.   Ed. A. W. Gibbons.

   ,,   ,,   Somerset.

   ,,   ,,   York (Arch. Assn.), Vols. 17, 23.

Surtees Soc. (York Manual, York Wills,
Vita S. Godrici, Gray's Register, Chantry
Surveys, etc.)

Worcester Historical Society.   Ed. J. Willis Bund.

City Records of Gloucester.   Ed. Stevenson, 1893.

   ,,   ,,   Northampton, II.   Ed. J. C. Cox.

   ,,   ,,   Norwich   Ed. Hudson and Tingey,
                                                1906.

   ,,   ,,   Nottingham.

HISTORICAL MSS. COMMISSION

4th R.— Aynho, Blyth, Brackley, Marlborough, Oxford, Romney, etc.

5th and 8th R.—Romney.

6th R.—Bridport, Hythe, Southampton, Winchester.

9th R,—Canterbury, Ewelme.

12th R.—Gloucester.

14th R.—Bury St. Edmunds.

1900, Beverley. 1907, Wells, Exeter.

COMMISSION FOR ENQUIRING CONCERNING CHARITIES

R. vi.—Bath.   R. viii.—Northallerton.

R. xxxii., Pt. vi.—London : Bethlehem, St. Bartholomew's, St. Thomas'.

TRANSACTIONS OF SOCIETIES

Bristol and Glos. Arch., VIII, XVII (Ciren-cester).	E. A. Fuller.
,, ,, ,, XX (Gloucester).	S. E. Bartleet.
Clifton Antiq. Club, I (St. Katherine's Hospital).	A. E. Hudd.
,, ,, ,, III (Seals).	R. H. Warren.
Cumb. and Westm., X (Leper Hospitals).	H. Barnes.
Arch. Cantiana, VII (Dover), VIII (Canterbury).	
Arch. Æliana, 1892 (Newcastle).	W. H. Knowles.
Somerset, XVIII, ii. (Taunton).	T. Hugo.
W. Salt Arch. Soc., 8 (Stafford).	T. J. de Mazzinghi.
Sussex, XXIV (St. Mary's, Chichester).	C. A. Swainson.
,, LI (,, ,,).	A. Ballard.
Wilts, XI (Heytesbury) X, XXVI (Wilton).	
Yorks, XII (Pontefract).	R. Holmes

ON LEPROSY

Archæological Essays, II, "On Leprosy and Leper Hospitals," etc.	J. Y. Simpson, ed. John Stuart, 1872.
British Arch. Assn., XI, 1855.	T. J. Pettigrew.
New Sydenham Soc., Prize Essay.	George Newman, 1895.
History of Epidemics, Vol. I, ch. ii.	Chas. Creighton.
Nineteenth Century, 1884, "Leprosy : Present and Past."	Agnes Lambert.
Leprosy and Segregation.	H. P. Wright, 1885.
[Cf. Statuts d'hotels-dieu et de léproseries.	Léon Le Grand, 1901.
Les Maisons-Dieu et léproseries de Paris.	,, ,, 1898.
Un règlement intérieur de Léproserie (Noyon)	A. Lefranc, 1889.
Danish Lazar-houses (New Syd. Soc.).	E. Ehlers, 1901.
Die Aussatzhäuser des Mittelalters.	E. Lesser, 1896.]

GENERAL INDEX

23

Clay, Rot[
The media[
of Englar[

WZ54

16411